I0814731

Stripe Press
Ideas for progress
South San Francisco, California
press.stripe.com

STEWART BRAND

MAINTENANCE: OF EVERYTHING

PART ONE

For wife Ryan Phelan, who maintains me.

Printed in Belgium
by Stripe Press / Stripe Matter Inc.

Stripe Press
Ideas for progress
South San Francisco, California
press.stripe.com

ISBN 978-1-953953-49-0 (print)
ISBN 978-1-953953-51-3 (ebook)

LCCN 2024056080 (print)
LCCN 2024056081 (ebook)
Library of Congress Cataloging in
Publication data is also available.

Also available in audiobook.

Table of Contents

Introduction

You should consider that the essential art of civilization is maintenance.
—Pete Seeger

Maintenance is what keeps everything going. It's what keeps life going.

Every living thing spends a great deal of time and toil in maintaining its own life and the life of the systems it depends on. Plants tend the life of the soil they grow in. Beavers maintain their dams and thereby the pond that protects them. Humans maintain their bodies, their vehicles, their homes, and their cities, along with much else. Nearly everything worth maintaining is nested in something larger, even more worth maintaining.

But so much of doing maintenance is tiresome. Brush the damn teeth, change the damn oil. They are unrewarding chores—repetitive, boring, often frustrating, and endless. Since that part of maintenance is a pain, we shirk it, defer it, fail to budget time or money for it, let it sink to the bottom of the priority list. That's easy to do because *the necessity of maintenance accumulates invisibly and gradually*. Then suddenly one day the thing breaks, the system falters, and everything stops in a turmoil of disruption, expense, and blame.

The apparent paradox is profound: Maintenance is absolutely necessary *and* maintenance is optional. It is easy to put off, yet it has to be done. Defer now, regret later. Neglect kills.

What to do?

Here's a suggestion: Soften the paradox, and the misbehavior it encourages, by expanding the term "maintenance" beyond referring only to *preventive* maintenance to stave off the trauma of repair—brushing the damn teeth, etc. Let "maintenance" mean the whole grand process of keeping a thing going. From that perspective, occasional repair is part of the process. Close monitoring is part of the process. Changing the oil is part of the process. Eventually replacing the thing is part of the process.

Maintenance, in this larger sense, has nothing optional about it. The necessity of maintenance doesn't accumulate invisibly; it is understood as a given. When you take responsibility for something, you enter into a contract to take care of it. If it's a child, to keep it fed. If it's a knife, to keep it sharp.

This series, I'm pretty sure, is the first to look at maintenance in general. It asks: What can be learned if you think about all the varieties of maintenance at the same time? I doubt there are any nontrivial laws of maintenance to be discovered. All I can offer here is to muse across a representative sample of maintenance domains and see what emerges.

The logic of the book is this:

- Start with a dramatic contest of maintenance styles under life-critical conditions—a true story told as a fable.
- Explore the insights from several domains of maintenance that everyone is aware of: vehicles, buildings, and cities.
- At the same time, see what social scientists and system engineers have to say about upkeep and repair in those familiar domains.
- Then, explore the most highly disciplined maintenance frontiers, which are exotic to most people: the military, manufacturing, aircraft and spacecraft, software, and Japanese culture.
- Apply what has been learned to the largest domains humanity is becoming obliged to take care of: civilization and the planet.
- Zoom back in to individual humans and their lifelong health.
- End with the nature of maintainers and the honor owed them.

This series is an invitation. Using maintenance as a frame of reference is—I hope to show—a fruitful way to rethink all manner of things.

The Path to Print

Given enough eyeballs, all bugs are shallow.
—Eric Raymond

Researching "all manner of things" these days is drastically easier than it used to be, thanks to the internet. You can use keyword- and AI-powered searches to find damn near anything. You can use images to find images. Often you can track important things down to their original sources. And when it comes to writing, plenty of cloud-based grammar checkers, synonym finders, and other aids smooth the process.

But what about questionable facts and tone-deaf language? To write authoritatively about subjects new to me, I needed access to experts who could help debug my prose toward accuracy. The internet has those, too. The question was how to find them or get them to find me. I wanted some kind of public drafting tool where early drafts of my writing and illustrations could be presented online in a form that invited detailed public comment.

Fortuitously, Stripe Press was interested in the same thing and had recently acquired an online publication called Works in Progress. Works in Progress created Books in Progress, the public drafting tool I'd yearned for. With this software, my book began to appear online in serial form. Every two weeks for six months in 2023, I published a new section of this book, available to read and comment on for free on the Books in Progress website. On Twitter (later renamed X), I announced each new section and invited readers to critique it. Stripe Press and Works in Progress did the same with their online channels.

We got traffic. Some 73,000 visitors showed up, and a good portion of them took the trouble to comment on the material and even comment on each other's comments. I was jubilant. Minds were reading my book while I was writing it! Book publishing's customary yearslong lag between writing and being read was gone. Most book authors have to write for an imagined future audience. I got to write for an audience that was real, present, and pitching in to make the book better. In this print version, I've added marginalia demonstrating how their comments were helpful.

Meanwhile, this is just Part One of what is shaping up to be a substantial book. Part Two (and beyond) is well underway. Drafts of my new sections appear online periodically at books.worksinprogress.co. If you like, come help sharpen their edge.

You're also welcome to comment on the material in this book online, because the Books in Progress version is a living document. It continues to evolve in response to my ongoing research and reader commentary.

—SB
May 2024

Credits!

Stripe Press

Rebecca Hiscott, managing editor; Tamara Winter, commissioning editor; Bobby Kessner, head of distribution and business operations; Kevin Wong, designer; Pablo Delcán, designer; Travis McCall, executive producer; Geoff Halber, creative director; Jennifer Yun, communications lead; Rachel Edwards, events lead; Robert Dolgonos, distribution coordinator; Nick Jones, web developer; Devin Jacoviello, art director and designer; Jess Pettet, web producer; Anna Stephenson, image researcher; Robin Lorsch Wildfang, fact-checker; Lynn Slobogian, proofreader; Ken DellaPenta, indexer; Rusty Sena, image correction specialist.

Works in Progress

Nick Whitaker, Ben Southwood, Saloni Dattani, and Sam Bowman, founding editors; And—Now, web designer; Peter Kranitz, copy editor.

Author's software

Scrivener (writing and organizing research); Books in Progress (public comments); X (public interaction); Google Docs (private comments); Google and Bing Copilot (search); Grammarly (grammar); WordHippo (synonyms); Amazon (books); Bookends (book citations); Scribbr (article and paper citations); Descript (transcription); Apple Notes (outlining); Bike (outlining); EasyCrop (image handling); GraphicConverter (image refining); Clipdrop (image enhancement and retouching); Keynote (image blending); Yandex (image search); YouTube (video research).

Commenters

My deepest thanks to everyone who made public comments on the drafts of each section we posted on Books in Progress. You helped refine the work for all the readers to come.

SLAPOUT9, MATISSE, MAKERJAK, PETERKRANITZ, GLENNMERCER, RYANPHELAN, CRANIAC, RHISCOTT,

TODD, GARREAU, INTJONATHAN, NICK, LYNDO, RACHELH, MLAURSEN, CABINETNOISE, JONATHANTAY, NIALLOLEARY, JUDE, 1RONNIE1, GP0129, DAVEBROSS, ABALL, RREINER, WEBBJE, FJSIMKIN, JOSHBLOOM, PAVANRIKKULA, RSTEPHENS, DEVESHBAJAJ, RIEMANNZETA, BJBOOGIE, RICKPOCK, GASCA, _BRIANPOTTER, BTWPHONES, BOB-RJ, FISCHER, JONSTEWART, DS1825, PCARTON, DAVIDTLANG, DGPINK, DGROVER, KAMIL, HUGHHOWEY, KATES, RBUS, TRAVERS, NICKIEGURNEY, INSTANT, ANDREWLAYMAN, JB21, KARINANGUYEN, PSCHWARTZ, BIKECOMMUTER, DECOM, VOELIZ, PHOUTZ, VANDAMARLOW, BIP-USH1, TIAGORECHAU, RAOUL, SHERLOCKIEEE, URIDON81.

A note to future commenters: I reply to every comment within 24 hours, and you're welcome to reply to my replies. Others may join the discussion on the point you raise.

—SB

CHAPTER ONE

THE MAINTENANCE RACE

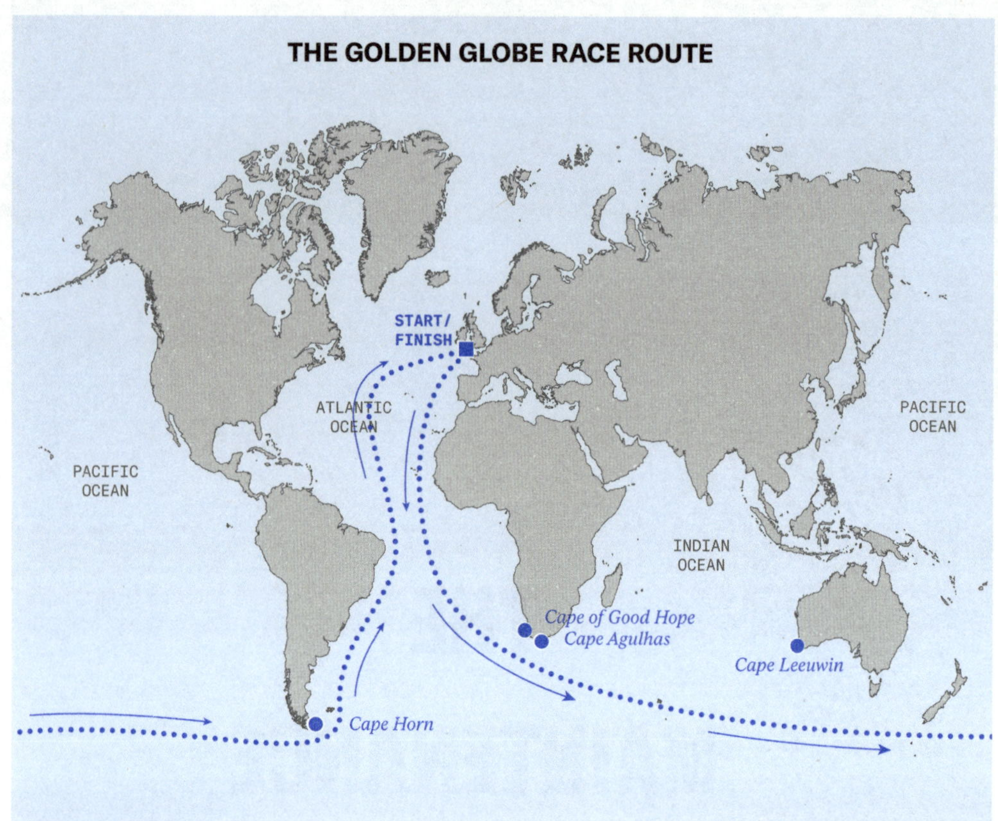

Figure 1. The Golden Globe Race route reads from the top (England) down and to the right past Africa and Australia, then from the left across the Pacific and around South America, back up to England. Thirty thousand miles; 10 months.

Probably a great many famous stories could be retold in terms of maintenance.

Here's one: the Golden Globe around-the-world solo sailboat race of 1968. Its drama continues to echo half a century later because three of the nine competitors became legendary: the one who won, the one who didn't bother to win, and the one who cheated. Their stories are usually told as a contest of wills and endurance, but at heart, it was a contest of maintenance styles.

The setup was this. In early 1968, editors and journalists at the *Sunday Times* in London noticed that several sailors were finding sponsors for their attempts at a new world record: to make the first solo voyage by sailboat around the world without stopping. The editors decided to co-opt the whole thing by declaring it a race. On March 17, they announced:

> The £5,000 *Sunday Times* round-the-world race prize will be awarded to the single-handed yachtsman who completes the *fastest* non-stop circumnavigation of the world departing after June 1 and before October 31, 1968...
>
> The *Sunday Times* Golden Globe will be awarded to the first non-stop single-handed circumnavigator of the world...
>
> The circumnavigation must be completed *without outside physical assistance* and no fuel, food, water or equipment may be taken aboard after the start.
>
> Those are the only conditions...[1]

There were two awards—one a cash prize, the other a trophy—because the sailors were planning to leave at different times; one might be the first to complete the trip, while another who left later might turn out to be the fastest. They were racing each other *and* the clock.

For the 30,000-mile circumnavigation, all the racers would sail from England down the Atlantic to the perilous Southern Ocean—the "Roaring Forties" latitudes between 40 and 50 degrees south of the equator—where storms and waves, sometimes immense, blast eternally from the west, uninterrupted all the way around the world. With that wind behind them, the racers would head east below Africa, then Australia, then South America. Then—if they got that far—they'd head north, back to England.

The racers were required to depart between June and October to arrive at the Southern Ocean between November and February, when the southern hemisphere summer makes the sailing a little less hazardous. It was expected that even the fastest competitor would take 10 months to get home. Some psychiatrists predicted that so many months totally alone, at times in extreme danger, might drive them mad.

Few modern ships use the far Southern Ocean. A boat in trouble could not count on help from anyone. GPS and electronic autopilots didn't exist in 1968, radio was primitive, and radar didn't fit on small boats. The mariners would navigate like their ancestors, solely by sextant, almanac, chronometer, and nautical chart. Without broadcast weather information, each sailor would have to make their own forecasts based on their barometer and what they could see of cloud, wind, and swell conditions. To free them from steering so they could sleep, cook, and do maintenance, they each relied on a complex self-steering device that kept the boat on a steady course in relation to the direction of the wind.

Every piece of equipment on board, and the structure of the boat itself, would be stressed for months on end. Since going ashore for repairs was forbidden, maintenance would have to be ceaseless and done at sea. Failure of a critical element at a critical time could mean death.

But the £5,000 award for the fastest trip was a serious incentive. These days it would be worth about $100,000. Fame, for the winners, would be worth far more.

The youngest of the three competitors who became legendary was Robin Knox-Johnston. Though only 29 years old, he could draw on invaluable experience. With some friends, he had sailed his 32-foot wood ketch *Suhaili* 17,000 miles from India to England, gaining crucial knowledge of the boat's seaworthiness and its match to his skills. In his account of the Golden Globe Race, *A World of My Own*, he wrote:

> Perhaps her greatest advantage... is that she is not complicated and there were very few maintenance tasks I could not carry out myself. The wear and tear and battering to be expected during a 300-day voyage meant that constant maintenance was essential, but this came easily to someone who had served an apprenticeship in the Merchant Navy...[2]
>
> ...[A bosun named Bertie Miller] taught us our knots and splices, canvas work, rigging, how to work a paintbrush properly, and the thousand-and-one finer practical points that make the difference between the seaman and a hand. It was Bertie who gave us a respect for the materials and the tools we

Figure 2. Robin Knox-Johnston's ketch *Suhaili* was built of tough Indian teak and designed for long ocean passages, but her length of only 32 feet made her slower than most of the other boats. (Bill Rowntree/PPL)

used and took tremendous trouble to see that we set about a job the right way and finished it off properly.[3]

Knox-Johnston had tried to build a boat specifically designed for sailing around the world, but he couldn't raise the money for it. Stuck with the wood 32-footer he had, he decided his governing principle would be "Make do and mend."

To prepare *Suhaili* for a 10-month passage, most of it in the world's roughest waters, he packed into his small boat all the materials and tools he could imagine he might need: specialized wrenches for every exotic nut on the boat; ditto for screwdrivers; a sailmaker's bag full of needles, sewing palms, and twine; a bosun's bag with every kind of shackle, thimble, and marlinespike for managing all his steel wire rope; a spare bilge pump and extra rubber pipe; 12 yards of canvas; caulking chisels and cotton; plenty of oil, glue, and Stockholm tar; spare parts for everything mechanical; and medical supplies for repairing himself.

Knox-Johnston's daring habit when the wind was light was to dive off his bow and swim alongside the boat for a while. Then he would grab a line trailing off the stern and climb aboard refreshed. His comfort in the water turned out to be crucial for dealing with his first crisis.

A month after his departure from England, it became clear that *Suhaili* had a very serious leak, forcing him to pump the bilges twice a day. On a calm day off the coast of West Africa, he went over the side with mask and snorkel and discovered two long gaps in the planking on each side of the keel, and they *moved* with the rolling of the boat. Over a cigarette, he considered the nature of the problem and what he might be able to do about it. (Skilled maintainers advise never trying to solve a new or complex problem without a thorough mulling first.) If it was a structural issue, it could cause the boat to eventually break apart, but she had been overbuilt of strong Indian teak, and maybe it was just a matter of caulking the gaps—*if* he could figure out how to do it all by himself at sea.

Dressing in a dark shirt and jeans to hide his white body from potential sharks, he dove down and tried wedging strips of cotton caulking into the gaps. But five feet under water, he couldn't hold his breath long enough to secure the caulking in place.

Knox-Johnston thought some more. Then he cut a one-and-a-half-inch canvas strip seven feet long, sewed caulking to one side of it, coated it with Stockholm tar, and pushed tacks through the canvas every six inches. With a hammer he kept suspended below the hull, he was able to pound in the tacks to hold the caulking in place, but he could only manage one tack at a time before having to surface to breathe. It took two hours.[4]

Then, worried the canvas strip might tear off eventually, he cut a long strip of copper that could be nailed over it. Meanwhile, a shark had arrived and was circling the boat. He fetched his rifle, shot the shark, and watched it sink out of sight, apparently without attracting other sharks. He went back into the chilly water hoping that was so.

He was successful with the copper strip, but the wind came up and he had to postpone sealing the second gap until another calm several days later. When that one was done, his leak was fixed.

Sometimes maintenance involves shooting the shark.

But he was unable to fix the overhead leaks from poorly fitted hatch covers. That meant he would never get dry. Peter Nichols, author of the book *A Voyage for Madmen*, drew on his own experience as a single-hander to describe Knox-Johnston's situation:

> With every wave that broke over the deck and cabin, salt water poured in through the companionway hatch and splashed

> over the chart table, the book rack, and the Marconi radio... The skylight dripped incessantly above his sleeping bag...
>
> A small boat at sea is its crew's only port in a storm, and if the boat is cold and wet below, its gear beginning to fail, the dismalness of such a situation can't be exaggerated.[5]

The constant motion also took a toll. Knox-Johnston noted that his tools were holding up well, except he was running short of drill bits, "mainly because when drilling in a moving boat one is constantly being thrown about and unless one withdraws the drill fast it gets snapped off." He added that his health remained good, "apart from the inevitable cuts, blisters, and bruises."[6]

One night in the midst of a gale, he lay in his bunk listening to the shrieking wind and tumult of breaking waves and chaotic cross seas. Suddenly he was hurled to the far wall and buried under everything loose in the cabin. He dug partway out, then was flung back across into his bunk as the boat righted itself after a complete knockdown. With the lamp out, he was in utter blackness. He groped his way out to the deck and felt his way around in the violent night to see if he had any masts left at all. He was surprised to find all his rigging intact, though the self-steering gear had been damaged.

He went below to pump out all the water that had come in during the knockdown and found that more was still coming in. To his horror, it was pouring in from gaps around the edges of the cabin, which had apparently been knocked partially loose from the deck. He knew that if the cabin got torn all the way off by another capsize, *Suhaili* would fill with water and sink. He reduced sail to improve his odds of surviving the night.

When the storm abated, he spent a whole day reinforcing the structure that held the cabin to the deck, another day rebuilding the self-steering apparatus, and then three days repairing the rudder. If he had not laid in a supply of materials, tools, and fasteners for such tasks, he would have had to quit the race. It was his thorough preparation that equipped him to "make do and mend."

But preparation can never be perfect. The radical part of Knox-Johnston's making-do was that he was never daunted by the lack of a crucial material or tool.

When he took apart his radio transmitter to find out why it had quit working, he discovered a wire connection so badly corroded it would have to be reattached, but he had no solder to do it with. So… he painstakingly melted and collected the tiny dots of solder from inside several navigation lightbulbs. That got the transmitter working again. (For a while.)

Another time, he figured out that his battery charger wouldn't run because of grease on the ignition points. He cleaned off the grease, then realised he couldn't reset the gap at the required 12 to 15 thousandths of an inch because he had no feeler gauge on board. So… he measured the pages in his logbook and found there were 200 to the inch, which meant one page would be five thousandths of an inch. Three pages did the trick. The charger ran again. (For a while.)

In his book he wrote, "Necessity is the mother of invention and I am always quite happy to leave things until I have to cope with them, and then throw myself happily into the problem."[7]

Coping worked well for him most of the time but not all of the time.

People on sailboats tend to be vaguely disapproving of and thus negligent about their engine. It's bulky, heavy, noisy, and hard to get at. Its prop drags in the water. Turning it on feels like a violation of the essence of sailing. But when the engine is really needed to get out of trouble, it had better work instantly.

One day Knox-Johnston wrote in his journal, "I decided to turn the engine today as it has not had any use for over two months." It wouldn't turn. Close inspection showed nothing obviously wrong. He wrote, "Whatever the trouble, it's my own fault for not turning it daily. Now I have a lot of work on my hands to get it free, even if I manage that."[8] Later, he completely disassembled the engine, discovered that the cylinders were rusted solid from condensed moisture, and broke several tools failing to clear them.

At a point halfway around the world, he had no engine and no radio transmitter. Then came what felt like the final straw. He was south of Australia when his last spare for a critical part of the self-steering rig broke off and sank. He knew that sailing long distances solo was considered impossible without self-steering gear. He wanted to head to Melbourne and quit.

But first he experimented to see if he could arrange his four sails—mizzen, main, and two headsails—in ways that would allow the boat to keep a course on any point of wind so he would not have to steer all day and night. To his amazement, it turned out he could. But he needed some way to know while he was sleeping if *Suhaili* was jibing or about to jibe, because the rigging was increasingly vulnerable to the shock of his mainsail suddenly slamming to the opposite side. His solution was to take the sideboard out of his bunk so he would be flung to the floor when the boat heeled unexpectedly. "This was a very effective alarm," he wrote, "and although I sustained a few bruises as a result, it was far better than damaging the boat."[9]

All the way across the southern Pacific, Knox-Johnston's boat took punishment. So did he. Years later, he recalled one incident:

> When you're looking at the stern and you see an 80-foot wave breaking at the top, stretching from horizon to horizon, don't tell me you're not a little bit scared... As the wave was breaking, I knew it was going to sweep the boat—and I realised I could not get down below where I was safe. So I just climbed the rigging and the wave covered the boat. It was me and two masts and nothing else in sight for about 1,500 miles in any direction. Then she popped up. The hatch had been knocked open, so I spent the next three hours pumping out three tonnes of water.[10]

Figure 3. The swamping of *Suhaili* by an 80-foot breaking wave on December 16, 1968, was depicted in 1989 by nautical painter Gordon Frickers. It was based on guidance from Knox-Johnston himself, who commissioned the painting. Titled *Roaring Forties*, the large painting—this is just part of it—has been widely reproduced as an illustration of the ferocity of the Southern Ocean. (Gordon Frickers)

By the time he turned north at Cape Horn toward England after four and a half months in the Southern Ocean, even his durable synthetic sails were disintegrating. "I spent more time repairing sails on the homeward run than any other form of maintenance," he wrote.[11] He had to devote three hours every day solely to tasks that would keep the boat sound enough to get all the way home.

Despite the endless ordeal, or maybe because of it, he reported, "I realised I was thoroughly enjoying myself." He loved being at sea. He loved exploring the extreme limits of his competence.

Ever the responsible merchant marine officer, Knox-Johnston concluded his book with an 11-page "Pilot's Notes," spelling out in detail everything he had learned about gear and technique on the voyage. He quoted from his journal this lesson in particular:

> The only way to overcome my present feeling of depression is to fully occupy myself, so I cleaned and served the remaining bottle screw threads and then gave all the servings a coat of Stockholm Tar. Next I polished the vents and gave them a coating of boiled oil. Whilst I had it out I dabbed the oil on wire and rust patches.[12]

Doing maintenance cures depression.

Donald Crowhurst counted on his race becoming legendary. To solve his financial problems, he desperately needed the money that would come with a famous victory.

Since he would be starting in late October, at the back of the pack, he figured he could beat the others with his talent for innovation. His specialty was electronics. He had devised a handy radio direction finder that he sold through his tiny business. Stanley Best, the principal backer of his company and, later, of his Golden Globe bid, said of him:

> I always considered Donald Crowhurst an absolutely brilliant innovator... but as a businessman, as someone who had to know how the world went, he was hopeless... He seemed to have this capacity to convince himself that everything was going to be wonderful, and hopeless situations were only temporary setbacks.[13]

The most innovative form of sailboat available in 1968 was the newly developed trimaran, a central hull between two large floats. Trimarans were so light they could sail twice as fast as traditional keel boats, but they had a serious potential problem. When a trimaran tipped over, it would stabilize upside down and could not be righted. For the boat he was building, Crowhurst came up with an intricate solution. There would be a buoyancy bag at the top of the mainmast that would automatically inflate when it sensed a capsize. Then water would be pumped into the uppermost float, which would become heavy enough to pull the boat back upright.

Unfortunately, the 35-year-old Crowhurst was too much of an optimist to take into account the complications that always arise between having an idea and getting it to work. The whole rushed process of building and outfitting his trimaran became a nightmare of argument, delay, extra expense, and chaos. As a result, when he set sail at the last permitted moment on October 31, the boat was unready. Electrical wires led everywhere, connected to almost nothing. The buoyancy bag was installed but inoperable. And accidentally left on the dock in the turmoil of departure were all the materials needed for repairing the boat: fasteners, plywood, and rigging gear. The only things he had in abundance were electronic parts and tools for his elaborate radio array. He overprepared for what he knew well and underprepared for nearly everything else.

Traditional systems (like wood-plank keeled boats) have an advantage over innovative systems (like the then-novel plywood trimarans) in that the whole process of maintaining traditional things is well explored and widely understood. Old systems break in familiar ways. New systems break in unexpected ways.

Figure 4. On his 41-foot trimaran, Donald Crowhurst was the last to start the Golden Globe Race. He hoped the boat's exceptional speed downwind would let him pass the other racers who had started months earlier. (Rolls Press/Popperfoto via Getty Images)

Once at sea, Crowhurst's boat began to torture him with its problems. His self-steering gear was so poorly secured to the deck that it kept vibrating the screws loose, and some fell out. "That's four gone now!" he wrote in his journal. "Can't keep cannibalizing from other spots forever!"[14] He had to take screws from elsewhere because he had brought no spares.

The hatch in the cockpit floor leaked and let in a deluge of salt water on the electrical generator, shutting down his treasured radios. He discovered that his bilge pumps couldn't work because the specialized piping they needed was never put on board. The water that kept seeping through leaky hatches into the floats and main hull had to be bailed out by hand with a bucket. That would be impossible in a storm, he realised.

It became clear that his boat had so much going wrong that it could never survive the Southern Ocean gales. Crowhurst knew he should quit the race, but he couldn't bring himself to do it. Then he found a way not to.

When he got the generator and radios working again, his brief communications with the world became increasingly vague about where he was, exactly. In parallel with his accurate logbook, he began writing a fraudulent second logbook with plausible positions and speeds that showed a fictional Crowhurst on track to win the race. The real Crowhurst was dawdling south in the Atlantic Ocean, which he now planned never to leave.

He was only as far as Brazil when he discovered an extremely serious three-foot-long split in his starboard float. Damage like that would have been an honorable reason to quit the race and go ashore, but he had already cabled to the public that he was making good time 3,700 miles east of where he actually was.

Lacking the materials for repair, he flouted the race rules. He snuck ashore in Argentina, lied to the locals about who he was, repaired the split with their plywood, and headed back to sea, continuing his sporadic cheery reports of rapid progress past Africa, Australia, and South America, disguising his radio signal so it seemed to be coming from those continents.

Optimists like Crowhurst—and me, I confess—tend to resent the need for maintenance and resist doing it. Maybe we prefer to think in ideals, and the gritty reality of things constantly decaying and breaking offends our sense of the world. Crowhurst referred to doing maintenance as "sailorizing." To keep himself motivated, whenever he completed something unpleasant he would reward himself with a drink. Before long, he was running out of rum and wine. In his journal he would diligently make a list of projects that needed to be done, do a few of them half-heartedly, and then lose interest. Since he never got around to organizing his stowage, he had to ransack everywhere to find things.

Months went by. Crowhurst got as far south as the

Falklands and then headed back toward England and the finish line.

Crowhurst was so good at fixing radios that he sought out reasons to do it while neglecting everything else. Toward the end of his trip, when his long-range transmitter was irreparably broken, he decided to convert his short-range radiotelephone to long-range Morse code capability. With no technical manuals on board, he derived what needed to be done from first principles. Testing gear he had to make from scratch. Sixteen hours a day for two weeks in tropical heat, he toiled over the innards of the radios. The whole cabin was covered with electrical parts.

And he succeeded! For a day, he exchanged cables with his backers, his wife, and the BBC. Then he got more ambitious. Longing to communicate by voice, he worked on the radio far into the night, trying to convert it from low-frequency Morse to high-frequency speech transmission. This time he failed.

On June 23, 1969, he sent a cable to his wife apologizing that they would not be able to talk, and another cable to the *Sunday Times*, who believed he was completing the fastest circumnavigation, asking permission to have transmitter parts delivered to him. Their answer was no.

It was his last sane day.

Crowhurst had been broadcasting an elaborate lie for seven months. By now he was sure he would be found out. He might be received back in England in triumph at first, but once his fake logbooks were examined closely, it would all turn to scandal and disgrace. His financial ruin would be complete. He would have failed his wife and four children. The prospect was intolerable.

On June 24 he began to take hope from a tremendous new idea that he was certain would liberate him and all of humanity if he could just explain it clearly enough. Adrift in the Sargasso Sea, he spent the next eight days and nights feverishly spelling out in his journal the origins and wondrous ramifications of his discovery that *reality could be stipulated* by a sufficiently brilliant mind. Abstraction was the ultimate power. The realization led to exhilarating revelations. In one statement that ended with 18 exclamation points, he wrote:

> And yet, and yet—*if* creative abstraction is to act as a vehicle for the new entity, and to leave its hitherto stable state it lies

> within the power of creative abstraction to produce the phenomenon!!!!!!!!!!!!!!!!![15]

He was confident that when mathematicians and engineers read what he was writing, they would understand it immediately, and "problems that have beset humanity for thousands of years will have been solved."[16] With intense, delusional invention he was trying to solve his own problem.

Mid-morning on July 1, 1969, he saw with dismay that his chronometer had run down. He started the clock again in order to keep precise track in his logbook of his countdown, insight by written insight, to the moment that would resolve everything. At 10:29:00 he wrote:

> It is finished
> IT IS THE MERCY

His last entry read:

> 11:17:00
> It is the time for your move to begin
> I have not need to prolong the game
> It has been a good game that must be ended at the
> I will play the game when I choose
> I will resign this game 11:20:40
> There is no reason for harmful[17]

Having come to the bottom of a page, he did not complete the sentence. Instead, taking the clock with him, he went out on deck and crossed his own finish line into the ocean—leaving behind the boat and the documents that he knew would reveal the truth of what had happened. He could have disguised his suicide as an accident and chose not to.

The trimaran was found nine days later by a British ship and hoisted aboard intact.

The tragic story of Crowhurst's deception usually ends with the note of redemption in his words "It is the mercy." But this is the maintenance version.

He was a remarkable man, intelligent and bold. The boat he abandoned, however, revealed how lax he was about nearly every aspect of maintenance. The exhaustively researched book *The Strange Last Voyage of Donald Crowhurst* by Nicholas Tomalin and Ron Hall has this indicative example:

> The cabin, after eight months of cramped, unmethodical male housekeeping, smelled as if cabbage juice had been poured over old bedding, allowed to ferment, then baked in a hot oven. Several days' plates, saucepans, and ripening curry lay in and around the sink; his bed stank.[18]

The authors added, "This smell was still pungent five months later."

Poor preparation and maintenance led to Crowhurst's cheat. The cheat led to his death. His excessively optimistic view of the world and of himself, which had worked well enough on land, was lethal for a man alone at sea in an unfit small boat, marinating for months in two contradictory realities. He had invested so much of himself in an illusion that when it shattered, he shattered.

Bernard Moitessier (pronounced "Mwa-TESS-ee-ay"), at 46 years old, was the most experienced of the nine Golden Globe competitors. For years he had vagabonded alone in small boats all over the world and then, in 1966, made an epic sailing trip with his wife from Tahiti to Spain via Cape Horn. At the time, it was history's longest nonstop passage by a yacht.

Compare Moitessier's first knockdown in the Roaring Forties with what three of his competitors experienced.

You'll recall it took Robin Knox-Johnston five days of repair to recover from his capsize. Another sailor, Loïck Fougeron, endured something similar. Beset on his 30-foot steel cutter at night in a gale, he was violently thrown to the side of his cabin and buried under all his stuff, certain he was going to die. When the boat came upright, he decided instantly to quit the race and sail to shore in Africa.

It was even worse for Bill King. His 42-foot junk-rigged schooner was thrown over on its side by a massive wave and turned all the way upside down. When it finally came back up, his masts were broken. By sheer luck, King happened to be in the cabin fetching a rope when the knockdown occurred. If it had come 30 seconds earlier or later, he would probably have died. Under a makeshift rig he also sailed to Africa to quit.

Moitessier's turn came in a fierce storm with rough cross seas. He was relaxing in the cabin. He wrote, "I... put on my slippers and roll myself a cigarette. A spot of coffee? Why not! God, it's good to be inside when things are roaring out there." Suddenly, "an enormous breaking sea hits the port beam and knocks us flat." After his boat came back up, Moitessier went

Figure 5. Bernard Moitessier on his waterproof 39-foot steel ketch *Joshua* in 1968. The boat was designed and built to be low maintenance, highly durable, and simple to handle solo. Note the extremely high reef bands (row of dots) on the two aft sails. (Barry Pickthall/PPL)

on deck to check for damage and make adjustments to the sails. The aft boom had swung and broken the wind vane off the self-steering gear. He wrote, "Not serious: half a minute is all it takes to change the vane, thanks to a very simple rig. I have seven spare vanes left, and material to make more if necessary."[19] The boat sailed on as if nothing had happened.

Moitessier had dealt with most of his maintenance issues *in advance*. Everything about the design and construction of his boat and everything about his outfitting for the race was the result of his decades of learning exactly what it takes for a small boat to thrive in the brutal Southern Ocean. He knew that once at sea, the need for maintenance had to be minimal, and doing it had to be easy.

The boat was named *Joshua*, after Joshua Slocum, the first person to sail around the world alone (though with many stops along the way). It was a traditional two-masted ketch like Knox-Johnston's, but at 39 feet it was seven feet longer and therefore faster. With money from an admirer, Moitessier had it built of heavyweight steel in France. "Ah, steel," he wrote. "Watertight bulkheads, tanks welded right to the hull, incomparable rigidity, welded chain-plates, and an absolutely watertight boat that you clean with a broom and dustpan instead of a bilge pump."[20]

The critical maintenance issue with steel is corrosion. The answer, he wrote, is "paint, paint, and more paint."[21] Noting that the French Navy puts on 10 coats of paint before any launch, he went with seven coats. But not just any paint.

It had to be what he considered the best paints in the best sequence: two coats of anticorrosion zinc silicate Doxanode, followed, after two weeks of drying, by two coats of a zinc chromate paint and three coats of two-part epoxy. (Obsession with detail is a hallmark of the most successful maintainers.)

For strength and simplicity, *Joshua's* masts were inexpensive recycled telephone poles. Moitessier installed steps up the sides of the masts so he could comfortably climb them weekly to inspect for problems and oil the halyard blocks at the top. Far more importantly, he would be able to reach the mastheads instantly in an emergency.

"The one thing that any singlehander fears," Moitessier's competitor Knox-Johnston wrote, "is something breaking at the top of the mast."[22] Like most sailboats, Knox-Johnston's *Suhaili* had no mast steps. He had to hoist himself aloft in a bosun's chair, which could only be done safely in a dead calm. He tried it once in rough seas when a halyard broke and he could no longer raise or lower his mainsail. Thirty feet up in the chair, he was flung away from the mast and nearly killed.

Moitessier's sails were made of the same high-strength synthetic as Knox-Johnston's, but he had no need to spend countless hours repairing them because he had his made "small, light, easy to handle, with very high reef bands and reinforcements that would take a sailmaker's breath away."[23] He was six months at sea before he had to get out his sewing palm at all.

He even added a unique element for heavy-weather sailing. In order to steer *Joshua* from inside the cabin, he made a small windowed dome out of a wash basin and attached it to the roof of the main hatch. Perched safe and dry on a seat under the dome next to the interior wheel, he could see conditions outside and adjust his course as needed.

"*Joshua* is just simple," Moitessier once told an interviewer. "Simplicity is a form of beauty."[24] That principle governed everything for him. "Given a choice between something simple and something complicated," he wrote, "choose what is simple without hesitation; sooner or later, what is complicated will almost always lead to problems."[25] Only simple things, he noted, can be reliably repaired with what you have on board.

His self-steering gear was easy to repair because it had none of the usual complicated linkages or line attachments. He didn't bother to install interior heating because, thanks to a watertight cabin, reliably dry clothing would keep him warm enough. He hated electronics on boats, so there was no battery charger to worry about. To substitute for what he described as "two or three hundred pounds of noisy radio equipment," he had a slingshot for launching film canisters containing messages onto the decks of passing ships. His cabin light was a kerosene lantern.

Moitessier emptied his boat of absolutely everything but the basics. With less stuff, there was less to maintain. With less weight, he would sail faster. Before departure, he off-loaded his engine, his dinghy, four anchors, 900 pounds of anchor chain, the anchor windlass, surplus books, surplus paint, and half the water he usually carried. It added up to a ton of weight and distractions gone. Later, at sea, he purged still more, heaving over the side 375 pounds of food, kerosene, and rope he decided he wouldn't need.

Thanks in part to his paring down, even though he had left England more than two months after Knox-Johnston, he was sailing so much faster that he might well catch up.

As Moitessier approached Africa's Cape of Good Hope, he wanted to let the world know what a sensational passage he was having. He sailed up to a freighter and slingshotted a message onto her deck saying he had two packages of information to throw to them. Their skipper obliged by turning the stern toward him, and the packages were passed.

But then the overhanging stern of the freighter caught Moitessier's mainmast. He wrote, "My guts twist into knots. The push on the mast makes *Joshua* heel, she luffs up toward the freighter… and wham!—the bowsprit is twisted 20 or 25 degrees to port."[26] He was horrified.

His bowsprit was a steel pipe, so it bent instead of broke, but he knew he could not continue the race if it stayed bent, because the symmetry of the stays that supported his masts was now so compromised that he could lose his whole sailing rig in a storm. How could he possibly fix it at sea alone? He wrote, "I did not want to crystalize my thinking prematurely." He thought about the problem for two nights and a day before proceeding.

His carefully considered solution was elegant, combining a four-part block and tackle with his cockpit winch for sufficient force and using a staysail boom to get the right leverage. Bowsprit straightened, he sailed on exultant.

I once got to know Moitessier a little bit. In 1981 he was living aboard *Joshua* in Sausalito, California, close to where I had a sailboat berthed. One time, when I remarked on how fit his boat looked, he said, "My rule is, a new boat every day."

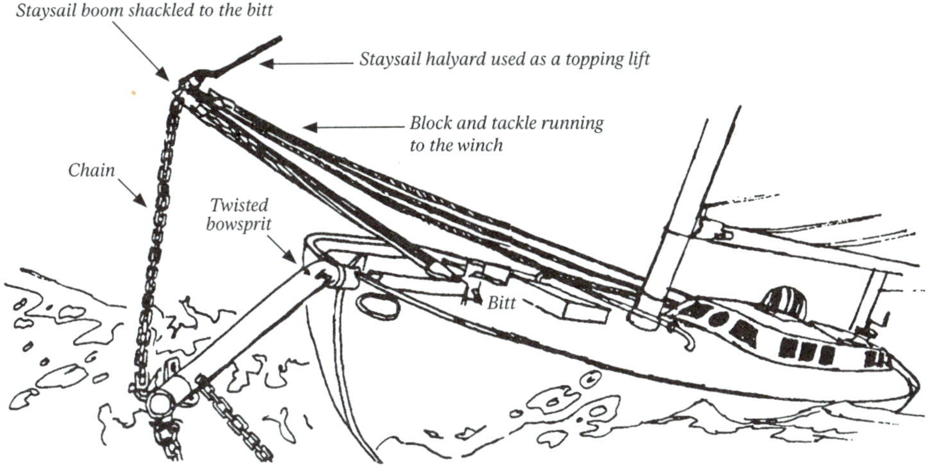

Figure 6. Moitessier's solution for straightening his bent bowsprit, combining a four-part block and tackle with his cockpit winch and using a staysail boom to get the right leverage. (Bernard Moitessier, *The Long Way*, illustration by Marc Berthier)

His years at sea had taught him that if you don't fix something when you first see it beginning to fail, it is very likely to finish failing just when it is the most dangerous and the hardest to deal with, such as in the midst of a storm.

Moitessier loved doing routine maintenance. He wrote:

> I work calmly at the odd jobs that make up my universe, without haste: I glue the sextant leg back on with epoxy, adjust the mirrors, replace five worn slide lashings on the mainsail and three on the mizzen, splice the staysail and mizzen halyards… to freshen the nip on the sheaves.[27]

His reward for a boat functioning like new every day was this: "I spend my time reading, sleeping, eating. The good, quiet life, with nothing to do."[28] That was in fair weather. Storms were as arduous for him as ever, but he was unafflicted with worry that his gear might fail.

He also took care to maintain his own health, physical and mental. When he found himself exhausted after rounding the Cape of Good Hope, plagued by an ulcer and considering giving up, he began doing yoga every day. "My ulcer stopped bothering me," he wrote, "and I no longer suffered from lumbago. But above all, I found something more. A kind of undefinable state of grace."[29]

Moitessier was at the peak of his skills—at one with his boat, the sea, and himself. He began wanting it to go on and on.

All across the Southern Pacific he was catching up to Knox-Johnston, who had started 69 days before him. They rounded South America's icy Cape Horn only 20 days apart, with 10,000 miles to go to England. The London press began predicting that Moitessier would not only win the £5,000 prize for the fastest solo round-the-world trip but might also finish first, taking the Golden Globe award as well. France was preparing a fleet of naval ships and yachts to accompany their hero home, where he would receive the nation's highest tribute, the Legion of Honour. No yachtsman in the world would be more famous.

Moitessier dreaded all that. He wrote, "I really felt sick at the thought of getting back to Europe, back to the snakepit."[30] He asked himself, "How long will it last, this peace I have found at sea?... Don't look beyond *Joshua*, my little red and white planet made of space, pure air, stars, clouds and freedom."[31]

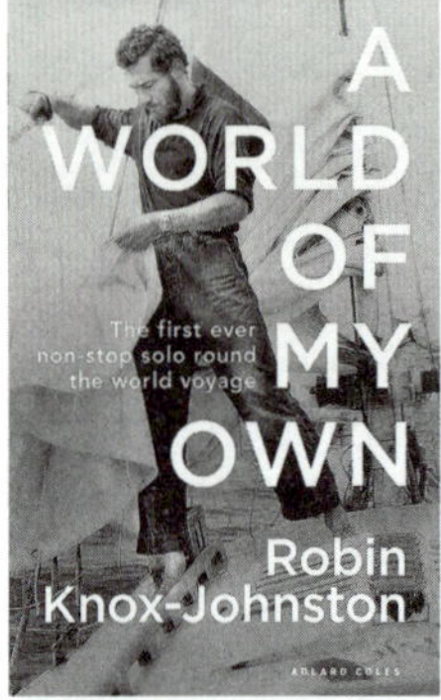

Figure 7. *A World of My Own* by Robin Knox-Johnston, originally published in 1969. (Adlard Coles)

And yet he longed to see his wife and friends. He could really use the prize money. What had he sailed so fast for, if not to win?

Race watchers in England calculated that Moitessier must be far up the Atlantic toward a double victory when word came from South Africa of a message received by slingshot on a tanker in Cape Town Harbour. It read:

> My intention is to continue the voyage, still nonstop, toward the Pacific Islands, where there is plenty of sun and more peace than in Europe... I am continuing nonstop because I am happy at sea, and perhaps because I want to save my soul.[32]

Figure 8. *The Strange Last Voyage of Donald Crowhurst* by Nicholas Tomalin and Ron Hall, originally published in 1970. (Hodder and Stoughton)

So it was Robin Knox-Johnston who won both the Golden Globe and the prize of £5,000, which he gifted to Donald Crowhurst's bereaved wife and young children. By the time he was knighted by the Queen in 1995, he had become Britain's most distinguished yachtsman. His 1969 book, *A World of My Own*, continues to be read 50 years later as a model of audacious seamanship and British pluck. The boat he had dauntlessly kept afloat for 312 days and 30,123 miles was exhibited for years at the National Maritime Museum in Greenwich and later returned to him. He still sails *Suhaili* at times.

No other competitor completed the race.

For the investigation that led to *The Strange Last Voyage of Donald Crowhurst*, the authors sought the advice of psychiatrist Glin Bennet. Bennet wrote that Crowhurst's final writings amounted to

> the most completely documented account of a psychological breakdown... The steps towards the final disintegration proceed with the remorselessness of a Greek tragedy... It is a private tragedy but with a richness of texture that has immortalized the name of Donald Crowhurst in a way he could never have intended but in a way he might possibly not have regretted.[33]

Over the years, Crowhurst's story has been retold in six novels, many poems, many songs, an opera, several plays, several documentary films, and three major movies. Has any other failure succeeded so well?

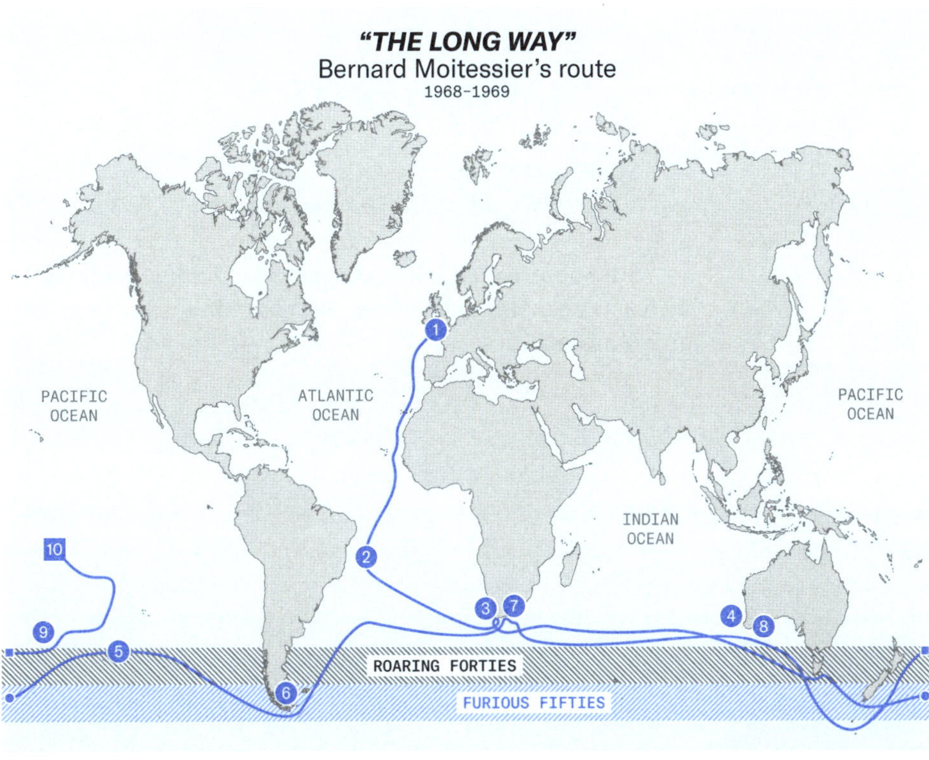

Figure 9. Moitessier's route from Plymouth in England in 1968 to Tahiti in 1969.

1. August 22, 1968 Leave Plymouth, UK
2. October 1, 1968
3. October 20, 1968 Cape of Good Hope
4. December 7, 1968 Cape Leeuwin
5. January 1, 1969
6. February 2, 1969 Cape Horn
7. March 18, 1969 Cape of Good Hope
8. April 27, 1969 Cape Leeuwin
9. May 20, 1969
10. June 21, 1969 Arrive in Tahiti

Figure 10. *La longue route* (*The Long Way*) by Bernard Moitessier, originally published in 1971. (J'ai Lu)

Bernard Moitessier finally docked in Tahiti 303 days after leaving England, worn out from 37,455 miles at sea—which is still considered "the world's longest recorded nonstop solo sailing voyage."[34]

In Tahiti, it took him two years to craft a book about his voyage that satisfied him. It quickly joined the canon of most-loved sea books, providing inspiration and, with its 60-page appendix of technical advice, instruction for generations of cruising sailors to come. Like Thoreau's *Walden*, Moitessier's *The Long Way* is a masterwork about solitary transcendence, practical and lyrical at the same time.

The different maintenance styles of the three sailors led directly to their different outcomes.

Knox-Johnston's style was:
"*Whatever comes, deal with it.*" And he did.

Crowhurst's was:
"*Hope for the best.*" It killed him.

Moitessier's was:
"*Prepare for the worst.*" It freed him.

Sir Robin Knox-Johnston won the Golden Globe Race. With a more maintainable boat, Bernard Moitessier went even farther, faster.

Figure 11. Moitessier liked to sign things with a tiny drawing of *Joshua*, a sunset, and an island. The drawing is on his gravestone in Le Bono, France, where he was buried in 1994. Not far away in La Rochelle, berthed at the Musée Maritime's sailing school, *Joshua* lives on, still teaching. (© Flammarion, Paris, 1986, 2005, 2011)

Figure 12. Harley-Davidson turned a common motto among motorcyclists into a company slogan. Here it's used to decorate the fuel console door on a deluxe Harley motorcycle. (Steve Skjold/Alamy)

CHAPTER TWO

VEHICLES (AND WEAPONS)

Figure 13. Philosopher Matthew Crawford at his motorcycle repair shop in Richmond, Virginia. (Rob Adamo)

2.1 What Motorcycles Teach About Maintenance

Start with the motorcycle. A motorcycle is a two-wheeled, unstable, heavy, complex machine that you wrap your delicate body tightly around and ride at high speed. The combination of exceptional intimacy and exceptional danger invites exceptional bonding. Nobody proclaims "Live to ride! Ride to live!" about cars. Philosophers don't write extremely popular books about repairing cars, but two have about repairing motorcycles. Examining what interests them about fixing a motorcycle might turn up some instructive ways to think about repair in general.

The books are Matthew B. Crawford's *Shop Class as Soulcraft: An Inquiry into the Value of Work* and Robert M. Pirsig's *Zen and the Art of Motorcycle Maintenance: An Inquiry into Values*. Crawford's *Soulcraft*, with a motorcycle on the cover, was the surprise hit of 2009, an instant bestseller that went through five printings in three weeks. Pirsig's *Art of Motorcycle Maintenance*, with a wrench on the cover, was turned down by 121 publishers before finally being released by Morrow in 1974. It sold six million copies in 27 languages, bent the culture of the day toward honoring maintenance, and was celebrated as "the most widely read philosophy book ever."[35]

My original line here described Crawford's book as "the sleeper hit of 2009, an instant bestseller that went through five printings in three weeks."

RACHELH commented: "If it's a sleeper hit, it wouldn't be an instant bestseller, right? It was a surprise hit."

Right! I corrected the word in the next draft.

Both authors use the details of motorcycle maintenance—especially the trauma of repair—to ground-truth their philosophies, and their philosophies are deployed as a source of insight into the nuances of motorcycle maintenance. In both books, the motorcycle material serves as a framing device. Crawford uses it to celebrate the intelligence embodied in blue-collar work: "There was more thinking going on in the bike shop," he notes, "than in my previous job at the think tank."[36] Pirsig uses motorcycle maintenance as a model for figuring out the structure of reality.

Matthew Crawford got his PhD in political philosophy at the University of Chicago and currently does research at the University of Virginia in Charlottesville. He is also a professional mechanic; for years he ran a repair shop for vintage motorcycles in Richmond. Robert Pirsig studied philosophy at Banaras Hindu University in India and the University of Chicago, then taught creative writing at Montana State University and the University of Illinois. He became a journeyman technical writer and computer programmer.

My original line was "the university of Virginia in Richmond."

RBUS corrected me and added details and links: "The University of Virginia is in Charlottesville, Virginia, not Richmond. Crawford's research institute is the Institute for Advanced Studies in Culture affiliated with the University of Virginia. Crawford's repair shop was in Richmond and is now called the Reclaimed Vehicle Fabrication Laboratory."

While Pirsig was an amateur working on his own bike, Crawford was a professional, paid to repair and upgrade other people's motorcycles. One time, when a customer asked him to help revive a beloved 1983 Honda Magna V45 that hadn't been driven for two years, Crawford responded, "Assuming it's got all the usual problems from sitting, you're looking at a thousand dollars to get it back on the road. The carbs will need to be gone through, it'll need new fork seals, new battery, new tires, probably new hydraulic lines, and who knows what else. Have you kept the valves adjusted?"[37]

The need for maintenance doesn't stop when usage stops. The upkeep of any machine is largely about tending to the four sources of most problems: moving parts, flowing fluids, flowing electricity, and temperature stresses. Every bit of the moving, flowing, and stressing causes wear and tear, but damage also comes from not moving, flowing, or stressing. Nonmoving parts seize up. Nonflowing fluids leak or curdle into gunk. Rubber starts to rot. Corrosion gets into everything. Crawford told his customer with the half-dead Honda, "You might want to just get rid of it."[38]

My original line here was "Crawford points out that before problem solving comes problem finding."

RACHELH opined: "I might want a transitional sentence or clause here."

Done!

Crawford emphasizes that repair comes in two stages—that problem *finding* comes before problem *solving*: "You try to think logically about a sequence of investigations and fixes that will reveal the most serious problems sooner rather than later."[39] Diagnosis is often more convoluted than a simple decision tree. He gives the example of dealing with evidence of a serious oil leak:

> A thick three-dimensional layer of caked-on grime covers the bottom half of the engine and frame. It could be something easy to fix (a leaking oil tank, or an external oil line), or it could be something requiring a complete teardown of the motor (certain oil seals, for example)... But to make this determination, you have to first figure out where the oil is leaking from... Oil flings everywhere in the blast of wind that comes with speed, so it's near impossible to say where the oil is leaking from unless you first get everything clean and dry, and cleaning the bike is a big deal. You poke halfheartedly at it with a screwdriver... and watch chunks of shit-colored bike cheese fall off onto the lift. Next come the rags, lots of them, and various caustic substances.[40]

Once the motorcycle is clean, it still has to run before the leak can be detected, and getting it to fire up may require "removing carburetors, disassembling and cleaning them, sorting out buggered wiring, and who knows what all."[41] After all that, the oil leak could turn out to be so deeply buried that the bike should just be scrapped. Part of pragmatic diagnosis is being realistic about when to abandon repair and think about buying a new motorcycle or giving up on riding.

Most of the time, when a machine stops working, it's obvious to a skilled mechanic what is wrong and what to do about it. But what about when it's not obvious? Both philosophers have the same advice as the sailors Knox-Johnston and Moitessier: Stop and think. Crawford writes:

> You have to step back and get a larger gestalt. Have a cigarette and walk around the lift. Any mechanic will tell you that it is invaluable to have other mechanics around to test your reasoning against, especially if they have a different intellectual disposition.
>
> Some diagnostic situations contain so many variables, and symptoms can be so under-determining of causes, that explicit analytical reasoning comes up short. What is required then is the kind of judgment that arises only from experience; hunches rather than rules.[42]

Maintainers learn to be causation experts when dealing with repair. They build two narratives: one for finding the problem and one for solving the problem. Working backward from the visible part of the problem to the issues hidden behind it is detective work into what caused what. Then, with a solution (or plausible hypothesis) in hand, they have to figure out the correct repair—how to re-ravel the skein of causation in a way that avoids collateral damage and ensures the problem will go away and stay away. That can be an elaborate caper story, carefully linking one crafty ploy after another in the most efficient sequence.

This line aroused a dialogue:

RHISCOTT: "This is just a beautiful turn of phrase."

STEWARTBRAND: "Thanks! I worried it might seem too abstruse."

MAKERJAK: "I love it as well."

Every noteworthy fix is a detective story or a caper story or both, and that's how they're told among mechanics.

It's a chancy situation. Repair is nearly always a disruptive intervention in an intricate system. Some of history's worst disasters came from mismanaged maintenance. A bungled routine system test caused the nuclear meltdown at Chernobyl in 1986. The catastrophic fire at Notre-Dame cathedral in 2019 came during a renovation of the badly rotted spire. In hospitals, when a medical examination or treatment *causes* illness, it's called "iatrogenic." Beware iatrogenic repair—when a sloppy attempt to fix a problem makes the problem worse or adds a new one.

Another author worth citing here is John Jerome. His 1977 book *Truck*, chronicling his yearlong project to revive a broken-down 1950 Dodge pickup, is regarded as a classic of truth telling about repair. For instance, when he thought his rebuilt engine wouldn't start because he had mounted a component backward deep inside the engine, he vented:

> Just because this stinking sag-ass trash heap happens to have its cam in backwards, let us not lose our patience. Just because the God damned ball-breaking ass-licking rotten scum-bag of a pig fucker is eating me alive, driving me right into the ground from fatigue and drudgery and boredom and hate and despair. Patience.[43]

Robert Pirsig honors the aggravation. "Motorcycle maintenance gets frustrating," he writes. "Angering. Infuriating. That's what makes it interesting."[44] His approach is to inspect the aggravation itself. He proposes that when you're baffled, it means your current theories about how to proceed aren't working. You have to empty your mind of them, Zen-style, which takes time. He advises:

> Just *stare* at the machine... Watch it the way you watch a line when fishing and before long... you'll get a little nibble, a little fact asking in a timid, humble way if you're interested in it...
>
> After a while you may find that the nibbles you get are more interesting than your original purpose of fixing the machine... Then you're no longer strictly a motorcycle mechanic, you're also a motorcycle scientist, and you've completely conquered the gumption trap of value rigidity.[45]

Three terms in his last sentence bear examining. Pirsig's technique for becoming a "motorcycle scientist" is through studying how he arrives at solutions. By "value rigidity" Pirsig means "an inability to revalue what one sees because of commitment to previous values."[46] (Once, during the Golden Globe Race, the skilled radio technician Donald Crowhurst had a shrewd wrong theory about why one of his radios wouldn't work and took it completely apart to find the elusive problem. It turned out the actual problem was a blown fuse, something he should have checked first.)[47] As for "gumption trap," the term and concept is Pirsig's most heralded contribution to the field of maintenance. To push through frustration takes a level of zeal that he calls "gumption." But certain situations in a repair job "destroy enthusiasm," he says, "and leave you so discouraged you want to forget the whole business. I call these things 'gumption traps.'"[48]

Of the seven gumption traps he names, Pirsig says five lurk in the mechanic; he calls them "hang-ups." The other two are in the machine; he calls those "setbacks." *Value rigidity* is one hang-up in mechanics. Another, he proposes, is an oversize *ego* and the defensiveness that goes with it. You need an unhindered, open mind to detect subtle signals from the machine you're trying to repair. If you can't think that way, Pirsig has a profound suggestion: Just fake it. Pretending to be open-minded can work well enough to reward you into gradually developing the real thing. (This works for a great many desired practices.)

Another hang-up is *anxiety*. When you're in a state of agitation, Pirsig writes, "you fix things that don't need fixing and chase after imaginary ailments. You jump to wild conclusions and build all kinds of errors into the machine because of your own nervousness."[49] To break the cycle, he advises first reading everything you can find that is relevant. It will be calming as well as helpful. Then, before you start the repair, map it all out on paper. As you keep adjusting the sequence of what you will do, ideas will come to you and your confidence will grow.

Impatience is another form of agitation that can lead to rushing into big mistakes. Pirsig has two recommendations here. One is to allow what at first seems like an excess of time for your tasks, because things almost always take longer than expected. The other is to take time to put away your tools periodically. It's a calming thing to do, and when your tools are where they belong, you won't get frantic trying to find them. (My further suspicion is that tidiness, like cleanliness, is a social signal, as much to oneself as to others. It's visible evidence that something is respected.)

Then there's the drain of gumption that comes with *boredom*. In that case, Pirsig's advice is to do something else for a while. Sleep is ideal. If you can't stop, dose yourself with coffee. Another solution is to treat the boring task as a ritual, alive with aesthetic nuance and a welcome respite from the clamor of thinking. Find your own contemplative practice in motorcycle maintenance.

As for the gumption traps that lurk in the ailing bike itself, a classic setback is what sometimes happens when the work is almost done. You've triumphantly reassembled the whole machine, and… "What's this? *A connecting rod bearing liner?!…*

Oh Jesus, everything's got to come *apart* again!"[50] To head off the crushing *out-of-sequence reassembly setback*, Pirsig again offers two techniques. One is to keep a notebook in which you write down every step of the disassembly process with reassembly in mind. The other is to lay out every disassembled part on a safe surface in precise sequence, left to right, top to bottom—every screw, washer, and pin.

Finally, an all-too-common gumption killer is the maddening *intermittent failure*. The power shorts out at times while you're riding. Back home, you do something you think will fix it, but on your next ride it's shorting out again, and you realize the problem will always disappear entirely in the shop. Despair ensues. Pirsig advises taking some tools with you on rides so you can stop immediately when there's a short and look for the problem while the machine is in the condition that caused it. "When intermittents recur," he suggests, "try to correlate them with other things the cycle is doing. Do the misfires... occur only on bumps, only on turns, only on acceleration? Only on hot days? These correlations are clues for cause-and-effect hypotheses."[51] Science your way out of the trap.

In the book, Pirsig explains that he was motivated to become an expert motorcycle mechanic by two disasters. First, on an earlier road trip with his son, his bike quit in the middle of a rainstorm. Pirsig figured that the rain caused the problem but nothing he tried would restart the engine, so he had the bike trailered home. Later he realised the problem wasn't the rain; it was him. He had simply run out of gas in the main tank and didn't think to turn on the petcock to the reserve tank, where there was plenty of gas. His one wrong theory about the cause of the problem had destroyed the trip.

The second disaster was the near destruction of his motorcycle by a pair of careless mechanics. Pirsig took it to them because it was overheating at high speed, causing the bike to seize dangerously. They began by misdiagnosing the problem: "Oh yeah. Tappets." Following expensive tappet work, the bike kept seizing. Three laborious, ineffective overhauls later, Pirsig watched one of the mechanics misuse a wrench so badly he rounded off the bolts holding both tappet covers. Pounding the bolts with a hammer and cold chisel to free them, he punctured the tappet covers and began damaging the engine. Pirsig stopped the work and drove the bike away. It was vibrating so badly that he pulled over and discovered that the mechanics had left the engine fastened to the frame by only one of its four bolts.[52]

After that, Pirsig decided to study everything he needed to know to fix his motorcycle himself. (Close examination of his motorcycle revealed the real cause of the overheating at high speeds: Oil flow was partially blocked by a tiny internal pin that had been sheared off by an earlier careless mechanic.) Driven by bad mechanics to become his own good mechanic, Pirsig learned that he had to acquire "a certain nondivided relationship between the mechanic and motorcycle, a craftsmanlike feeling for the work."[53] He says the essence of that relationship is *caring*.

Pirsig proposes that to become expert at keeping anything in good repair, you need to understand it in two ways: *how it works* and *how it's made*. How it works will be relatively straightforward and universal to similar machines. There are *operator-controlled* functions such as steering, throttle, and brakes, and *standard running* functions such as the actions of a four-cycle engine: intake, compression, power, and exhaust. Repairing your specific machine requires knowledge about how it was made—the nested component assemblies of the particular make and model you have. Pirsig writes:

> The engine consists of a housing containing a power train, a fuel-air system, an ignition system, a feedback system and a lubrication system.
>
> The power train consists of cylinders, pistons, connecting rods, a crankshaft and a flywheel.
>
> The fuel-air system components...[54]

This kind of understanding, Crawford writes in *Soulcraft*, is what it takes to become "masters of our stuff."[55] Just owning and using something is not yet mastery. We need "a basic intelligibility to our possessions: in their provenance, in their principles of operation, in their logic of repair and maintenance."[56]

Another element of mastery, says Pirsig, is to acquire the best tools you can afford and become skilled with them. Like the Golden Globe winner Sir Robin Knox-Johnston, Pirsig revels in listing the tools and spare parts he packed on the bike for a long road trip:

> A large, adjustable open-end wrench. A machinist's hammer. A cold chisel. A taper punch. A pair of tire irons. A tire-patching kit. A bicycle pump. A can of molybdenum disulfide

spray for the chain... Impact driver. A point file. Feeler gauge. Test lamp.

...Plugs. Throttle, clutch and brake cables. Points, fuses, headlight and taillight bulbs, chain-coupling link with keeper, cotter pins, baling wire. Spare chain.[57]

A large part of maintenance is routine inspection. Pirsig's habit on the trip was to take advantage of any pause to "check the oil level and tires, and bolts, and chain tension."[58]

In Pirsig's book there is never a mention of the make and model of his motorcycle. He did write, "I don't think I'll ever sell it. No reason to, really. They're not like cars, with a body that rusts out in a few years. Keep them tuned and overhauled and they'll last as long as you do. Probably longer. Quality."[59]

Robert Pirsig's motorcycle, a 1966 Honda Super Hawk, did outlast him. After he died in 2017, the Smithsonian National Museum of American History acquired what they described as "the most famous forgotten motorcycle in American history and literature."[60] Along with the carefully maintained bike, they procured his leather jacket, his favorite tools, and his worn 1966 Honda shop manual for the Super Hawk.

Motorcycle maintainers take heart from what they repair *for*—the glory of the ride. Crawford writes, "Fixing bikes is... meaningful because not only the fixing but also the *riding* of motorcycles answers to certain intuitions I have about human excellence. People who ride motorcycles have gotten

Figure 14. Robert Pirsig's *Zen and the Art of Motorcycle Maintenance* is a novelized account of a real road trip he took in 1968 with his troubled 11-year-old son Chris. One of their partners on the trip took this photo. (Pirsig and Chris wore helmets when riding.) Over the course of a month, they traveled 5,700 miles from Twin Cities, Minnesota, to San Francisco and back. His motorcycle was a 1964 Honda CB77 Super Hawk, Honda's first sport bike. The model's speed, power, and reliability made it a standard setter for modern motorcycles. (Sylvia Sutherland, courtesy of Mariner Books)

Figure 15. Pirsig's 1966 motorcycle was still in good repair and running in 2019 when his wife Wendy donated it to the Smithsonian. It showed 33,213 miles on the odometer. (Smithsonian)

something *right*, and I want to put myself in service to it." He describes riding behind an expert customer, who

> leans hard through a corner on the Blue Ridge Parkway, to the point of deliberately dragging his well-armored knee on the inside. This moment of faith, daring, and skill casts a sanctifying light over my work. I try to get his steering head bearings as light and silky as they can be without free play, and his swing arm bushings good and tight, because I want him to feel his tires truly. Only then can he make the road fully his own... I want to *hear* the confidence he has in the chassis I have tuned, expressed by the way he rolls on the throttle, brashly, through the exit of a turn. He is likely to pull away from me; I may find him waiting for me at Cumberland Gap with a verdict that lighter fork oil is called for, to get less damping in the front end.[61]
>
> Ride to live.

2.1a

VANDAMARLOW marked this passage and noted: "My doctor friends in the ER call motorcycles 'donorcycles'... and your stats prove what they see all too frequently."

Motorcycle Footnote 1: Ride to Die

Motorcycles tangentially confer a public benefit. Fatally injured motorcycle riders are in great demand at hospitals looking for transplantable organs because, one, the donor riders are often young and healthy, marred only by what killed them; and, two, there are quite a lot of them—around 5,400 a year in the US currently, a death rate 27 times greater per vehicle mile than in cars.[62]

The spare parts most needed for repairing humans in America are kidneys, livers, hearts, lungs, pancreases, and intestines. Tissues that can be grafted include bones, tendons, ligaments, skin, heart valves, blood vessels, and corneas. There are never enough donors to meet demand—over 100,000 patients are usually waiting for a donor organ, and 7,000 die every year because an organ could not reach them in time. The supply of organs and tissue from motorcycle riders has gone up in recent decades, especially in the 28 states that still don't require adult riders to wear helmets.

2.1b Motorcycle Footnote 2: The Instruction in Disassembly

This is a story of three generations in the family of the eminent mathematician-physicist Freeman Dyson, who died in 2020. In 1913, his father, Sir George Dyson, was a music teacher at Marlborough College in England. A friend related this anecdote to Freeman:

> Your father had just bought his first motorcycle. They wheeled it up to the top of the school playing fields behind the College, next to the open grassland of the Wiltshire Downs. Your father then proceeded to dismantle the machine entirely, laying out all the different parts neatly on the ground. Then he reassembled it again, putting it all back together correctly, so that when he filled the tank with petrol and turned on the motor, it started immediately. He mounted it, and drove off at speed.

When I heard this story from Freeman's son, science historian George Dyson, I asked him, "Did your dad do that kind of thing? Do you?"

Sir George's grandson George wrote back:

> Freeman, yes, but in a totally different non-physical way. I think anything he looked at he mentally dismantled down to the level of quantum field theory (below the level of even atoms or elementary particles) and then reassembled it before trusting it. I think that's how he could just walk into any field and make sense of it. But he didn't do it with his hands. I'm more like his father—physically taking things apart. Still maintain a 37-year-old Volvo, etc.[63]

2.2 Three Maintenance Philosophies Fought for Control of the Auto Industry

A fundamental question that will keep coming up is this: What are the best ways to *design* for maintenance? At the very beginning of the auto industry, no less than three radically different design-for-maintenance philosophies fought it out. One lost but not because of maintenance issues. The other two won big by rejecting each other's approach to maintenance.

Electric automobiles were the first to market, almost fully formed by the 1890s. In his 1988 book *The Evolution of Technology*, historian George Basalla writes:

> The electric car appeared to have all of the good points of the horse and buggy with none of its drawbacks. It was noiseless, odorless, and very easy to start and drive. No other motor vehicle could match its comfort and cleanliness or its simplicity of construction and ease of maintenance. Its essential elements were an electric motor, batteries, a control rheostat to regulate speed, and simple gearing. There was no transmission and, hence, no gears to shift.[64]

By the first decade of the 20th century, dozens of manufacturers in America and Europe were offering electric automobiles. New York, London, and Paris had fleets of electric taxis and delivery vehicles.

Gasoline-powered internal combustion engines were arriving at the same time, but they were a pain to run. Owners who could afford it hired a chauffeur to repair and drive the complex machines. The electric vehicles, by contrast, were so easy to use that they were marketed especially to women. An advertisement for the Rauch & Lang Carriage Company listed the advantages:

> **Electric Car Supremacy**
>
> ...Every member of your family can drive it—no chauffeur needed. It offers all of the best qualities of a gasoline car without any disagreeable features—danger from gasoline—offensive odors of oil—grime, dirt and the difficulties attending its operation.
>
> ...Its upkeep is far below that of the gas car, to say nothing of the depreciation difference...
>
> No machinery to get out of order—no mechanician needed—no engine trouble—no nerve racking gear clashing—no exhaust noise to disconcert the timid—nothing, but *just* the enjoyment of rapid transit in an easy, luxurious, delightful manner.[65]

Electric cars scored high on all issues of vehicle maintenance. Compared with gasoline engines, they had far fewer moving parts and almost none of the problems that come with

Figure 16. Looking exactly like horseless carriages, the first electric cars were simple to drive and maintain. This gentleman wore formal dress at the tiller of his early electric in 1899. (Steering wheels came later.) (Alamy)

Figure 17. Electric lorries being recharged at St. Pancras goods depot in London in 1917. The Midland Railway company had a fleet of 84. During World War I (1914–1918), the War Office encouraged the use of electric vehicles to free up petrol and horses for the military. The wooden wheels on these trucks indicate that they may have been manufactured in the US. Certainly the batteries were—the metal plate at lower left reads "Edison Accumulators."* Thomas Edison patented, promoted, and sold nickel-iron batteries that he claimed were better than the standard lead-acid batteries of the time. They were remarkably maintenance-free and long-lasting, but their low efficiency and high cost kept them from taking over the market. (SSPL/Getty Images)

*See Caption Notes on page 207.

Figure 18. A woman poses with a hand-cranked battery charger for her electric Columbia Mark 68 Victoria automobile in 1912. (Getty)

fluids—no explosive gasoline, no scalding water steaming out of the radiator, no oil to change. The electrics ran cool and quiet, with none of the high temperatures and percussion of internal combustion engines. Only the lead-acid batteries needed frequent attention; their water had to be checked and refilled, the accumulated sludge removed, and the positive plates cleaned.

The main limitation of the electrics was the short distance they could travel on a battery charge. Since they were at their best in cities, they were tailored for the urban wealthy with luxury items such as "upholstered chairs, clock, reading lights, lady's toilet case, gentleman's smoking set, flower vase of cut glass, and silk curtains," according to one chronicle of the age.[66] Shopping districts lured affluent customers with free charging stations. Owners who could afford it hired service centers near their homes to pick up, charge, clean, and maintain their electrics at night and deliver them the next day. The cars were stabled at night, like a horse.

Henry Ford's wife, Clara, loved her 1914 Detroit Electric Model 47 brougham and drove it well into the 1930s, even as her husband's mass-produced Model T was displacing cars like hers. A deluxe electric like Mrs. Ford's cost about $3,000. The Model T, in contrast, cost $300.

Aside from cost difference and traveling distance, other forces were at work to displace the electrics. Gasoline got steadily cheaper, thanks to widespread petroleum discoveries. And the invention of the electric self-starter in 1912 was a breakthrough. Drivers no longer had to risk broken teeth or a dislocated shoulder hand-cranking their car to start it; all they had to do was push a button. In addition, bicycle enthusiasts had founded the Good Roads Movement to force the government to pave rural roads, and early drivers of touring gas cars joined the movement. As soon as dirt roads began to be paved in the 1920s, gas cars sped far into the countryside and left the city-bound electrics behind.

Maintenance for electrics was easy thanks to their simplicity. A completely different kind of low maintenance arrived with the most epic exploit in early automobile history.

It took place in England and Scotland in the summer of 1907, when the demonstration model of a new internal combustion car was driven for 40 days straight—14,000 miles over mountainous country, in all weathers, at up to 80 miles an hour. An official judge from the Royal Automobile Club was on board to chronicle the number and nature of breakdowns during the endurance test. He recorded no breakdowns at all, apart from occasional stops to repair tire punctures common to all vehicles then. (A car doesn't just have moving parts; it *is* a moving part.)

Though the car was still running perfectly at the end of the test, the manufacturer disassembled the entire vehicle

Figure 19. The original 1907 Rolls-Royce, with its polished aluminum body and precisely tailored engine and drivetrain, ran so quietly it earned the name "Silver Ghost." Photographed in 1930. (Alamy)

anyway just to see which parts showed signs of wear. Several pins and a fan belt were replaced and a valve was reground. That was all. The company made sure that everything about the test and its results was celebrated in the press.[67]

The manufacturer was Rolls-Royce. The car was called the Silver Ghost, so named because of its swanky color and stealthily quiet running. Its price was high, but buyers deemed it an investment. They figured the value of a durable, gorgeous car widely described as "perfect" could only increase with time. Sure enough, a century later, most of the early Silver Ghosts are still running, each worth a fortune. (In 1921, a Silver Ghost was purchased in America for $12,000, about $190,000 in current dollars. According to the classic-car sales site Classic.com, of 31 Silver Ghosts sold between 2018 and 2023, six fetched over $1 million.)[68]

It was simple for salesmen to awe reporters and customers. They would place a coin balanced on edge or a brimming martini atop the Greek-portico radiator and invite the potential buyer to put the gearshift in neutral and accelerate the massive engine to full power. The balanced coin would not fall over; the martini would show not a ripple; the only sound was an intense, exhilarating purr.

Superb performance and reliability were designed into Rolls-Royces through how they were made. Each Silver Ghost was manufactured as a bespoke, unique vehicle, meticulously crafted by a dedicated team led by Henry Royce, the partner responsible for engineering. The experts assembling the car were armed, according to journalist Simon Winchester's 2018 book *The Perfectionists*, with "their loupes on lanyards, their slide rules, micrometers, calipers, verniers, and pressure gauges."[69] Charles Rolls, the partner who handled marketing, told a reporter:

> To produce the most perfect cars you must have the most perfect workmen, and having got these workmen, it is then our aim to educate them so that each man in these works can do his particular work better than anyone else in the world.[70]

Peak output from the Rolls-Royce factory, in the early years from 1908 on, was two cars a day.

Henry Ford, meanwhile, started manufacturing Model Ts, also in 1908, with the opposite goal. In order to build a car so cheap that his own factory workers could afford it, he abandoned construction by craftsmen and bet everything on a revolutionary substitute: the assembly line. His strategy came from a philosophy of precision and maintainability that was the reverse of the Rolls-Royce model.

At the Rolls-Royce factory, highly skilled workers used files to minutely adjust every part to fit perfectly in the car they were working on. At the Ford factory, files were forbidden on the assembly line because anyone using a file to improve a part would slow or stop the line. The parts would arrive at each station *perfect enough* that no microadjustments were needed.

Figure 20. Built in 1913, Ford's 100-acre factory in Highland Park, Michigan, was the largest in the world and the first to employ a moving assembly line. By 1924 it was producing 2 million Model Ts a year. This photo from 1915 shows the chassis assembly line at the point where the pre-assembled dashboards were mounted and hooked up to the engine. The chain-driven assembly line reduced the man hours it took to build a Model T from 12.5 hours to 1.5 hours. (Henry Ford Museum)

The worker's job was limited to assembly, usually of just a small portion of the car, and his moderate pay reflected the modest skill required. Thanks to the resulting efficiency, a finished Model T came off the line every three minutes.

The whole process depended on the manufacture of *truly interchangeable parts.* That was where Ford directed *his* obsession with precision. The specialized machine tools upstream of the assembly line had to make provably identical parts, which depended on extremely accurate measurements—finer than one ten-thousandth of an inch.

The two approaches to precision deployed by Henry Royce and Henry Ford led to two versions of success. Rolls-Royce produced the best cars in the world—nearly 8,000 of them in 20 years. In the same 20 years, Ford made the most popular cars—over 15 million. Royce hired and trained the world's best workmen; Ford hired and unleashed the most innovative production engineers. In his 1984 book *From the American System to Mass Production, 1800–1932,* historian David A. Hounshell writes:

> Ford had attracted to his factory a core of perhaps a dozen or a dozen and half young, gifted mechanics, none of whom had developed set ways of doing things. Encouraged by Ford, this group carried out production experiments and worked out fresh ideas in gauging, fixture design, machine tool design and placement, factory layout, quality control, and materials handling.[71]

By selling Silver Ghosts only to the rich, the former newsboy Henry Royce became wealthy himself. By pricing his Model Ts to sell to the middle class and poor, Henry Ford, born a farm boy in Michigan, became the richest man in the world. When he died in 1947, he was worth about $200 billion in current value. With every year of the Model T's production, he improved its quality and lowered its price. In 1908, a Model T cost $825. In 1916, it was $345. And in 1925, it was down to $260. (The equivalent decline these days would be from $28,000 to $4,600.)

At that time, nearly everyone lived and worked on farms or ranches and in small towns. Most of them were proudly self-reliant, skilled at repairing anything they owned. Ford knew that and designed for it. In his 1922 book *My Life and Work,* he wrote, "I believed... that it ought to be possible to have parts so simple and so inexpensive that the menace of expensive hand repair work would be entirely eliminated. The parts could be made so cheaply that it would be less expensive to buy new ones than to have the old ones repaired."[72] The car had only 100 different parts, and they remained standard from the first Model T to the last, from 1908 to 1927. Every junked car was a trove of reusable parts.

Ford built the car to be so robust that you could drive it anywhere, and so simple and transformable that you were invited to adapt it to your own needs. Wikipedia's entry for the Model T has this to say:

> It could travel a rocky, muddy farm lane, cross a shallow stream, climb a steep hill, and be parked on the other side to have one of its wheels removed and a pulley fastened to the hub for a flat belt to drive a bucksaw, thresher, silo blower, conveyor for filling corn cribs or haylofts, baler, water pump, electrical generator, and many other applications.[73]

The huge aftermarket for Model T add-ons and parts filled pages of the Sears, Roebuck catalog and the shelves of specialty shops. Conversion kits proliferated for Model T-based tractors, trucks, taxis, rail cars, snowmobiles, boats, and even airplanes.

In a revered 1936 *New Yorker* essay titled "Farewell, My Lovely!" E.B. White wrote:

> When you bought a Ford, you figured you had a start—a vibrant, spirited framework to which could be screwed an almost limitless assortment of decorative and functional hardware...
>
> ...you bought a Ruby Safety Reflector for the rear... a fan belt guide to keep the belt from slipping off the pulley...
>
> ...a radiator compound to stop leaks... special oil to prevent chattering... a tool box which you bolted to the running board, a sun visor, a steering-column brace... and a set of emergency containers for gas, oil, and water...
>
> ... Owners... invented gadgets to meet special needs. I myself drove my car directly from the agency to the blacksmith's, and had the smith affix two enormous iron brackets to the port running board to support an army trunk...
>
> ... Everybody carried a Jiffy patching set, with a nutmeg grater to roughen the tube before the goo was spread on. Everybody was capable of putting on a patch, expected to have to, and did have to.[74]

Figure 21. In 1915, auto dealer Ned Land adapted his Model T with tractor rear wheels to disk and seed his fields in north Texas. (Courtesy of Blake Cathey)

Figure 22. The Snowmobile Company of West Ossipee, New Hampshire, sold a popular conversion kit for the Model T. The kit was patented in 1917; this photo was taken in 1926. (Getty)

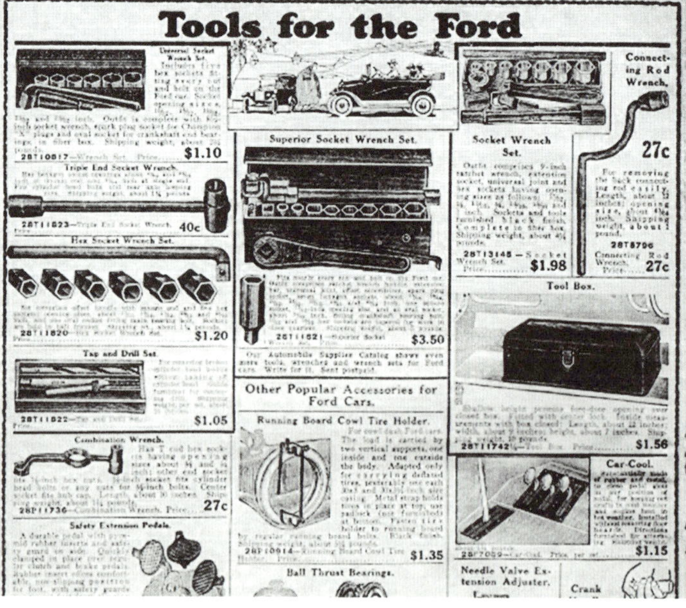

Figure 23. The 1919 Sears, Roebuck mail-order catalog offered many pages of parts, embellishments, and tools for Model T owners. (Sears, Roebuck and Co.)

Figure 24. This shop, photographed circa 1921, was dedicated solely to accessories and parts for the Model T. Visible are tire pumps, jacks, accessory brakes, side lights, and custom steering wheels (including the "fat man" wheel, which could be slid upward on the steering column for easier entry). (Source unknown)

Figure 25. The writer E.B. White and his wife, Katharine, in a 1923 Model T in 1940. White drove his first Model T across America in 1922, when it was a hero's journey to undertake. He was 23. (E.B. White, *Farewell to Model T*)

(Those days are gone. Nowadays, most drivers in developed countries don't know how to change a car's tire, much less how to patch an inner tube. On one-third of new cars there's no spare tire at all.)

It wasn't just the tires that needed diligent maintenance. Because the Model T had a simple, cheap "splash" lubrication system, its level had to be kept just right, and since there was no oil filter or pump, the oil would get dirty quickly and need replacement. Likewise, the simple, cheap "thermosiphon" water cooling system had no pump or thermostat, so the resulting slow flow easily collected dirt, rust, or air bubbles and clogged the radiator. The Model T's low-compression engine used low-octane gasoline, which led to carbon buildup on the valves and pistons. Staying ahead of those hidden problems took constant vigilance.

The owner had to learn certain skills to keep the car running. For example, you had to know what to do when the car wouldn't start no matter how hard you cranked it. The problem would almost certainly be the ignition or the fuel. To check the ignition, you would have to have someone else crank the engine while you determined whether electricity was getting to all four spark plugs. To avoid getting shocked, you would have to use a wood-handled screwdriver, touching its end to the engine block and leaning it close to each spark plug. A nice fat spark at all four spark plugs would impress bystanders and tell you the ignition was okay, so it must be a fuel problem. You would then have to start at the gas tank (empty?) and its vent (blocked?), then—groan—the carburetor. You would examine the spray needle setting, the choke valve, the drain valve, and so on.

When the engine started knocking, an experienced driver could tell from the sound whether it was caused by carbon buildup, a loose piston, a connecting rod, a main bearing, or a piston pin. The guilty cylinder could then be identified with a variation of the wood-handled screwdriver trick. With the engine idling, the screwdriver could be used to short the engine block to the exposed end of each spark plug to make its cylinder cease firing. When the knocking went silent, that was the problem cylinder.[75]

DGROVER: "John Steinbeck wrote in *Cannery Row*, 'Someone should write an erudite essay on the moral, physical, and esthetic effect of the Model T Ford on the American nation. Two generations of Americans knew more about the Ford coil than the clitoris, about the planetary system of gears than the solar system of stars. With the Model T, part of the concept of private property disappeared. Pliers ceased to be privately owned and a tyre-pump belonged to the last man who had picked it up. Most of the babies of the period were conceived in Model T Fords and not a few were born in them.'"

There were so many Model Ts that the specialized knowledge needed to keep them running became common knowledge. Anyone who tried to customize a Silver Ghost would probably screw up its tightly integrated perfection, so no one did. Every Model T, on the other hand, required some customization just to function well, and that inspired owners to devise all manner of new features and functions. A Rolls-Royce, impressive as it was, had just one use. When Ford put the power to make changes in the hands of his millions of customers, the Model T evolved rapidly in all directions and was put to countless uses.

Royce served his customers well by crafting a vehicle they could trust as totally reliable; it would never embarrass them by not running beautifully. Ford did a different favor for his customers: He designed a car so cheap that anyone could buy it and so uncomplicated that anyone could learn to do the

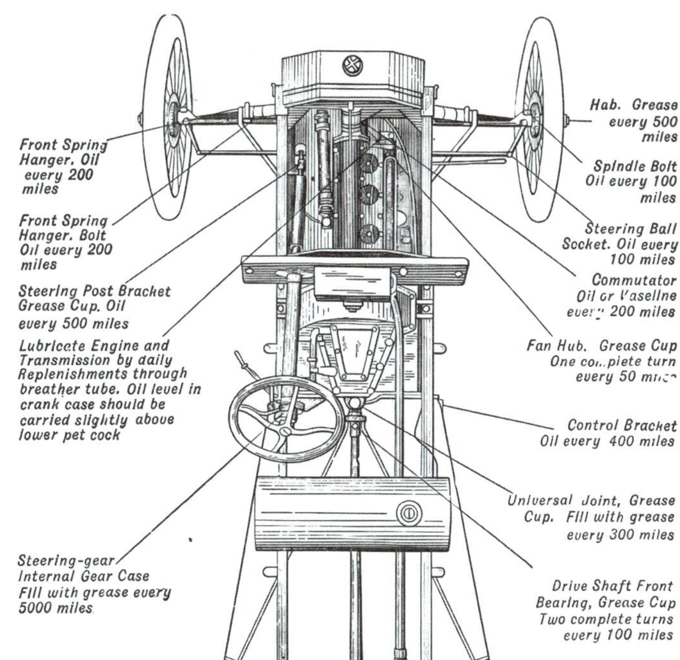

Figure 26. The Model T had 24 lubrication points that needed periodic servicing. If you didn't fill the grease cups and apply a grease gun to the fittings, your car would soon wear out as the moving parts turned into grinding parts. Often the grease would get so dirty on America's dusty, muddy roads that it would need to be completely replaced. (Victor Page, *The Complete Ford Model T Guide*)

Figure 27. Model T owners learned mechanic skills. This group may have stopped for a rest when they felt like it, or their Model T may have stopped when *it* felt like it. In either case, the four-cylinder, 20-horsepower engine evidently needed attention. Note the spare tire (not wheel). (US Census Bureau)

maintenance it required. Once customers took that on, they discovered that the *power to maintain is the power to improve*. The Model T inspired user creativity at a massive scale worldwide.

Decades later, something similar occurred when personal computers, then cell phones, then the World Wide Web unleashed user inventiveness at a massive scale. As each of those took off exponentially, the result was explosive. The Model T showed how that could happen.

2.3 Digression 1

Precision: How America Made Machines Make Machines

Some subjects helpful for thinking about maintenance don't really work as chapters, but they can be rooted in a chapter. Call them "digressions." This one looks at how something called "armory practice" eventually made it possible for Ford to fabricate the truly interchangeable parts that made 16.5 million Model Ts so cheap to produce and easy to repair. Achieving that level of uniformity took over a century of relentless obsession with *precision* in manufacturing.

My short history draws largely on two books: *The Perfectionists: How Precision Engineers Created the Modern World* (2018) by Simon Winchester and *From the American System to Mass Production, 1800–1932: The Development of Manufacturing Technology in the United States* (1984) by David A. Hounshell. In *The Perfectionists,* Simon Winchester declares:

> For precision to be a phenomenon that would entirely alter human society, as it undeniably has done and will do for the foreseeable future, it has to be expressed in a form that is duplicable; it has to be possible for the same precise artifact to be made again and again with comparative ease and at a reasonable frequency and cost.[76]

The governments of three nations—England, France, and America—forced the issue with their quest for uniformity in their military weapons.

In the 18th century, the military establishments of France and England were highly interested in cannons, primarily to use against each other. Before 1774, the big guns were inaccurate and often dangerous because of how they were made. The cast iron for each cannon was poured around a clay cylinder in the shape of the desired bore, but the result was uneven.

Then, in 1774, in England, a patent was issued for "a new method of boring cannons" to an ironmaster known as John "Iron-Mad" Wilkinson.[77] His innovation was to cast the cannon solid instead of around a clay cylinder. Running the cutting tool into the uniform iron produced a perfectly straight and smooth bore. Soon he was selling hundreds of accurate, identical cannons to the Royal Navy.

The following year, 1775, Wilkinson ordered one of James Watt's new steam engines to pump the bellows for his iron foundry's furnace. The massive engine arrived with a major defect that had frustrated Watt for years. Its efficiency depended on tightly sealing the steam in the six-foot-wide hammered-iron cylinder so the steam could drive the piston with maximum force, but there were gaps up to half an inch wide between the piston and the cylinder. The engine could barely run, thundering out clouds of waste steam through the gaps.

When Wilkinson applied his cannon-boring technique to Watt's steam engine cylinders, the gaps were reduced to one-twentieth of an inch. The tenfold improvement in precision, from half-inch cylinder gaps (the width of your little finger) to one-twentieth of an inch (the thickness of a dime), made all the difference. In short order, Wilkinson was providing hundreds of cylinders for the smooth-running steam engines that powered the Industrial Revolution. The first use of the enormous coal-burning steam engines was to pump water out of soggy England's coal mines. The more steam engines, the more coal. The more coal, the more steam engines. By 1800 there were 2,000 steam engines in England; by 1850, there were 10,000.[78]

Meanwhile, in France, the inspector of artillery, Lieutenant General Jean-Baptiste Vaquette de Gribeauval, was also introducing lighter, more accurate cannons bored from solid iron. (The process had been separately invented in 1734 by Swiss engineer Jean Maritz.) His new cannons were designed to be part of what came to be known as *le système Gribeauval*. It gave France the best artillery in Europe. Hounshell explains why:

> Beginning in 1765 Gribeauval sought to rationalize French armaments by introducing standardized weapons with standardized parts. The uniformity system, Gribeauval reasoned, would allow complete interchangeability in the French military; parts of small arms and artillery pieces could be easily interchanged.[79]

FISCHER: "I ran across a bit from Alice Rawsthorn in the design documentary *Objectified*. She mentioned that Ying Zheng, first emperor of China, designed standardized arrows and bows. Before that, each soldier created their own arrows, which would not fit in their comrade's bows."

STEWARTBRAND: "Fascinating. I will use the Ying Zheng story in the next chapter. Thank you for it."

The idea of interchangeable parts was something new in the world. Its supporters knew it could change the world, but they quickly discovered how hard it would be to accomplish, for social as well as technical and financial reasons.

An innovative Paris gunsmith named Honoré Blanc became a protégé of Gribeauval. In response to demand by the military for cheaper manufacture of the army's flintlock muskets, Blanc developed a rigorous procedure that required each of the complex parts in the musket's flintlock-and-trigger assembly to be a perfect replica of an ideal model. The parts were handcrafted with file and lathe to match the model, using

Figure 28. Honoré Blanc designed and handcrafted the flintlock mechanism of France's famed Model 1777 Dragoon Muskets to have the world's first interchangeable parts. Pictured here is a Model 1777 An. IX Dragoon Musket, dated 1811. (Royal Armouries)

gauges and calipers for exact measurement and jigs to support and guide the shaping of each component. The technique yielded parts standardized to a tolerance of one-thousandth of an inch.

In 1785, Blanc stunned French government officials with a public demonstration before a large audience. He disassembled 25 lock assemblies, tossed the dozens of separate parts into boxes, and shook the boxes. With parts randomly selected from each box, he reassembled 25 new locks. They all worked perfectly.

A guest at the occasion was the minister to France from the new United States, Thomas Jefferson. He was so intrigued he went to visit Blanc's factory. In a report to John Jay, the American secretary for foreign affairs, Jefferson wrote:

> [Blanc] presented me with the parts of 50 locks taken to pieces and arranged in compartments. I put several together myself taking pieces at hazard as they came to hand, and they fitted in the most perfect manner. The advantages of this, when arms need repair, are evident.[80]

Three years later, Jefferson urged Secretary of War Henry Knox to adopt Blanc's techniques for the American military. Knox paid no attention.

In Paris, Gribeauval provided Blanc with a government-supported workshop, which produced quantities of identical muskets for the next four years. It ended in the upheaval of 1789, when supporters of the French Revolution, who called themselves sansculottes, destroyed Blanc's workshop. According to Simon Winchester,

> there was a fast-growing, eventually fanatical, opposition among the sansculottes toward mechanization, toward efficiencies that favored the middle classes, toward techniques that put the honest work of artisans and craftsmen to disadvantage. By the turn of the century, the idea of interchangeable parts had withered and died in France.[81]

It was a triumph of Rousseau's romanticism over Enlightenment rationality. Craft was extolled; uniformity was deplored. That sentiment would bedevil technical progress ever after. Romantics always side with John Henry against the Rationalists' steam drill. But I propose that in all cases of machines threatening labor, it's worth looking closely at the welfare of the customers as well as the workers. Blanc's use of gauges to make interchangeable parts did indeed threaten the practices of the gunsmith's guild. But the guild, like others at that time, was secretive, intensely protective, conservative, and politically powerful. It protected its members at the expense of their customers, who had to put up with guns that were often shoddy and always expensive.

Blanc provided his customers, the soldiers of France, with the best—and most repairable—muskets in Europe. The revolutionaries who wrecked his shop were protecting the commercial interests of a few instead of the use interests of the many. Thirty years later, the French military was stuck with the worst muskets in Europe. In his 1997 book *Engineering the Revolution*, historian Ken Alder writes that the result was 50 years of "technical amnesia" that caused France to "miss the boat on the Industrial Revolution then unfolding in Britain."[82]

America's earlier and more conservative revolution led to the opposite of France's outcome. Secretary of War Knox may have shown no interest in French muskets with standardized parts, but American military officers paid close attention to the thinking of their French allies in the revolution—especially to Louis de Tousard, one of Lafayette's senior officers. After the war, Tousard returned to France and studied the advantages of *le système Gribeauval*. Back in America, he joined the US Corps of Artillerists and Engineers as a major and became the leading champion of weapons standardization in the War Department.

Figure 29. Described as "the greatest disgrace ever dealt to American arms" in the Oxford History of the United States,* the Battle of Bladensburg took place in August 1814. This carefully researched illustration shows the critical moment just before the poorly equipped and poorly led American troops (in blue), who outnumbered the British four to one, panicked and fled the battlefield. The redcoats then marched into an undefended Washington, DC, and burned the government buildings. One consequence of the defeat was that a reform-minded War Department resolved to never again arm its troops with weapons that could not be repaired in the field with interchangeable parts. (US National Park Service)

President Washington encouraged Tousard to write a book on the subject. While working on his three-volume *American Artillerist's Companion*, Tousard proposed building a school to train officers. That led directly to President Jefferson creating the US Military Academy at West Point in 1802. Every officer in the US military studied Tousard's textbook, in which he warned, "Want of uniformity impeded for a long time the progress of the French military, as it will that of America, unless a similar system is adopted."[83]

Then came the War of 1812 with Britain and the most humiliating battlefield defeat in American history. In the summer of 1814, just northeast of Washington, DC, a force of 1,500 British regulars routed 7,000 American troops in the infamous Battle of Bladensburg, then burned all of the public buildings in the nation's new capital. As a result, the US Army Ordnance Department was given new powers and new leadership: West Point officers who had been inspired by Tousard. Hounshell describes their motivation:

> From their experience in the War of 1812, when a vast number of arms had been damaged beyond repair in the field but could have been fixed had parts simply interchanged, the ordnance officers believed that uniform parts manufacture... would be worth almost any price.[84]

Historian Merritt Roe Smith, who studied the matter even more closely, explains how what began as a goal became an obsession. In his 1977 book *Harpers Ferry Armory and the New Technology*, he writes that the department's leaders were determined to eliminate the

> costly maintenance and repair problem that had plagued military authorities since the days of the Revolution. Intrigued,

even infatuated with the possibility of making arms with interchangeable parts, [they] became zealous advocates of the "uniformity system" and relentlessly pursued the idea of introducing it at the national armories.[85]

The War Department was committed to the idea of standardized weapons, but it would have to deliver the institutional clout, cash, and patience to make it happen—if such a breakthrough at scale was even possible. Though nothing like it had been attempted before in the new nation, early steps in the process looked promising. Yankee ingenuity began developing transformative tools at the nation's two armories: the Springfield Armory on the Connecticut River in Massachusetts and the Harpers Ferry Armory on the Potomac River in Virginia.

The first consequential innovation came at the Springfield Armory in 1819 with Thomas Blanchard's invention of the soon-famous Blanchard lathe.

Wooden gunstocks on muskets had never been uniform because they had to be hand-carved into their irregular shape. Blanchard devised a machine tool that could rapidly carve the complex shape because it was guided by an identically shaped cam. The Springfield Armory describes it this way: "An iron master form, in the shape of the musket stock, slowly rotates,

Figure 30. The Blanchard lathe carves the wooden gunstock on the left into a perfect replica of the metal form on the right. As the gunstock and metal form revolve slowly in unison, the belt-driven cutting wheel on the left moves with the tracking wheel on the right, carving, in just nine minutes, a gunstock identical to every other gunstock produced by the machine. The lathe in this photo was manufactured in Massachusetts and purchased by the British government in the 1850s. It was used at the Enfield Royal Small Arms Factory in north London for 100 years. (American Precision Museum and Springfield Armory)

allowing a guide wheel to roll over it and to direct, in turn, the cutting wheel as it makes identical movements on the slowly rotating wooden stock blank."[86]

Blanchard's invention was important; his patent earned him a lifetime of royalties as the idea was widely applied to shaping axe handles, shoe lasts, and the like. Even more significant was how he set up the gunstock operation. By 1826 he had created a sequence of 14 special-purpose machine tools to do the interior carving that made each gunstock ready to receive its metal barrel and lock-and-trigger mechanism. The process was quick, precise, and uniform. Work previously done by 75 men now required only 17. "Blanchard," writes Hounshell, "had shown Americans the meaning of mechanization."[87]

Blanchard's lathe made him rich, but the main breakthrough to uniformity came down south at the Harpers Ferry Armory. A man from Maine named John Hall created a two-leveled invention like Blanchard's: a novel device followed by a machine-based system to manufacture it at scale. His device was a new kind of rifle that loaded from the breech instead of the muzzle. When the Ordnance Department tested Hall's prototype breechloaders, they found that soldiers could fire the guns three times faster than traditional muzzle-loading rifles with equal accuracy. The War Department ordered 1,000 Hall rifles in 1819 and subsidized their manufacture at the Harpers Ferry Armory. That was new—the government committed to pay both for the guns *and* for developing the novel process that could fabricate them.

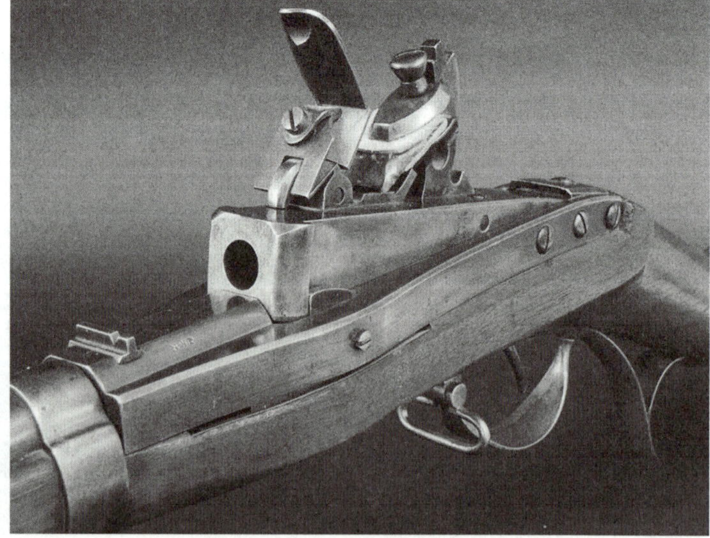

Figure 31. The world's first machine-made, mass-produced interchangeable parts were in John Hall's breech-loading flintlock rifles, commissioned in 1819. This one has the breech receiver open, ready to be loaded with gunpowder and a round lead bullet. All of the 20,000 rifles manufactured at the Harpers Ferry and Springfield Armories had completely interchangeable parts, made possible by John Hall's system of extremely precise gauges and machine tools. (Museum of Connecticut History, Connecticut State Library)

1. Jaw screw
2. Cock (bottom is tumbler)
3. Cock screw
4. Pan & touch hole
5. Trigger & dog
6. Main spring
7. Main spring screw
8. Sear spring
9. Sear spring screw
10. Catch spring
11. Catch spring screw
12. Catch
13. Axis pin hole
14. Trigger stop pin
15. Chamber
16. Supporters
17. Hammer or frizzen
18. Frizzen spring
19. Frizzen spring screw
20. Frizzen screw
21. Set trigger adjustment screw
22. Catch pin
23. Preventer or shoulders

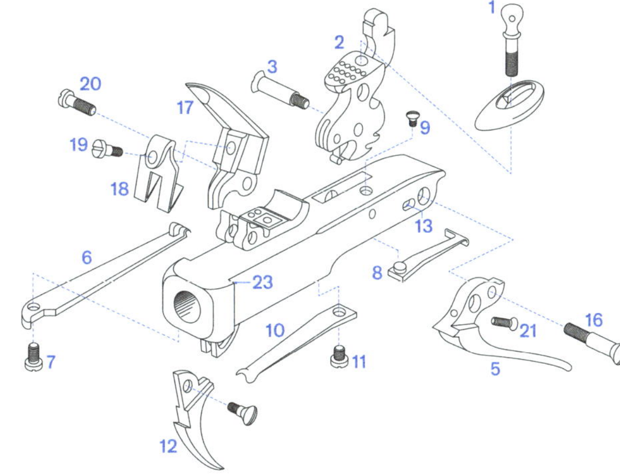

Figure 32. John Hall's breech-loading rifle lock had 23 identically machined parts. Standard flintlock muzzle-loading muskets of the time had only 11 parts.

Several features were unique to Hall's manufacturing system. The most important was his commitment to creating genuinely interchangeable parts entirely with machines instead of handcrafting them with file and lathe, as Blanc had in France. According to Simon Winchester,

> for a lock merely to work required a tolerance of maybe a fifth of a millimeter; to ensure that it not only worked but was infinitely interchangeable, he needed to have pieces machined to a *fiftieth* of a millimeter.[88]

Figure 33. John Hall's workers used inspection gauges, like these for the later Model 1841 rifle, to verify the exact dimensions of every part before assembly. The gauges would gradually lose accuracy with use and had to be calibrated against a master set of gauges and adjusted or replaced when they deviated from the required tolerance. (Smithsonian)

To achieve that degree of precision, Hall took gauges—hardened steel templates into which the various dimensions of the parts had to fit exactly—to a new level. He used 63 gauges in three sets. One set was used by the fabricators of the parts and another by the inspectors. The third set ruled them all. It consisted of 63 master gauges against which the other two sets were checked when a discrepancy was detected between them. Using gauges this way was a laborious, painstaking process, but no one could duplicate Hall's success in making interchangeable parts without it.

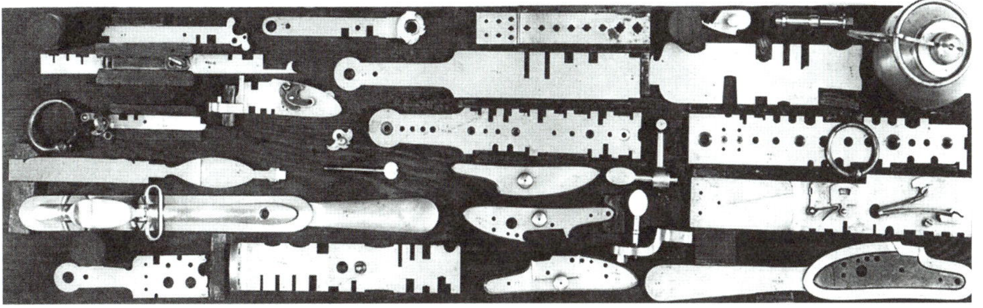

Like Henry Ford a century later, Hall focused on perfecting the *system* that fabricated the product. He employed as many mechanics to work *on* the machines as there were operators *of* the machines. In Hounshell's words, Hall recognized "that skill within this system was confined to construction and maintenance of machines and tools rather than to the production of the good itself."[89] Most of the operators were unskilled boys aged 12 to 15. Hall proudly declared that "one boy by the aid of these machines can perform more work than ten men with files, in the same time, and with greater accuracy." The skilled men in his shop were paid $1.75 a day; the boys got 35¢ a day. Each boy could run three or four machines at a time because, thanks to another innovation, the machines would stop automatically after completing a task. (Presumably, some of the boys grew up to become readily employable skilled mechanics. As America industrialized, veterans of armory work were in high demand everywhere.)

Hall's mechanized technique of making guns was considered such a perversion of the traditional craft of gunsmithing that the director of the Harpers Ferry Armory, James Stubblefield, sought to undermine Hall at every opportunity. In 1826 Stubblefield instigated a congressional investigation into what he called "the waste & extravagance of the Publick money on the Patent Rifle."[90] Accordingly, a team of three expert examiners was sent to Harpers Ferry to report on the conduct and value of Hall's system. They immersed themselves in the operation for three weeks and returned to Washington with a 17-page report that had language rare in government writing. It read in part:

> Capt. Hall has formed & adopted a system, in the manufacture of small arms, entirely *novel* & which no doubt, may be attended with the most beneficial results to the Country...
>
> The machines we have examined, effect this with a certainty & precision, we should not have believed, till we witnessed their operations...
>
> In point of accuracy, the quality of the work is greatly superior to any thing, we have ever seen or expect to see... It fully demonstrates the practicability of what has been considered almost or totally impossible by those engaged in making arms, viz., of their perfect uniformity...[91]

As described in the report, Hall's special-purpose machine tools were uniquely sturdy and massive, made totally of metal, unlike the wood-framed machines in other shops. The belts driving his machines could be finely adjusted to run up to 3,000 revolutions a minute without vibration. The report noted that his system was expensive to build, but once it was running, it could turn out large quantities of perfectly identical rifles at a low cost per rifle. That raised the question of maintaining Hall's machines over time. The examiners reported:

> The cost of keeping them in repair, it is believed, will be small, as their constituent parts are generally made extremely strong & provision is made for detaching all such parts, as are most liable to get worn, and for repairing them, whenever they may require it.[92]

Hall paid the same attention to the repairability of the rifles themselves. In a manual he wrote for their operation and maintenance, he noted:

> The guns will seldom or never require to be taken apart—for the lock will go quick and easy, even when very dirty, in consequence of its peculiar construction; but whenever it may become necessary to take it apart, the operation may be performed easily without a vise, and with barely the aid of a screwdriver.[93]

He made sure that each rifle's kit included an elegant tool he'd designed, a combination screwdriver and touchhole pick. When the rifle was not in use, Hall advised that it be left with its breech receiver open, but if "by negligence or by accident the receiver has long been left shut, and has become rusty," it might be hard to open. In that case, he said, "strike on the

Figure 34. A steel combination tool was issued with every Hall rifle. The pick was used to clear the flintlock's touchhole; the screwdriver disassembled the lock mechanism for cleaning.

barrel just in front of the receiver with a piece of wood repeatedly, and the receiver will gradually be forced up."

Hall's manual even included a trick for undoing a common mistake he had noticed. In cleaning the barrel, the soldier might forget to begin with a wet wad of cloth on the cleaning rod and start with a dry cloth instead, which would get solidly stuck in the barrel. Now what? "A little water may be poured into the muzzle to moisten it, it will then move easy; as the receiver is open, the chamber will remain dry," Hall wrote.[94]

A rifle manual that tells you where to whack it or pour water in it when it gets stuck exudes the "practicability" that so impressed the congressional investigators of Hall's system. Everybody in America's budding manufacturing industry learned about the system, because the Ordnance Department insisted that all innovations at the national armories were the opposite of secret and could be copied royalty-free. This was done to ensure that private manufacturers of firearms for the government were up to speed with the armories, and that the development of all American machine tools kept pace with the best. Armory visitors were encouraged to make drawings, borrow patterns, and study any technique they might want to employ in their own shops.

Of course, the new methodology and skills were transmitted mainly via the minds and hands of the increasingly expert workers who moved freely between the government armories and private factories. None of that would have happened without the determined leadership of the Army Ordnance Department, particularly by Colonel George Bomford, who headed the department for 20 years, from 1821 to 1842. According to Merritt Roe Smith,

> Bomford would do more than any other person to make the uniformity system an American reality...
>
> ...The development of uniform standards required a total investment exceeding two million dollars... Only the federal government could have financed such a massive undertaking. That it did so over a forty-year period underscores the importance not only of capital but also of longevity as a key ingredient in the evolution of complex technological systems.[95]

(Conversely, in France, an equally determined bureaucrat prevented the Industrial Revolution from taking root in his nation for half a century by enforcing his belief that social harmony was more important than manufacturing uniformity. Jean Jacques Basilien Gassendi was a lifelong enemy of Gribeauval. After Gribeauval's death in 1789, Gassendi had Napoleon appoint him to Gribeauval's old position as head of artillery. Gassendi then subverted the arms testing process to support his lie that interchangeable parts could never be "achievable, affordable, or desirable,"[96] and he made sure that became the official position of the French government. America, meanwhile, was proving the opposite.)

An unscheduled test of Hall's system came in 1852, when a catastrophic flood at Harpers Ferry damaged 9,000 percussion muskets manufactured by Hall's machines. Nine thousand muskets had to be disassembled, cleaned, and reassembled randomly. They all worked perfectly.[97]

Smith writes that Hall's achievement "formed the taproot of modern industrialism."[98] He adds:

> Armory practice spread to technically related industries and by the late 1850s could be found in factories making sewing machines, pocket watches, railroad equipment, wagons... [and later] agricultural implements, bicycles, gramophones, cameras, and automobiles.[99]

In 1854, British inventor Joseph Whitworth reported to Parliament in London what he had observed on a tour of American factories. Americans, he wrote, "call in the aid of machinery in almost every department of industry. Wherever it can be introduced as a substitute for manual labor, it is universally and willingly resorted to."[100]

How armory practice played out in 19th-century American factories is worth a close look because, while the public sector had the deep pockets, perseverance, and leadership to build the mechanized interchangeability that the military required, it took two special skills of the private sector to bring manufacturing to a level that would enable Henry Ford to soar. The skills were mass production and mass marketing on a global scale.

The Ordnance Department at that time had no occasion to manufacture a million *anythings* and no interest in marketing except to their paymasters in Congress. Samuel Colt, by contrast, was a marketing maestro. He was a popular lecturer before he secured patents in the US and Britain in 1836 for

Figure 35. Samuel Colt invented product placement advertising. In 1855 he commissioned George Catlin, the famous artist of the American West, to produce a series of paintings and lithographs featuring the new Colt guns. The subtitle in this lithograph reads, "I gave five shots to the right and left, four of which were fatal to the heart and all in less than half a minute." (British Museum)

his handgun combining a rotating cylinder of preloaded chambers with a fixed barrel. After a few missteps, he established a large factory in Hartford, Connecticut, that embodied the maturing of armory practice with 400 specialized machine tools. Hounshell notes that Colt opted for "overwhelming emphasis on mechanization rather than on the pursuit of precision" because the "parts of the Colt revolver... did not come close to being interchangeable."[101] If you needed to replace a part in your Colt pistol, you had to go to a gunsmith to get the part crafted to fit your gun.

The public thought the parts were interchangeable because Samuel Colt never ceased telling everybody that they were. He paid reporters to write laudatory articles and gave their editors a free revolver. He paid popular artist George Catlin to include Colt guns in his paintings. He flooded newspapers with ads. A slogan he promoted—"God created men, Colt made them equal"—became a popular adage in America. (The idea of self-defense has sold countless guns since then.)

When Colt realised that foreign heads of state would not receive him without a title, he had the governor of Connecticut appoint him as a colonel in the state militia. "Colonel" Colt then gifted the leaders and celebrities of Europe with gorgeously engraved Colt revolvers.[102] At the Great Exhibition of 1851 (also known as the Crystal Palace Exhibition) in London, where the Colt exhibit was a hit, he demonstrated the interchangeability of the weapon's parts by disassembling 10 guns, mixing the parts, and reassembling them.[103] (They were specially prepared guns.)

When Colt built a second factory in London, it became

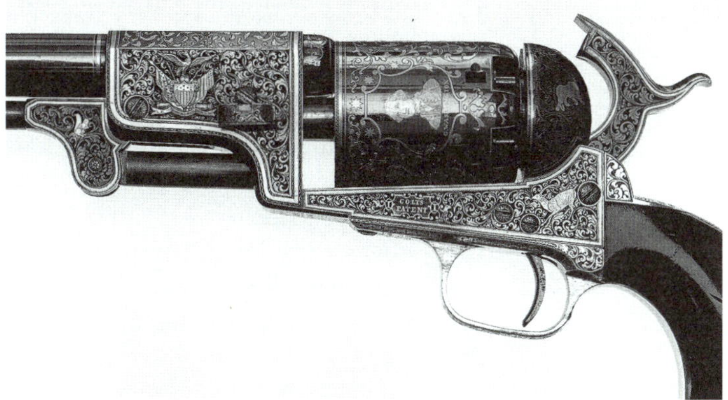

Figure 36. In 1854, "Colonel" Colt presented the mate of this engraved revolver to the Czar of Russia, Nicholas I. German artists at Colt's factory in Connecticut engraved the blued steel with dense scrollwork and elaborate gold inlay portraying patriotic American imagery along with Colt's name. At the time, Russia was at war with Britain and France in the Crimea. Colt enthusiastically sold weapons to both sides. This pistol is on display at the Metropolitan Museum in New York. (Metropolitan Museum of Art)

the embodiment of what Europeans called "the American system" of mechanized manufacturing. Charles Dickens himself paid a visit and praised the factory. According to a historian at the Smithsonian, Colt's guns were becoming "America's most exportable manufactured item."[104]

The guns soon found a vast new market in America. With the coming of the Civil War, Colt's Connecticut factory had 1,500 workers producing 150,000 guns a year, used by Confederate and Union soldiers alike. Another market opened out West for the frontier's Indian fighters, sheriffs, and outlaws. All that time, the revolver's design kept evolving toward its peak in the 1873 Colt Single Action Army revolver. Known to the trade as the "Peacemaker" and to legend as the six-shooter that won the West, it is still in production today—presumably now with interchangeable parts.

Samuel Colt had a good product, a great manufacturing system, and world-class marketing. Yet his success was surpassed by the humble sewing machine. It was the first mechanical device developed for domestic use by women, a tool for repair as well as for creating. Two American companies dominated the emerging mass market for sewing machines. Both adopted Colt practices but in different ways.

The first to take the lead was Wheeler & Wilson. Its factory in Connecticut was run by a former Colt mechanic who turned it into a duplicate of Colt's armory, then refined the process until it could produce genuinely interchangeable parts. By 1860, the totally mechanized factory was turning out 25,000 sewing machines a year. That same year, Wheeler & Wilson's main competitor, I.M. Singer & Co. in New York, made only half as many, in part because its sewing machines were built by hand like Honoré Blanc's dragoon muskets back in the

1770s, only without Blanc's insistence on precision. Even when Singer came to dominate the industry from the 1870s onward, it didn't bother to make machines with interchangeable parts.

What happened? "While Wheeler & Wilson was busy perfecting a manufacturing plant," writes Hounshell, "Singer laid out a worldwide marketing strategy."[105] Like Samuel Colt, Isaac Singer advertised extensively in newspapers. Like Colt at the 1851 Great Exhibition in London, Singer made a splash at the 1855 Paris Exposition, winning first prize. As with Colt, brilliant marketing was more important than perfect uniformity in the product. By 1861 Singer was an international company, selling more of its sewing machines overseas than in America.

Singer specialized in paying close attention to its clientele, deploying an army of women trained to teach customers how to use the sewing machine. Purchase was made easy with a rent-to-buy arrangement. The most popular model, designed for home use, had sales of 4 million units in 18 years. Mass marketing had arrived.

Figure 37. In 1857, Singer had an opulent showroom on Broadway in New York City to demonstrate its sewing machines. The company produced only 3,500 that year. By 1886 Singer was manufacturing a million a year, still without interchangeable parts, and the company name had become a synonym for "sewing machine." This illustration is from *Frank Leslie's Illustrated Newspaper* in 1857. (Alamy)

America's bicycle craze of the 1890s brought a new kind of vehicle to the world. It also introduced a swarm of innovations that paved the way for Ford's assembly line.

Bicycles had been invented in France, developed in England, and came to America primarily through the efforts of a Bostonian named Albert Pope. In 1878, Pope started importing "high-wheel" bicycles from England. Then he took over an old rifle factory in Connecticut that had been converted to a sewing machine factory and converted it into a bicycle factory. There he perfected his own flavor of armory practice, making the nation's highest-quality bicycles under the brand name Columbia.

Figure 38. In 1895, Madison Square Garden in New York City hosted America's first National Bicycle Exhibition, with hundreds of exhibitors. By then, nearly 1 million bicycles were sold each year. Trade shows like this one were later repurposed to sell automobiles. (*Scientific American*)

Figure 39. In 1897, the New York-based satirical weekly *Judge* featured this cartoon with the caption "A Modern Street Scene." Some of the signs read: "PARK: Only those mounted on wheels will be admitted," "We Have Given Up Making Sewing Machines and Manufacture Only BICYCLES," and, under a crossed-out "Livery Stable," a new sign reads "BICYCLE RIDING ACADEMY." (Judge Publishing)

The market took off after 1887 with the arrival from Coventry, England, of a new design for bicycles that anyone could ride. John Kemp Starley's innovation had two wheels of the same size with the rear wheel driven by a chain. It was called a "safety bicycle" to distinguish it from the high-wheel bikes that were anything but safe, given how far the rider was from the ground, seated precariously on top of the towering front wheel.

Bicycle design matured with astonishing rapidity. In "A Tale of Invention: The Birth of the Modern Bicycle," science historian John S. Reid explains why: "The requirement to make the bicycle light, strong and efficient because of the personal limitations of its power source... pushed the bicycle into the forefront of mechanical technology."[106] To reduce friction, ball bearings were developed to make the pedals, cranks, and wheels spin easily. Mounting the saddle on a spring made the ride less jarring. So did the introduction of inflatable tires, and their rubber gave riders the traction and flexibility over bumps needed for a vehicle whose power source was onboard. The best configuration of wheel spokes was determined to achieve a rigidity that could support a load 10 times the weight of the wheel. By 1897, some American bike manufacturers were

Figure 40. Bicycles from 1887, 1897, and 2018. Only intrepid men could ride the 1887 high-wheel bike. The 1897 Columbia "safety" bicycle was configured for women in long skirts. So was the 2018 Raleigh bike, some 120 years later. Both weigh about 30 pounds. Developed in just 10 years, nearly all the design elements and features of the 1897 bicycle are still standard. (Clockwise from top left) 1887 high-wheel bicycle (Alamy), 1897 "safety" bicycle (Alamy), 2018 Raleigh bicycle (Raleigh).

experimenting with handlebar controls for a gearshift and braking calipers.

Most of the design refinements came from Albert Pope's factory, where innovative scientific testing of each component kept reducing the bike's weight while improving its reliability. Every chain was stress-tested to just below the breaking point before assembly. A device for distorting the frame, Hounshell writes, "enabled Pope designers to change frame designs to minimize usage of tubing while maintaining frame strength and rigidity."[107] The hundreds of parts were machined to perfect interchangeability as precise manufacturing finally came to full maturity in America's bicycle factories.

An eyewitness of the phenomenon was Fred H. Colvin, a lifelong chronicler of machine tools and coauthor of the authoritative *American Machinists' Handbook*. In his 1947 memoir, *60 Years with Men and Machines*, he had the following observations about what bicycles wrought:

> The advent of the bicycle gave the first real impetus to the designing and building of machine tools for mass production... The greatest single contribution that the safety bicycle

has made to mechanical progress was the ball bearing, the manufacture of which... has developed into a vast industry involving a large number of new tools, new machines, and new processes... The need for strong, light wheels led wire-makers to investigate thoroughly the tensile properties of various kinds of steel wire for the spokes; the desire for a pneumatic tire that could be repaired on the road led to the development of the inner tube and to extensive research into the technology of rubber... The theory and practice of mass production was applied for the first time on a large, international scale in the bicycle industry, which had some 25 million customers at the turn of the century.[108]

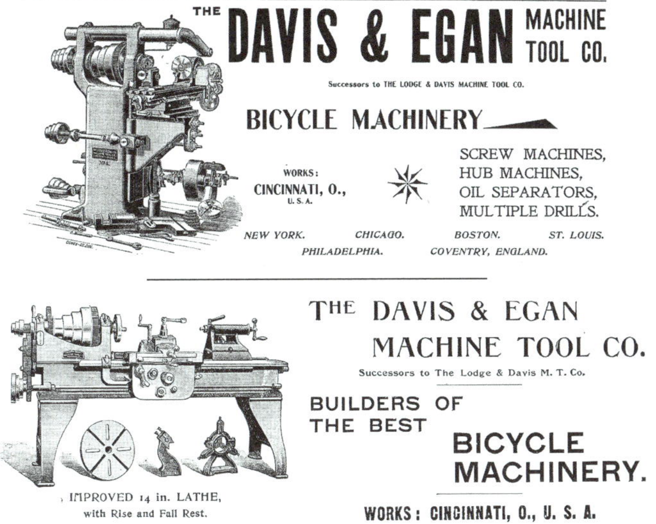

Figure 41. Two machine tools invented in America transformed manufacturing for the bicycle boom: the universal milling machine (top) and the horizontal manual turret lathe (bottom). The graduated spindles on the left allowed the belt-driven machines to run at varied speeds and, if you made a half-twist in the belt, in either direction. (*American Machinist*)

Two American machine tools in particular made bicycle mass production possible: the universal milling machine, invented in 1862, and the turret lathe, invented in 1845 and automated in 1873.

On the lathe, the "turret" is a rotating tool holder that can quickly switch multiple cutting tools in perfect alignment, allowing for multiple operations on the same workpiece without manually changing tools. Representing a huge improvement in efficiency and accuracy, the machine was ideal for the mass production of identical parts such as screws, bolts, nuts, valves, and fittings. Automated turret lathes of the time could turn out 200 flawless screws an hour. The universal milling machine, meanwhile, could cut, drill, shape, or mill a workpiece from any angle at any speed, even cutting the helical

Figure 42. For the first hundred years of machine tools, factories were a forest of belts. The leather straps transferred power from overhead shafts driven by a waterwheel or steam engine down to the spindles of each machine. In this 1909 photo of a bicycle factory in Coventry, England, the female workers have their hair tied up to avoid being caught in the hazardous belts. By the 1890s, Coventry led the industry, with 40,000 workers in 250 factories making bicycles. (Alamy)

flutes in twist drills. It was ideally suited for fashioning the intricate parts of bicycles such as gears and flat-link chains.

The bike factories of the East Coast were producing bicycle parts like gun parts, by drop-forging each part in solid steel and extensively milling it. Then, a former toy factory in Chicago called Western Wheel Works introduced a breakthrough in metalworking. The company showed that by feeding sheet steel into power presses for punching and stamping, it could shape nearly every component at a lower cost than with forging and without sacrificing quality. Its bicycles were lighter and cheaper than anything the competition could offer. As a result, Western Wheel became America's leading bike manufacturer, and everyone else, including Pope, adopted its steel stamping techniques. (So did Henry Ford. In 1911, he bought a New York company that stamped bicycle parts from sheet steel and moved it to Michigan to do the same for the Model T. The technique became standard in the auto industry.)

Back at Columbia, Albert Pope devoted as much of his entrepreneurship to building the market for cycling as he did to crafting the company's brand. In 1880 he initiated two magazines, *The Bicycling World* and *The Wheelman.* Along with promoting bicycling clubs, he founded the League of American Wheelmen, which, with his financial backing, launched *Good Roads* magazine and the Good Roads Movement. He even donated $6,000 to MIT to create a department of road engineering.[109] Like England's Roads Improvement Association, also founded by bicyclists,[110] the Good Roads Movement in

Figure 43. Western Wheel Works in Chicago introduced steel stamping machines that could turn out top-quality parts that formerly required laborious milling, including "hubs, steering heads, sprockets, frame joints, crank hangers, fork crowns, seats, handlebars, and brackets."* (Western Toy Company)

America successfully lobbied local and national legislators to begin paving the nation's dirt roads.

One of Pope's most popular schemes was a series of monthly contests and exhibitions of posters promoting Columbia bicycles. Many of the posters depicted bicycles as a mode of liberation, especially for women. In 1896 the leading pioneer of women's rights, Susan B. Anthony, discussed bicycling in an interview with Nellie Bly for the *New York World*. Bly reported:

Figure 44. Albert Pope's advertising posters often celebrated the freedom bicycles gave to women. (Alamy)

> "Let me tell you what I think of bicycling," Miss Anthony said, leaning forward and laying a slender hand on my arm. "I think it has done more to emancipate women than anything else in the world. I stand and rejoice every time I see a woman ride by on a wheel. It gives [a] woman a feeling of freedom and self-reliance. It makes her feel as if she were independent. The moment she takes her seat she knows she can't get into harm unless she gets off her bicycle, and away she goes, the picture of free, untrammeled womanhood."
>
> "And bloomers?" I suggested, quietly.
>
> "Are the proper thing for wheeling," added Miss Anthony promptly. "It is as I have said—dress to suit the occasion. A woman doesn't want skirts and flimsy laces to catch in the wheel. Safety, as well as modesty, demands bloomers or extremely short skirts. You know women only wear foolish articles of dress to please men's eyes, any way."[111]

There was such an appetite for the novelty of independent, adventurous transportation that well over a million bicycles were sold every year in the mid-1890s. Thanks to the bicycle craze, Americans were feeling the call of the open road, and factories equipped with a new generation of machine tools were mass-producing innovations such as ball bearings, stamped metal parts, and pneumatic tires. With these elements in play, the market and manufacturing were ready for the advent of automobiles. Why pedal when you could *drive?*

Henry Ford industrialized precision at a scale that changed the world. Shortly before he started making cars, the machine tool industry had been transformed by a new kind of extremely tough high-speed tool steel developed by what was called the taylor-white process. For the first time, pre-hardened steel components could be machined with high accuracy and consistency. Ford deployed the new capability throughout his Highland Park factory.

Figure 45. All in one operation, the Model T's engine block had 24 holes simultaneously drilled and reamed in three sides by the kind of special-purpose machine tool that made Ford's factory, pictured here in 1914, such a miracle of efficiency. (Henry Ford Collections)

An abiding problem in manufacturing was the lack of a uniform standard of extreme precision for calibrating all of the measuring tools in a factory. This problem was solved in 1896 when Swedish machinist Carl Edvard Johansson conceived the idea of 103 perfectly dimensioned gauge blocks that could, in combination, make 20,000 measurements in increments of a thousandth of a millimeter. By the time he set about crafting nonmetric sets based on fractions of an inch, his "Jo blocks," as they were called, had become so popular that his compromise between the British inch and the microscopically larger

American inch caused both nations to convert their standards to his. He settled on 25.4 millimeters to the inch, and that's where it remains today. In 1923, Henry Ford bought Johansson's operation and made it part of the Ford Motor Company.

_BRIANPOTTER: "Fun fact: During World War I, Jo blocks had to be smuggled past German blockades. Ford bought the rights in response to ensure the US would maintain access to the technology."

Henry Ford's 1930 book *Moving Forward* has a chapter titled "A Millionth of an Inch." In it, Ford declares, "Without the Johansson blocks and tools, our tool rooms would be blind."[112]

A factory's toolroom is the heart of the operation. The highly skilled technicians in the toolroom, called tool and die makers, are responsible for the reliability and accuracy of all of the machine tools on the production line. In Ford's factory, that accuracy depended on 140 complete sets of all 103 Johansson gauge blocks. They were crafted in Johansson's laboratory on-site, which was kept perpetually at 68 degrees

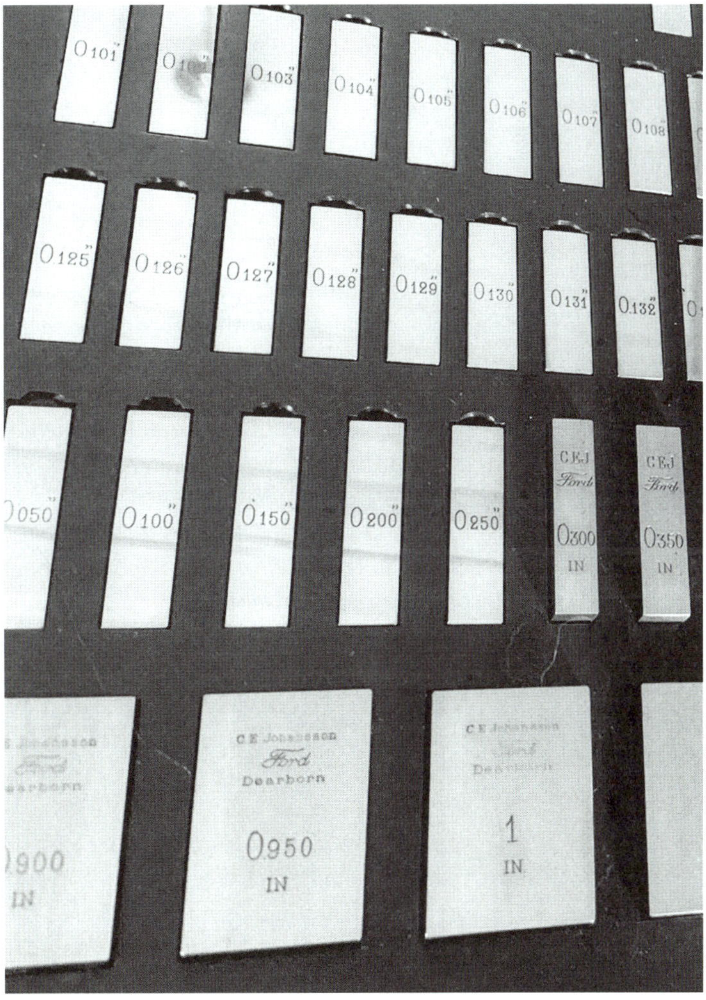

Figure 46. This set of 103 gauge blocks made by C.E. Johansson for the Ford factories was presented by Henry Ford to his friend Thomas Edison. It is now on display at the American Precision Museum in Windsor, Vermont. Gauge blocks are crafted to be so ultraflat and smooth that they stick together when placed against each other. They can only be parted by "wringing"—slide-twisting—them apart. Thus, when stacked, the sum of the amounts on each stacked block is accurate within a millionth of an inch. (American Precision Museum)

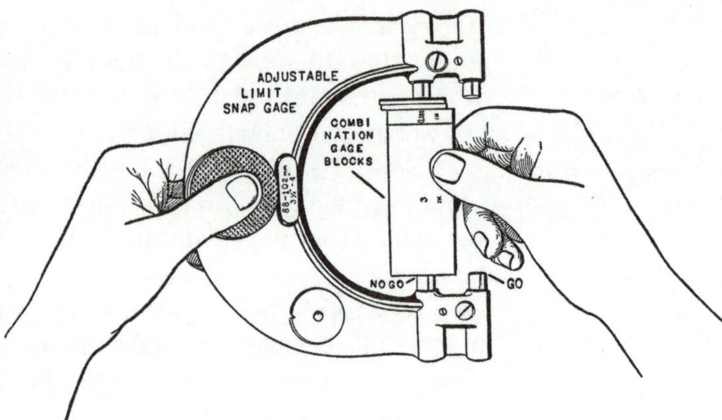

Figure 47. Here, a combination of Johansson gauge blocks is used to calibrate a go/no-go gauge (sometimes spelled "gage"). Henry Ford described its use for rapidly measuring the exact diameter of a rod: "The gauge would consist of four pieces of steel, set in a horseshoe-shaped holder, two far enough apart to allow the rods to pass between them... and the other two close enough together to keep the rods from passing between them... The points may be spaced to the specified distances apart by setting them to gauge blocks, or combinations of them, of the measure value desired." In order to be within the limits, the part should be able to pass through one set of steel pieces but not the other: "If the part passes through both, it is too small; if it passes through neither, it is too large."* (Robert H. Smith, *Book of Advanced Machine Work*)

Fahrenheit (20 degrees Centigrade) to ensure that thermal expansion did not affect the precision of the blocks.

The century-long development path from government guns to private guns to sewing machines to bicycles to Ford automobiles radiated to the world because Ford invited the world to study his innovations in detail. David A. Hounshell writes:

> The Ford company was completely open about its organizational structure, its sales, and its production methods... Ford engineers had no skeleton closets in their factory. Proud of their work, they were anxious to have technical journalists tour the shops and write extensive articles about Ford methods...
>
> As a consequence of Ford's openness, Ford production technology diffused rapidly throughout American manufacturing.[113]

And if anyone wanted to achieve the highest level of precision in their factories, Ford had Johansson gauge blocks to sell them. For him, transparency and marketing were both parts of one grand tactic: Be the news.

It had all started with a simple-seeming goal: weapons with parts so interchangeable that soldiers could easily make repairs in the field. The precise manufacturing that solved the problem made mass production possible. Mass production, in turn, made every kind of complex mechanism cheap, reliable, and readily available—clocks, reapers, typewriters, cameras, on and on through all the consumer goods of the 20th century.

Did Henry Ford know the names of the giants whose shoulders he stood on? He probably knew about the marketing

Figure 48. An inspector at a Ford plant in 1924 uses a Johansson-calibrated go/no-go gauge to ensure that a part has precisely the correct diameter. Every part in the car was tested this way. The inspection gauges had an accuracy of plus or minus four-millionths of an inch. The master gauges against which they were checked every day had an accuracy of plus or minus two-millionths of an inch. (Henry Ford Collections)

genius of Albert Pope, Isaac Singer, and Samuel Colt. He always honored inventors like Thomas Blanchard and John Hall. But he likely remained unaware of the goal setters and resolute funders behind it all: the government bureaucrats Jean-Baptiste Vaquette de Gribeauval in France's War Ministry and Louis de Tousard and George Bomford in the US War Department. In a sense, Ford's Model T was just another uniform device to emerge from Gribeauval's *système*—now renamed "the American system"—and far from the last.

America's experience in the 19th century proved that government funding and oversight could accomplish seemingly impossible technological breakthroughs. Merritt Roe Smith points out that fully mechanized manufacturing was only the first such outcome. Later products of what he calls "military enterprise" include:

> Computers, sonar, radar, jet engines, swept-wing aircraft, insecticides, transistors, fire- and weather-resistant clothing, antibacterial drugs, numerically controlled machine tools, high-speed integrated circuits, nuclear power—these are but some of the best-known industrial products of military enterprise since World War II.[114]

Military enterprise to accelerate innovation was institutionalized in 1958, when President Eisenhower established the Advanced Research Projects Agency (ARPA) within the Department of Defense. A by-product of America's Space Race with the Soviet Union, ARPA was generously funded to pursue blue-sky, high-risk research projects under rigorous supervision by the agency. Later renamed DARPA—the D is for "Defense"—the agency had such spectacular success that it became the model for other government departments: IARPA for the intelligence community, ARPA-E for the Department of Energy, and ARPA-H for the Department of Health and Human Services.

Back in 1775, a twentieth-of-an-inch tolerance was a breakthrough for steam engines. One hundred and thirty-three years later, the tolerances of a millionth of an inch at the Ford factory amounted to a 50,000-fold improvement in precision. In Simon Winchester's *The Perfectionists*, the automobile chapter ends just halfway through the book. There is always a use for more precision. He goes on to chronicle such feats as the accuracy of atomic clocks in GPS satellites (millionths of a second) and the beyond-microscopic dimensions that extreme ultraviolet lasers can reach for fabricating transistors in computer chips: five nanometers.[115] (A nanometer, they say, is to a tennis ball as a tennis ball is to the Earth.) GPS and extreme ultraviolet lasers were both invented at DARPA.

Each new product of greater precision has to provide affordances for maintenance and repair, and every new user has to learn them—how to tune a carburetor, how to replace a typewriter ribbon, how to back up a computer—and then, in time, has to forget them as even more precise devices come along that require different skills.

Although precision in manufacturing was initially driven by the quest for conveniently interchangeable parts, it soon proved to be about something far deeper than maintenance and repair. The progress from efficient steam engines to an efficient assembly line to the extreme density of nanoscale microchip fabrication is a saga of multiplying capabilities for humanity. Simply by becoming masterly at doing ever more with ever less, again and again, we live in a time of such potency that we have to be careful about what we wish for. Maybe considerations of long-term maintenance of the whole process can help us frame our desires judiciously. Bear in mind: Tinier always means faster.

Meanwhile, some other modes of progress *are* driven by straightforward maintenance issues. The endless battle against corrosion is one. I'll come back to it in a later digression.

2.4 What the Three Most Popular Cars in History Have in Common

The three most popular cars ever made have this in common: they were cheap, they retained their basic design for decades, and they invited repair by the owner. The Ford Model T sold

16.5 million units between 1908 and 1927. The Volkswagen Beetle sold 21.5 million between 1938 and 2003. The Lada "Classic" from Russia sold 20 million between 1970 and 2012.[116] (Other cars with best-selling reputations, such as the Toyota Corolla, Toyota Hilux, and Ford F-Series pickups, retained only their brand names while changing radically in design.)

Just as Henry Ford in 1908 designed the Model T for a dirt-road America, the designers of the Lada—it was just a beefed-up Fiat sedan—in 1970 were realistic about what their customers would have to deal with in the Soviet Union. The country was vast, the roads terrible, and the winters brutal. There were no repair shops. Fuel quality was unreliable. Potential customers had barely any money. So Ladas were made as cheap as possible. (A joke of the time: "How do you double a Lada's value? Fill it up with petrol.") One driver recalled the Lada's "strangely brittle plastic, lumpy foam and clingingly uncomfortable fabric, hideously inadequate fittings, parts that came off in your hand when using them; erratic gauges, either wildly optimistic or non-functioning; keys that broke in the locks; seats that listed drunkenly."[117]

Figure 49. A Lada owner in Borovsk, Russia, working on the exhaust system in 2019. This is my favorite photo of auto repair ever. The crushing car. The owner's embrace. The cry for help in open hood and trunk. The ramp and block of wood used as a jack under the rear tire. (Andrey Rudakov/Bloombery)

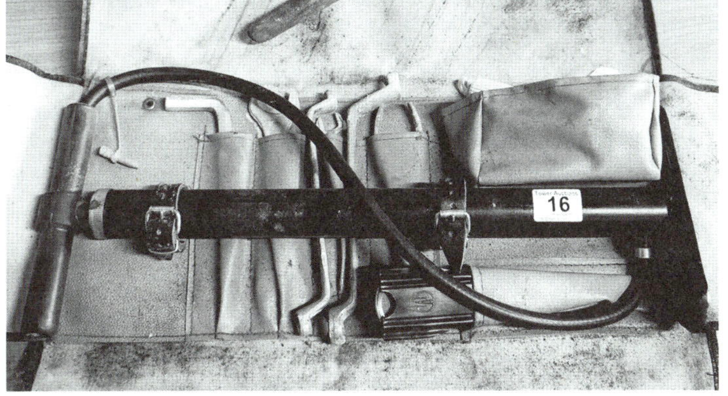

Figure 50. The toolkit provided with each Lada. From left to right: tire pump; Allen wrench (12 mm); two double-end wrenches (17 mm, 13 mm, 10 mm, and 8 mm); two double-offset box wrenches (13 mm, 12 mm, 19 mm, and 17 mm); slip-joint pliers; 12-volt yellow work light; and a tire pressure gauge in the black plastic case. (Tower Auctions)

In their favor, the Ladas were ruggedized with thicker steel panels than the original Fiat, as well as higher road clearance and sturdier transmission and brakes. The engine ran roughly, but it could handle any fuel. Since the cars required constant maintenance, they were designed so that the owner could do the work. Each Lada came with a set of tools for fixing it. The windshield wiper blades were made to be easily removed because in Russia, if the driver didn't lock them inside the car when parked, they would be stolen.

The Lada had a continuity advantage similar to Ford's Model T, remaining in production virtually unchanged for 32 years. Consequently, as one article points out, "While the car was notoriously unreliable, it was also ridiculously easy to fix. You could pluck a part from virtually any Lada ever made, jam it into yours, and get it going again."[118]

For many in Russia and the Eastern Bloc, and for millions of Lada export customers worldwide, it was their first car, and loved accordingly.

Volkswagens were similarly loved by my generation of hippies in the 1960s and '70s. Along with 21 million VW bugs, some 12 million boxy VW vans with the same air-cooled engine as the bug were sold between 1950 and 2013. (My van was made in 1962; I painted it military-spec jungle camouflage with a general's star on the door and often lived in the back, which I customized with plywood into an inviting bed.)

Figure 51. Hippies painted everything they owned. This was my VW van in 1968. (Stewart Brand)

The American appetite for do-it-yourself began long before our time. Farms and ranches had always depended on do-everything-yourself skills. A kid growing up there spent all day on maintenance chores, learning from older family members and ranch hands how to fix the tractor, mend barbed wire fences, manage the wood stove, and do the laundry. By the early 20th century, servants were disappearing in towns and home ownership was taking off. By the 1950s, doing one's own home repair and improvement became a popular weekend pastime. Retired men had a shop in the basement or garage. Teenagers hot-rodded their cars.

But as cars became more complex and costly, professional mechanics took over more and more of vehicle repair. If your car needed work, you were supposed to take it back to the dealer, which turned out to be both expensive and frequent.

LYNDON: "There's the phenomenon of the driveway mechanic. This winter in New Orleans I saw an engine swap happening over the course of a couple of evenings in the curb lane of a busy street (Esplanade Ave). You never see this in a polished place like Vancouver. It seems like the more relaxed a place, the more engine swaps you see happening on the streets in the evenings."

We hippies were so set on escaping dependency that we wouldn't listen to our elders, professionals, or even knowledgeable neighbors. Instead, we relied on books to teach us how to garden, raise goats, build geodesic domes, and do all the other "basics" we were determined to "go back to." Most of the generational techniques and tools hippies sought could be found in one place: the *Whole Earth Catalog*, a do-everything-yourself compendium I cofounded and edited from 1968 to the early '80s. Of course, one whole page was devoted to taking care of your VW. The star of the page was one of the best repair manuals ever created: *How to Keep Your Volkswagen Alive*, written by John Muir and illustrated with pizzazz by Peter Aschwanden.

Hippies had a peculiar aspiration about money. We aimed to live as adventurously as possible on as little money as possible. Travel was done by hitchhiking or driving the cheapest car we could find: the Volkswagen. Our imperative for self-reliance required that we repair it ourselves. John Muir saw that desire and met it with something revolutionary, a self-published book with a cheery, dead-accurate subtitle: *A Manual of Step-by-Step Procedures for the Compleat Idiot*. He assumed, rightly, that his readers had a funky car with funky problems and no idea how to solve them.

Figure 52. The cover of John Muir's legendary VW repair manual. (Peter Aschwanden)

First self-published in 1969, Muir's *How to Keep Your Volkswagen Alive* remains alive itself to this day. It's currently in its 19th edition, with updates by Tosh Gregg and illustrator Peter Aschwanden. Air-cooled VWs have not been manufactured since 1980, except for a few in Mexico until 2003. The

Figure 53. Muir's manual provides an overall understanding of the car's workings and nomenclature, as well as exhaustive details on how to fix everything that might go wrong. (Peter Aschwanden)

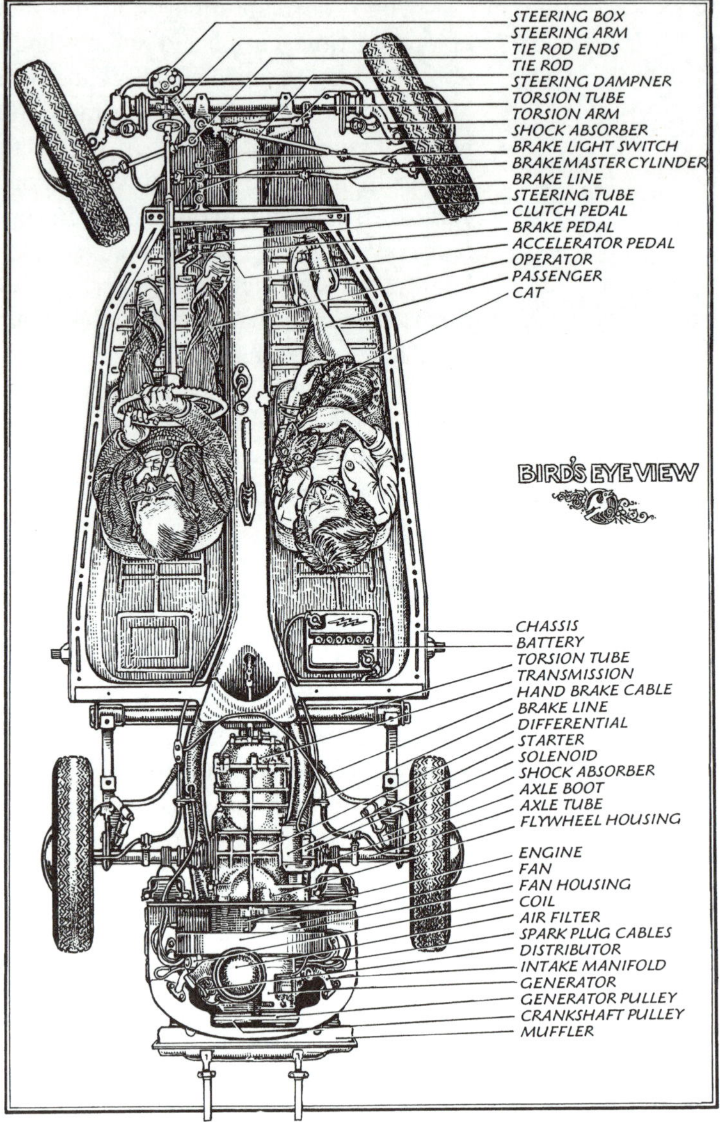

continuing popularity of Muir's book indicates that a hell of a lot of VWs have been kept alive, probably via his manual.

Muir organizes the book around the problems a VW owner might face, with chapters titled "Engine Stops or Won't Start," "Red Light On! (Generator or Alternator)," "Green Light On! (Oil)," "Maintenance (3,000 Miles)," "Volkswagen Doesn't Stop (Brakes)," "Shimmies and Shakes (Front End)," "Slips and Jerks (Clutch)," and "Grinds and Growls (Transaxle)."

Muir teaches how to listen for problems. If there's a funny noise and pushing the clutch down silences it, it's a transmission problem, but if it changes to a different funny noise, it's a

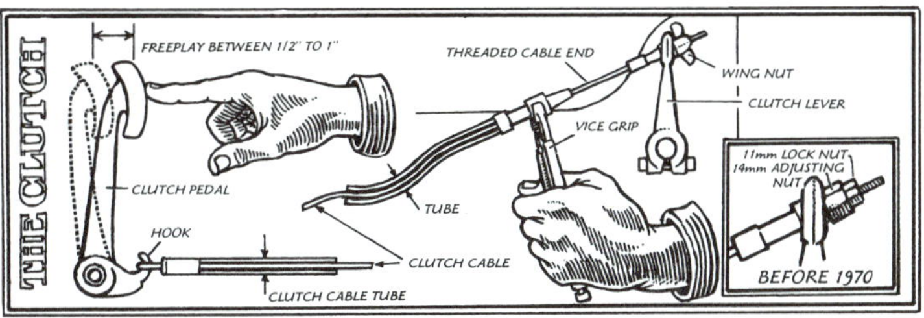

Figure 54. Muir on adjusting the VW's clutch: "Take the vice grip, the 14mm and 11mm end wrenches, plus the flashlight for locating things with you under the car. Scrooch under the car with your head almost under the left rear axle. Look up."* So begins his meticulous directions, including a note that if your car was built in 1970 or later, you don't need the end wrenches; your fingers are sufficient to turn the wing nut. This drawing covers both alternatives. (Peter Aschwanden)

LYNDON: "This is a beautiful point. Many in my generation (millennial) have never experienced this firsthand. You do not know the full meaning of ownership until you have maintained or modified the thing. You cannot buy full ownership; you must participate."

clutch problem. "Loose valves tweedle," Muir writes. "Very loose valves clatter."[119] He gives his reader the confidence to undertake even heroic tasks like diving into the engine's guts to adjust the valves every three months. He writes in capital letters: "DOING THE VALVES, TIMING, AND MINOR MAINTENANCE ON YOUR OWN CAR WILL NOT ONLY CHANGE YOUR RELATIONSHIP WITH YOUR TRANSPORTATION BUT WILL ALSO CHANGE YOUR RELATIONSHIP WITH YOURSELF!"[120]

(That general point is still valid, but car tune-ups are a thing of the past these days. Items that needed frequent adjustment, like the carburetor and distributor, have been entirely supplanted by electronic fuel injection and computerized ignition systems that adjust themselves. The new platinum spark plugs are so durable they seldom need checking or replacing. Those things came about because *low maintenance sells*. This fact is a key driver of progress in the world.)

While Muir teaches his readers every kind of repair their VW might ever need, he especially teaches them how to avoid having to do it. "Warm up the engine before moving—ninety percent of engine wear happens in the first fifteen minutes of operation," he advises. "Warming up the engine is a sacred rite... Do this warm-up thing and it will make your VW last a third longer, minimum."[121] He recommends that you idle for at least half a minute (up to three minutes in cold weather), then drive gently for the first mile. The point, he explains, is to give the engine cylinders time to get fully coated with oil. "Now when I put a load on the engine, it is the oil that carries the load, not the metal."[122] Modern engines are no longer so delicate about needing a warm-up, but their requirement for consistently renewed oil hasn't changed a bit.

Hippies were so dedicated to living in the moment that preventive maintenance was a difficult lesson for us. Something breaking is a big event. Repairing the broken thing is a big event. But preventing the thing from breaking is a nonevent. Doing a responsible task like changing the oil doesn't come naturally. It's a messy chore, tedious and thankless. There's no reward when you do it and no reward later—just the unnoticeable absence of pain.

To acquire the adult discipline of preventive maintenance, us flower children had to learn at soul depth the remorseless logic of "An ounce of prevention is worth a pound of cure." For example, being oblivious and lazy about the oil in a Volkswagen leads inexorably to a "tickety" sound in the engine becoming a "tockety" sound, Muir points out. Then a connecting rod bearing gives out and the broken rod bursts through the crankcase, at which point your car is not only dead in the road but you've also got to buy a new engine.

Once the pain of avoidable repair is severe and repeated a few times, the attraction of heading off the pain with preventive maintenance becomes compelling. Then all we need is knowledge of what to do and when and how to do it.

The universal advice from professional maintainers to every impatient equipment misuser is an expletive: "Read the fucking manual!" By which they mean: Part of taking proper ownership of something is to study its manual first. Along with offering a good introduction to the thing owned, owner's manuals are usually informative on preventive maintenance, and most provide a troubleshooting section for simple fixes. If you take the thing to a professional for what turns out to be something minor that is thoroughly covered in the manual, they may well charge you extra for being obtuse and annoying. If you ask online for a solution, you'll get the acronym version: "RTFM!"—typically used, according to Wikipedia, "to reply to a basic question where the answer is easily found in the documentation, user guide, owner's manual, online help, internet forum, software documentation, or Frequently Asked Questions."[123]

The *Whole Earth Catalog* eventually faded from usefulness, along with most printed manuals, because they were totally replaced by the internet. How that played out is worth another digression.

2.5 Digression 2: From Manuals to YouTube (with a Detour)

2.5a Six Great Manuals in History

The Wikipedia entry on John Muir says this:

> Muir's self-published edition [of *How to Keep Your Volkswagen Alive*] sold more than two million copies to become one of the

> most successful self-published books in history. Its wry subtitle… preceded (and perhaps inspired) the "for Dummies" books from IDG Publishing and the Complete Idiot's Guides from Dorling Kindersley.[124]

(About 2,500 *For Dummies* manuals have sold 200 million copies since 1991. Among them are books on beekeeping, motorcycling, pickleball, cybersecurity, and ukulele. The similar *Idiot's Guide* series has 120 titles in print, with subjects ranging from pregnancy for dads to flipping houses; a different *Complete Idiot's Guide* series has 183 titles, with subjects ranging from world history to street magic.)

Once a device has a large enough user base, two manuals are often considered essential. One is the shop manual that comes from the manufacturer. The second is an emergent third-party manual that goes deeper and wider, often with an artfulness and outsider attitude the manufacturer would never dare display. Robert Pirsig carried two manuals on his motorcycle along with his tools: the *Shop Manual* from Honda for the specifics of his Super Hawk and *Chilton's Motorcycle Troubleshooting Guide* for the then-current state of the art of motorcycle maintenance.

Unlike an owner's manual, a shop manual—sometimes called a workshop manual or service manual—is all about repair, complete with parts lists and wiring diagrams. The best ones have a hands-on, user-based perspective and lucid prose. The worst defy understanding. In *Shop Class as Soulcraft*, Matthew Crawford deplores how "the writers of modern

Figure 55. These two motorcycle manuals accompanied Robert Pirsig on the 1968 road trip that inspired *Zen and the Art of Motorcycle Maintenance.* His 1964 Honda *Shop Manual* is now at the Smithsonian National Museum, along with the Honda Super Hawk he rode in 1968. (Smithsonian)

manuals are neither mechanics nor engineers but rather technical writers."[125] Often, the clueless text for foreign-made items has gone through an even more clueless translator.

The best manuals for amateurs include point-of-view photos, often with a hand in the foreground using the right tool at the right place in the right way. The Haynes Repair Manuals are renowned for this. (The equally famous Chilton auto repair manuals, designed for professional mechanics, are richer with detailed advice than with photographs.)[126]

For usefulness and depth, nothing matches a comprehensive, encyclopedic manual. The bigger, the better. The 2019 edition of *iPhone: The Missing Manual* has 719 pages and weighs two pounds. The authoritative text for every known ailment of the human body is *The Merck Manual of Diagnosis and Therapy*; the 20th edition weighs in at six pounds and 3,530 pages. (That's the edition for medical professionals.

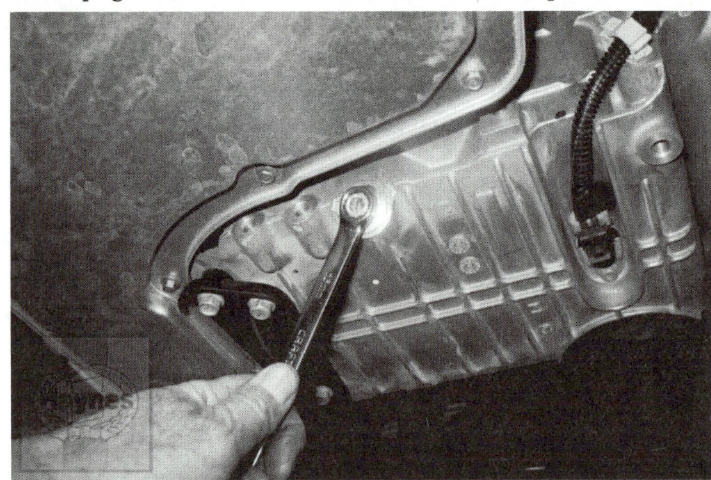

Figure 56. A good point-of-view photo. "Use the proper size box-end wrench or socket wrench to remove the oil drain plug and avoid rounding it off,"* advises the Haynes manual for the Pontiac G6. (Haynes)

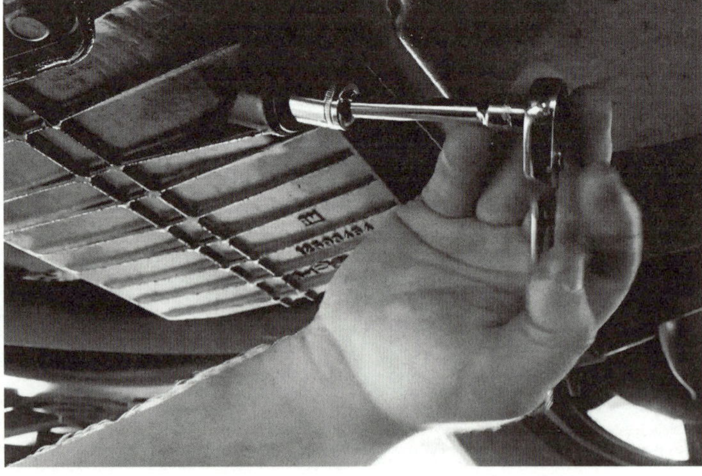

Figure 57. A YouTube video has all the advantages of a still photo, plus many more. In this video by T.J. Lewis for changing the oil on a Pontiac G6, you'll notice that you must turn the socket wrench *counterclockwise*, pushing with your thumb, to loosen the drain plug. Then you finish unscrewing it with your fingers. You'll probably get some oil on your fingers when it starts pouring out. (T.J. Lewis)

For family use, you get *The Merck Manual Home Health Handbook*—four and a half pounds, 2,500 pages.)

Manuals have long been the primary point of reference for maintainers, but most are ephemeral, confined to a subject and time that soon passes. But some, like John Muir's, have such uniqueness and impact on their times that they live beyond them. Here are six that strike me that way—three of which were created explicitly to break through class barriers.

Figure 58. "Test tightness of gasoline inlet needle by turning carburetor upside down, and sucking lightly on the fuel inlet elbow. If the needle is properly seated, the tongue or lips will stick to the elbow in the same manner as with a small bottle."* (*1909–1927 Model T Ford Service*)

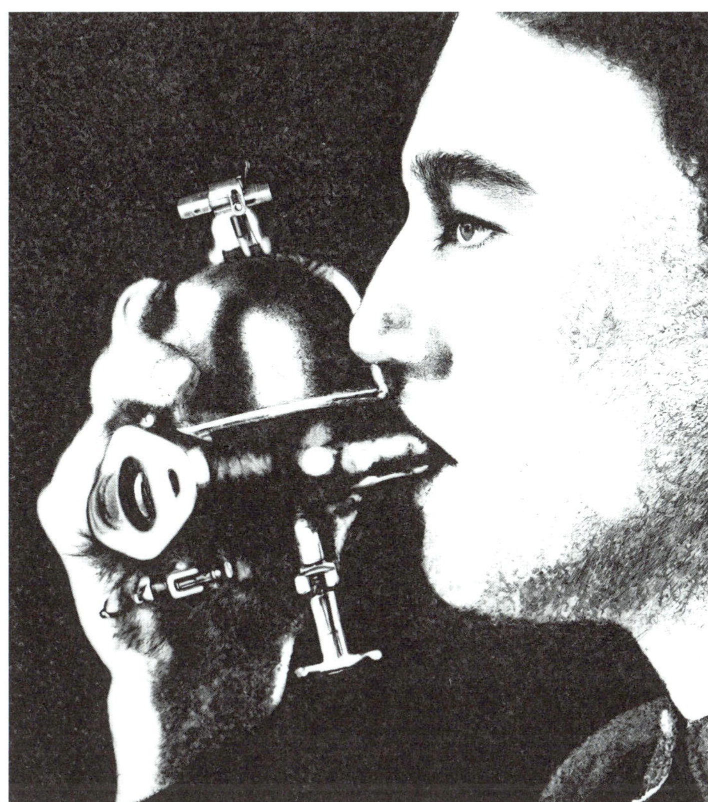

1. The Ford Model T service manual

Some manuals excel in evoking a sense of discipline. Ford's 1927 service manual for Model T mechanics begins: "We will first describe, step by step, the correct procedure in disassembling, and reassembling the car."[127] They mean the whole car, just like the elder George Dyson with his new motorcycle in 1913. The whole book is that thorough. When it comes to adding water to the batteries, Ford's advice is: "Distilled water or clean rain water that has not come in contact with metal should be used for this purpose."[128] Sucking on the carburetor to test it, collecting rainwater for the battery—those were the days.

Figure 59. Described as "the single greatest publication of the Enlightenment"* and "the greatest intellectual enterprise of the 18th century,"† France's *Encyclopédie, ou Dictionnaire raisonné des sciences, des arts et des métiers* took 25 years to complete. It contained 72,000 text entries and 3,100 engraved illustrations. (Christie's)

2. Diderot's *Encyclopédie*

In the 18th century, a manual-like set of volumes from the French Enlightenment transformed Western thought. It was the *Encyclopédie, ou Dictionnaire raisonné des sciences, des arts et des métiers* (*Encyclopedia, or Classified Dictionary of Sciences, Arts, and Trades*), published between 1751 and 1772. Despite its length—35 volumes filling a 12-foot shelf—it was a bestseller. The primary editor was a Parisian writer-philosopher named Denis Diderot, who specialized in warring with the powers of the ancien régime. "With the guts of the last priest," he wrote, "let us strangle the last king."[129]

Diderot's biographer, P.N. Furbank, writes that for Diderot the *Encyclopédie* was

> a rebuke to court culture and its attitudes, according to which it was below the dignity of a person of fashion or standing to know the technical detail of any craft... In the eyes of Diderot, the son of a master cutler, it was a matter of doing justice to a social species, the skilled craftsman, whose role in the national life was absurdly undervalued.[130]

Diderot once remarked, "Only the rich can afford to be stupid; for others, ability is a necessity, not an option."[131]

Figure 60. Maintaining a horse requires the services of a farrier to shoe the horse and treat its ailments. These plates in Diderot's *Encyclopédie* show in detail the work and tools of a farrier in 18th-century France. An apprentice holds the horse's hind foot (left) while the master demonstrates how to nail the horseshoe to the hoof. An apparatus (far right) is for keeping a horse immobile while workers lift one leg after another for shoeing. (Denis Diderot, *Encyclopédie*)

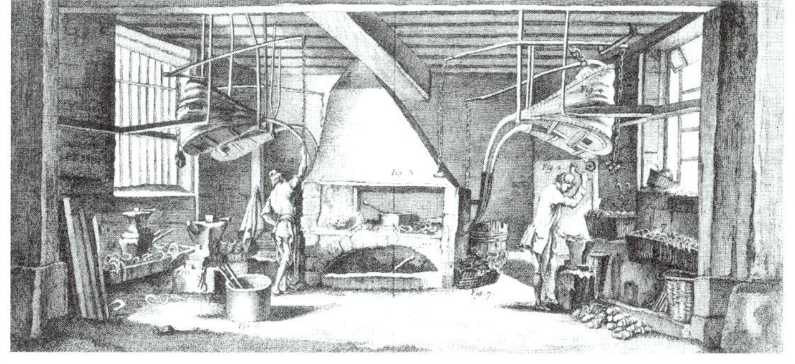

Figure 61. Here are two stages of the farrier's blacksmith work. He heats the forge by hauling on the chain overhead to expand the bellows (left). The weight of the rock hanging from the bellows then contracts the bellows rapidly to blast air onto the glowing coals in the forge. The smith hammers a red-hot horseshoe into shape on the anvil (right). (Denis Diderot, *Encyclopédie*)

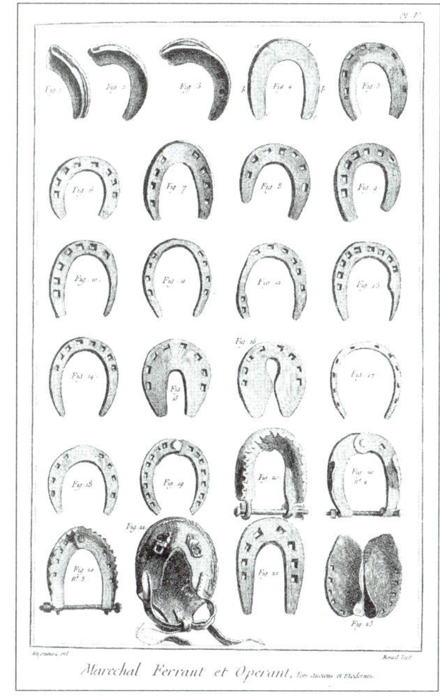

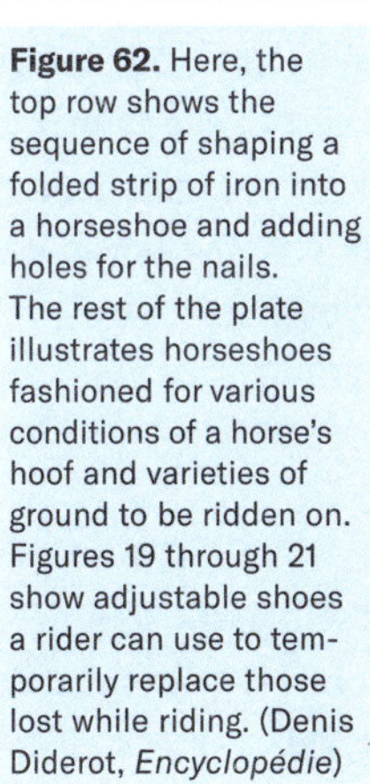

Figure 62. Here, the top row shows the sequence of shaping a folded strip of iron into a horseshoe and adding holes for the nails. The rest of the plate illustrates horseshoes fashioned for various conditions of a horse's hoof and varieties of ground to be ridden on. Figures 19 through 21 show adjustable shoes a rider can use to temporarily replace those lost while riding. (Denis Diderot, *Encyclopédie*)

Though the *Encyclopédie* had numerous contributors, Diderot himself wrote some 7,000 of the 72,000 entries, many of them about craft techniques he researched in person. He wrote:

> We addressed ourselves to the most skilled workers in Paris and the kingdom at large. We took the trouble to visit their workshops, to interrogate them, to write under dictation from them, to follow out their ideas, to define, to identify the terms peculiar to their profession.[132]

In an entry about "Art" (by which he meant "craft" or "technology"), he honored the industrial tools he encountered in the workshops:

> In what physical or metaphysical system do we find more intelligence, discernment, and consistency than in the machines for drawing gold or making stockings, and in the frames of the braid-makers, the gauze-makers, the drapers, or the silk workers?[133]

He often tried to operate the machines himself and discovered the difficulty of getting the process exactly right. He would, he said, "become an apprentice and produce bad results so as to be able to teach people how to produce good ones."[134]

The encyclopedia's entries were illustrated with some 3,100 plates portraying in meticulous detail the workshops and tools of every trade. The workers in the images are always depicted with dignity, performing their specialty with calm assurance. This accorded with the encyclopedia's credo, writes Richard Sennett in his 2008 book *The Craftsman*: "It celebrated those who are committed to doing work well for its own sake; the craftsman stood out as the emblem of Enlightenment."[135]

In his entry on the word "*métier*" (trade, profession, calling), Diderot wrote:

> We owe to the *métiers* all objects necessary in life. Those who take the trouble to go into the workshops will find usefulness & good sense everywhere... The poet, the philosopher, the orator, the minister, the soldier, the hero—they all would be naked & without bread without the artisan whom they all despise.[136]

A fellow troublemaker and close friend of Diderot's was Jean-Jacques Rousseau. Along with his acclaimed discourses on human inequality and the social contract, Rousseau wrote

Figure 63. Jean-Jacques Rousseau (left, 1753) was a good friend of Denis Diderot (right, 1767) and an early contributor to the *Encyclopédie*. Later, as Rousseau succumbed to growing paranoia, he became an enemy of the Encyclopedists and attacked Diderot. In the course of Rousseau's adult life, he went from being an influential participant in the French Enlightenment to its most lethal critic. (Maurice Quentin de La Tour, Louis-Michel van Loo)

several early entries for the *Encyclopédie*, drawing on his lifelong interest in music. But gradually he turned against the Encyclopedists and Diderot. He eventually assailed all his old friends and denounced the rationalism and practicality of the Enlightenment, celebrating instead emotion, intuition, and the primacy of personal passion. In his later writings, he relished parading his own melancholy and alienation. Diderot finally wrote of him, "This man is a monster."[137]

Much that became monstrous in the French Revolution emerged from popular devotion to Rousseau's ideas. One of his most fervent followers was the murderous Robespierre, who declared in a 1794 tract, "Terror is only justice prompt, severe and inflexible."[138] Arthur Herman's 1997 book *The Idea of Decline in Western History* makes a persuasive case that Rousseau's anti-rational Romanticism directly inspired two centuries of gaseous, heroic, often suicidal pessimism about civilization. Rousseau declared, "Everything degenerates in the hands of men."[139] Nietzsche echoed, "There is an element of decay in everything that characterizes modern man."[140] To my ear, the echoes continue today in every exuberant user of the words "existential threat to humanity."

RIEMANNZETA: "This feels like a profound and original insight into the nature of the similarities and differences in French and American culture, embedded in history and literature."

STEWARTBRAND: "Thanks! Have a look at Samuel Eliot Morison's book *The Conservative American Revolution*."

Two great political revolutions in the 18th century were inspired by the Enlightenment thinkers that included Diderot and Rousseau. The American one might be called Diderot's revolution—the creation of a nation founded on two Enlightenment documents, the Declaration of Independence and the US Constitution. The French Revolution was Rousseau's. What it did to Diderot's masterwork is summarized by Philipp Blom in his 2005 book *Enlightening the World*:

> The Revolution had no time for the generosity of spirit that marked Encyclopedist thought. The values espoused by the Encyclopedists, which had once seemed likely to dominate for decades, were swiftly crushed by Europe's first, though short-lived, totalitarian regime. When the monarchy was restored, the Encyclopedists were seen as sowers of unrest, rebellion, and impiety. The *Encyclopédie* was consigned to oblivion.[141]

General Gribeauval's rational system of uniformity in manufacturing similarly was canceled by the *sansculottes*, and the Industrial Revolution was kept out of France for half a century. By contrast, the triumph of the Industrial Revolution in Britain was closely linked with the lasting effects of the Scottish Enlightenment. Scotsman James Watt, inventor of the steam engine, communicated routinely with empiricist David Hume, economist Adam Smith, geologist James Hutton, and the scientist of gases and heat Joseph Black. They and the rest of the Scots intellectuals manifested what has been described as

> a thoroughgoing empiricism and practicality where the chief values were improvement, virtue, and practical benefit for the individual and society as a whole.
>
> Among the fields that rapidly advanced were philosophy, political economy, engineering, architecture, medicine, geology, archaeology, botany and zoology, law, agriculture, chemistry and sociology.[142]

The Scots intellectuals paid close attention to their French counterparts, especially Diderot. Of the 25,000 copies of his *Encyclopédie* printed, half were sold outside France.[143] As an immediate echo of the *Encyclopédie*, Scotsmen in Edinburgh created the *Encyclopedia Britannica*, published in three volumes in 1771.[144] Unlike Diderot's masterwork, the *Britannica* continued to grow in size and influence throughout the 19th century, peaking with its famed 29-volume 11th edition in 1911. Under American ownership, it continued as a massive, prestigious reference tool through the 20th century, until it was displaced by Wikipedia after 2004.

Figure 64. (Left) Nicholas Culpeper's manual for midwives was so popular it went through multiple printings. This 1666 edition notes that it is "Now newly Corrected from many gross Errors." (The vexation of authors with careless printers is an abiding feature of book publishing.) (Culpeper, *Directory for Midwives*)

Figure 65. (Right) According to his biographer, Culpeper understood the umbilical cord ("FF: The Navel-string") better than his famous contemporary William Harvey. Harvey thought the amniotic fluid nourished the infant through its mouth.* Culpeper wrote that the umbilical cord "is the nourisher of the infant even from the beginning of the conception, to the time of delivery, till it breath air and concoct its food as we do."† (Nicholas Culpeper, *Directory for Midwives*)

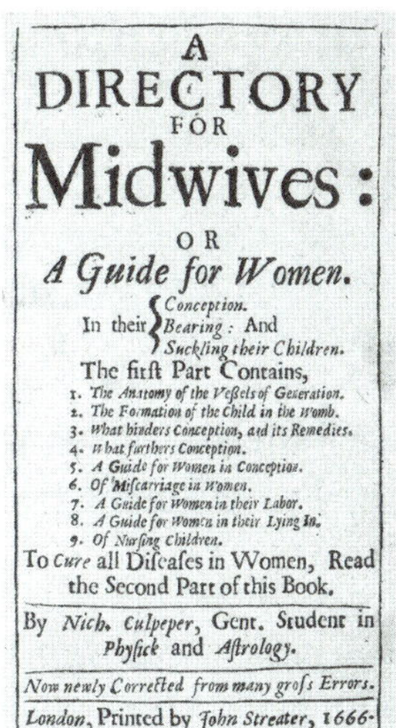

A
DIRECTORY
FOR
Midwives:
OR
A Guide for Women.
In their { *Conception.* / *Bearing*: And / *Suckling their Children.*
The firſt Part Contains,
1. *The Anatomy of the Veſsels of Generation.*
2. *The Formation of the Child in the Womb.*
3. *What hinders Conception, and its Remedies.*
4. *What furthers Conception.*
5. *A Guide for Women in Conception.*
6. *Of Miſcarriage in Women.*
7. *A Guide for Women in their Labor.*
8. *A Guide for Women in their Lying In.*
9. *Of Nurſing Children.*
To *Cure* all Diſeaſes in Women, Read the Second Part of this Book.

By *Nich. Culpeper*, Gent. Student in *Phyſick* and *Aſtrology*.

Now newly Corrected from many groſs Errors.

London, Printed by *John Streater*, 1666.

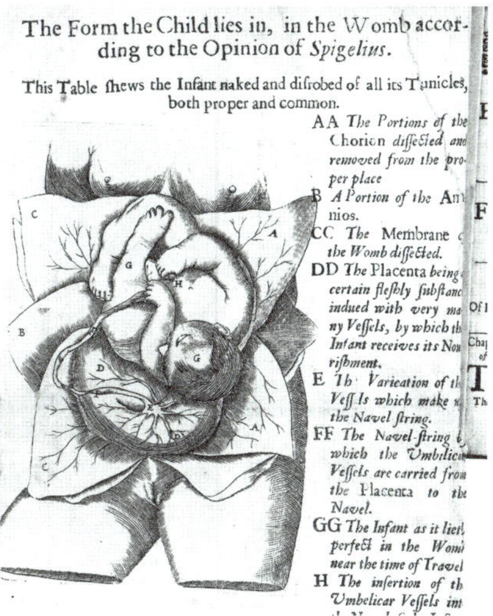

The Form the Child lies in, in the Womb according to the Opinion of *Spigelius*.

This Table ſhews the Infant naked and diſrobed of all its Tunicles, both proper and common.

AA *The Portions of the* Chorion *diſſected and removed from the proper place*
B *A Portion of the* Amnios.
CC *The* Membrane *of the Womb diſſected.*
DD *The* Placenta *being a certain fleſhly ſubſtance indued with very many Veſſels, by which the Infant receives its Nouriſhment.*
E *The Varication of the Veſſels which make up the Navel ſtring.*
FF *The Navel-ſtring by which the Umbilical Veſſels are carried from the* Placenta *to the Navel.*
GG *The Infant as it lieth perfect in the Womb near the time of Travel*
H *The inſertion of the Umbelicar Veſſels int*

3. Culpeper's *Directory for Midwives*

A century earlier in England, in the 1650s, an impulse similar to Diderot's drove a physician and herbalist named Nicholas Culpeper. He deplored the institutionalized secrecy and avarice of physicians. "No man," he wrote, "deserved to starve to pay an insulting, insolent physician."[145] He set up his apothecary shop in a poor part of London and saw as many as 40 patients a day. Physicians at that time used Latin as a private code for prescriptions, for the books they wrote, and especially for discussions that patients might overhear. Culpeper defied that practice by translating the *London Pharmacopoeia* of medicinal drugs from Latin to vernacular English.

Culpeper's biographer, Benjamin Woolley, describes him as a "pioneer of herbal medicine whose actions and beliefs revolutionized medicine and medical practice."[146] His reputation comes primarily from his 1652 publication, the *Complete Herbal*. It was, in effect, the *Merck Manual* of his time. The book described all the medicinal wild herbs in England and spelled out their properties, where to find them, how to prepare and preserve them, and how they could be used to treat all known ailments. He priced the book so anyone could buy it, at just three pence. And buy it they did. "It proved to be one of the most popular and enduring books in publishing history, perhaps the non-religious book in English to remain longest in continuous print," Woolley writes.[147] It is available today in several editions, most of them now illustrated.

A fundamental text on how to keep humanity going was Culpeper's hugely popular *Directory for Midwives*, published in 1651. "It was printed in pocket-sized octavo format, and written in an informal style, peppered with anecdotes and jokes," Woolley notes.[148] Along with detailed information on fertility, pregnancy, the development of the fetus, miscarriages, and childbirth, the book included lore about the sex organs. Unlike physicians such as the celebrated Dr. William Harvey, who discovered the circulation of the blood and wrote in Latin, Culpeper knew what the clitoris was and was for. He wrote, "In form it represents the yard of a man and suffers erection and falling as that doth; this is that which causeth lust in women and gives delight in copulation."[149] (Harvey, on the other hand, considered sex necessary but disgusting, something women must suffer.)

Childbirth in 17th-century England was hazardous for mother and child. Culpeper ended the book's preface with a message to the midwives he championed: "Let me intreat the favour of you all, that if you by your own experiences finds any thing which I have written in this Book, not to be according to truth... Acquaint me with them, and they shall be both acknowledged and amended."[150]

British novelist Ian McEwan read this section and responded with an addition: "Since you ask for suggestions, may I propose the history of manuals to the most complex thing we know? I'm thinking of childcare manuals. Over the last three centuries, their constant shifts in tone and emphasis give us a guide to the spirit of the age and its dreams of what we should be. In the 17th century, the business was to break the child's will, for such was God's will and children were little more than small, unreasonable adults. In the 18th century, romantic Rousseau-esque notions of the child trailing clouds of glory; then Victorian strictness, Edwardian sentimentality; in the 1920s and '30s, horrific 'science-led' regimes and behaviourist nightmares. Not picking up the screaming child—it must learn who's in charge. Feeding only every four hours on the dot. Lots of fresh air, resist cuddling. Then came Spock and child-centered care. Until recently, these manuals were mostly written by men to be read by women. The best guide to these guides is *Dream Babies* by Christina Hardyment."

Figure 66.
Enlightenment-era childcare advice was personified in the twin boys of the Blunt family in England circa 1767. Philosopher John Locke urged that children be respected and challenged. "Following his ideas," writes Christina Hardyment in *Dream Babies*, "parents dressed their toddlers in loose clothes and gave them small versions of adult tools to play with."* (Johann Zoffany, Birmingham Museum and Art Gallery)

4. Moxon's *Mechanick Exercises: Or, The Doctrine of Handy-Works*

The first modern-style do-it-yourself manual was titled *Mechanick Exercises: Or, The Doctrine of Handy-Works*. It was written and self-published in the 1670s by a different sort of leveler. While Diderot in the next century was an aristocrat writing for aristocrats about the trades of common people, the printer Joseph Moxon was a tradesman writing for tradesmen—and also for England's intelligentsia. Among Moxon's customers and sponsors were mathematician Isaac Newton, astronomer Edmond Halley, microscopist Robert Hooke, architect Christopher Wren, and naval administrator Samuel Pepys.

In 1678, Moxon was the first tradesman invited to join the scientists of the Royal Society, which had been purchasing his maps, globes, and mathematical texts since its founding in 1662. The Royal Society had long wanted to compile a book of tradecrafts, but the scholarly thinkers didn't have trade experience and tradesmen didn't write. Joseph Moxon was a tradesman who did. His self-printed *Mechanick Exercises* was the first-ever serialized book, released in 14 installments between 1678 and 1683. In the preface he wrote, "Tho' the Mechanicks be by some accounted ignoble and scandalous, yet it is very well known, that many Gentlemen in this Nation of good Rank and Quality are conversant in Handy-Works."

Moxon declared he was "for many Years conversant in" all the skills he wrote about: blacksmithing, joinery, house carpentry, lathe work, bricklaying, and printing. His book had 26 plates illustrating the tools of each craft and explaining their use. He began with blacksmithing, noting that its reputation as a "Vulgar Art" was misplaced because it is foundational to everything else.

Following 62 pages of instruction on blacksmith practices, Moxon ends with this note: "Only this general Rule observe, from an old *English* Verse us'd among Smiths, when they Forge Edge-tools, *He that will a good Edge win/Must Forge thick and Grind thin.*"[151]

Further on, in the carpentry section, where he explains "the pretty skill in driving a nail," he mentions a diverting "little trick." You "privately touch the Head of a Nail with a little Ear-wax" and then wager another carpenter that he can't pound the nail in with three blows.[152] His "*Hammer* no sooner touches the Head of the Nail," writes Moxon, "but instead of entering the Wood it flies away." (Workplace pranks are a constant throughout history, throughout the world.)

Figure 67. Whereas Diderot's encyclopedia would feature the classy blacksmith shop of France's Great Stables, Moxon showed the reader how to build and equip his own shop. He advises, for example, that the anvil should be mounted on a block of wood "about two foot high from the floor, or sometimes higher, according to the stature of the Person that is to work at it."* For this illustration he spells out the names and uses of the large and small tongs (Figs. 4 and 3), hammer and sledge (Fig. 5), pole vise and hand vises (Fig. 6), pliers (Fig. 6), and screw plate and taps (Fig. 7). (Joseph Moxon, *Mechanick Exercises*)

In 1683, Moxon published a second volume, this time focused on his own trade. Titled *Mechanick Exercises: Or, the Doctrine of Handy-Works Applied to the Art of Printing*, it has been called "a pivotal contribution not only to the mechanical art of printing but also to the standardisation of editorial practice."[153] It remained the authoritative text on the subject for a century. Moxon begins it by describing his own role in the complex process of printing a book:

> *First* The *Master Printer*, who is as the Soul of *Printing*; and all the Work-men as members of the Body governed by that Soul subservient to him; for the *Letter-Cutter* would Cut no Letters, the *Founder* not sinck the *Matrices*, or Cast and Dress the

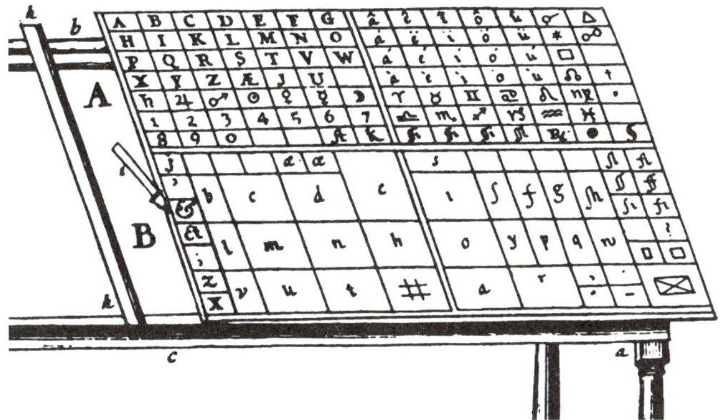

Figure 68. Moxon has 24 plates in his volume on printing. In this one, he explains how the cases of letters are laid out for letterpress printing. In the upper case, the capital letters are arranged in alphabetical order, but in the lower case, "*Letters* that are most used are laid in the biggest *Boxes*, about the middle of the *Case*, That the *Compositor's* hand may have the quicker access to them."* (Another term for the letters we still call lowercase is "minuscule.") At the left of this plate is the composing stick, marked "i." (Joseph Moxon, *Art of Printing*)

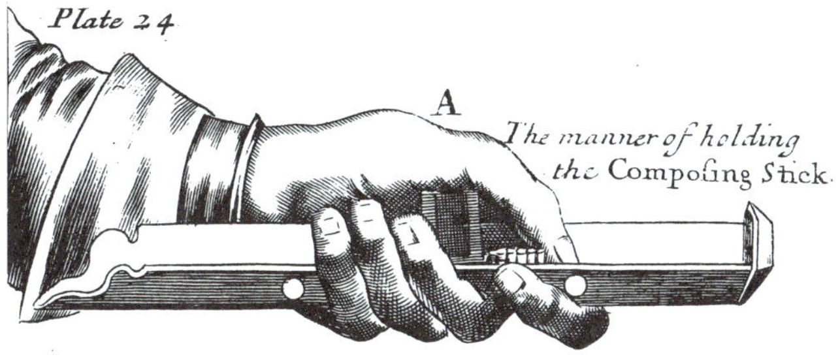

Figure 69. Moxon's technique of handling the composing stick is still used by letterpress printers today: "When he *Composes* the *Letters* he holds the *Composing-stick* in his Left Hand, placing the Second Joynt of his Thumb over the moving *Cheek* of the *Stick*, and the end of the Ball of his Thumb reaches down to the bottom of the *Cheek* and *Stick*; so that with the end of the Ball of his Thumb he gently presses the *Letter* close to the *Cheek*, and keeps the *Letters* tight and square together, as he places them in the *Stick* successively."* (Joseph Moxon, *Art of Printing*)

> Letters, the *Smith* and *Joyner* not make the *Press* and other Utensils for *Printing*, the *Compositer* not Compose the Letters, the *Correcter* not read Proves, the *Press-man* not work the Forms off at the *Press*, or the *Inck-maker* make *Inck* to work them with, but by Orders from the *Master-Printer*.[154]

Joseph Moxon lived and suffered 17th-century London to the full. When he was 10 years old, in 1637, his printer father was such an outspoken Puritan that he got in trouble with the government, and the family had to flee to Holland. Once Oliver Cromwell made London safe for Puritans, the Moxons returned in 1643 and put to use all they had learned about printing in Holland. Remarkably, by 1662 Joseph's reputation as a printer of charts and globes was so strong that it outweighed his history as a Puritan, and the newly installed Restoration monarch Charles II appointed him to a salaried position as hydrographer (cartographer) to the King.

In London's plague year, 1665, Moxon lost his mother, brother, wife, and their two children to the disease. The following year, 1666, the Great Fire of London destroyed his print shop and most of his stock. Yet he recovered and prospered.

His most popular product was a series of "pocket globes" depicting the world's geography on a three-inch sphere encased in two half-spheres with a map of the heavens inside. Moxon's biographer, Derek Long, writes that they "became both influential and fashionable... They were much sought after, and some of Moxon's globes found their way into royal and imperial collections."[155]

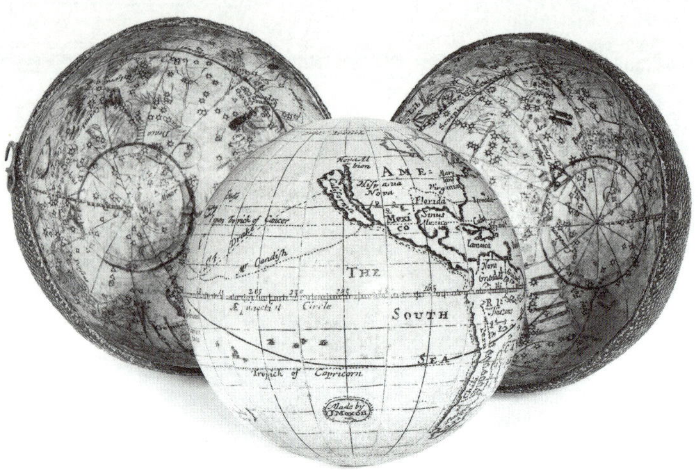

Figure 70. One of Joseph Moxon's pocket globes, dated about 1675. At the upper center of the globe, California is shown as an island intersected by a dotted line, indicating Sir Francis Drake's 1579 expedition. The cartouche "Made by J. Moxon" is visible (lower center). One of 11 pocket globes made by Moxon thought to still exist, this globe was purchased for $240,000 in 2021 at a Bonhams auction in London. (Bonhams)

5. *I.33*

The first self-defense manual dates to 1320 AD, the late medieval period in Europe. Called a "fight book"—*fechtbuch* in German—it taught the form of sword fighting then popular both for sport and for defense against real danger in public and in war. The combatants had no armor, so the sword-and-buckler technique emphasized defense and counterattack. The sword's edge was as deadly as its point; the buckler was a small shield for the left hand, usually positioned to protect the fighter's sword hand and forearm. Once the fight began, the buckler was light enough to shift rapidly from one purpose to another in the flurry of combat.

The most treasured document at England's Royal Armouries Museum, the manual has attracted enormous interest, inspiring books and videos on how to use it as a martial arts guide. Everyone calls it by its shelf name, *I.33* (pronounced "one thirty-three"; the first number is a Roman numeral one). The 64-page parchment manuscript illustrates 36 combat sequences between two fighters, a priest and his student. How it works as a manual is described by its leading scholar, Jeffrey L. Forgeng, this way:

Figure 71. The earliest sword-fighting manual, from 1320 AD, has 128 illustrations of the sword-and-buckler technique. Most of the actions are shown in sequence, as here. The teacher, left, is a tonsured priest; his student is on the right. In the top illustration, the combatants take up their Guard positions, with the priest using what was called "Guard #5" and the student in the "Longpoint" position. As they engage, both adopt the standard use of the buckler to protect their sword hands and forearms. Here, the student is successfully deflecting the priest's sword. The manual recommends that he follow up by using the buckler in his left hand to "shield-strike" the priest's buckler and sword aside while his right hand swipes his sword upward to the priest's unprotected head. A Latin verse between the two illustrations reads: "The deflector and the deflected are opposed and angry; the deflected flees to the side; I pursue." (Royal Armouries)

> More than anything else, *I.33* documents an interpretive system that seeks to make combat intelligible. What *I.33* teaches is not so much how to fight or train with a sword and buckler, as how to think about sword-and-buckler combat. Specifically, *I.33* uses the tools of intellectual discourse to break down the dynamics of combat—in this case, the tools of late medieval scholasticism... Its characteristic feature is reductive analysis, subdividing the subject matter into component elements (such as the schematised stages of each encounter), and... a simplified scheme of... structural elements (such as the seven basic guards)... The chaotic process of combat is rationalised to resemble the structure of an academic disputation... The author's schematic model of combat is excellently packaged for expression through words and images.[156]

Sophistication often comes early to weapons. The same goes for training in their use, as in this gorgeous manual.

6. Swiss Environmental Action Foundation's *Dry Stone Walls*
Occasionally a manual comprehensively spells out the whole world of a particular subject—the context that surrounds it as well as the lore you need to execute it well. A tome published in

2019 by the Swiss Environmental Action Foundation titled *Dry Stone Walls* is exemplary in this regard.

I once spent a couple of weeks in France supposedly learning how to build traditional drystone walls. I would have done better with just this book. Far more than most manuals, it teaches the *principles* of the craft.

A poem by Gary Snyder titled "Riprap" begins:

> Lay down these words
> Before your mind like rocks.
> placed solid, by hands[157]

Dry Stone Walls explains how the "solid" part actually works. Its principles apply metaphorically to anything that has to hold itself together—a poem, a theory, a software program.

In drystone walling, the mortar that holds everything together better than mortar can is gravity plus friction. All the tricks of construction put gravity and friction to work. One principle states, "All stones are placed slightly sloping towards the inside of the wall." Another declares, "Stones must touch all their neighbors and should not be able to move."[158]

The best stones are big, wide, rough-surfaced, and somewhat rectangular (called "ashlar"). The proper technique, the manual advises, is to always place "one stone on two, two stones on one" to ensure stability along the length of the wall. For cross-sectional stability, you must position each stone so that its long dimension reaches into the wall rather than along the outside and include some "throughstones" extending all the way across the wall. To ensure that each stone touches all its neighbors and is immovable, "wedge-stones" can be placed from inside the wall before the small "hearting stones" are poured in to fill the inner cavity. (Wedges placed on the outside will fall out.) With a hammer and chisel, you can level up the surfaces of irregular stones so they bed well with the stones around them.

Structured so, a seemingly inert wall actively defends its integrity for a long and useful life, exuding a geological-feeling permanence on the land. The book notes that

> professionally built dry stone walls can exist for centuries without significant maintenance or repairs being necessary. However, often a certain degree of management is required because dry stone walls interact strongly with their environment.[159]

Figure 72. A drystone wall needs five kinds of stones to ensure stability. Next to the foundation trench in this drawing, the largest stones are placed in the trench as foundation stones. Outside them on the ground are the many wall stones used for the facing. The through-stones (lower right) reach across the whole wall; there should be at least one every meter along the wall. The piles of small rocks are hearting stones, to be placed by hand inside the lower part of the wall. The cover stones (upper left) top off the wall. (Swiss Environmental Action Foundation, *Dry Stone Walls*, illustration by Dani Pelagatti, CC-BY-SA-4.0)

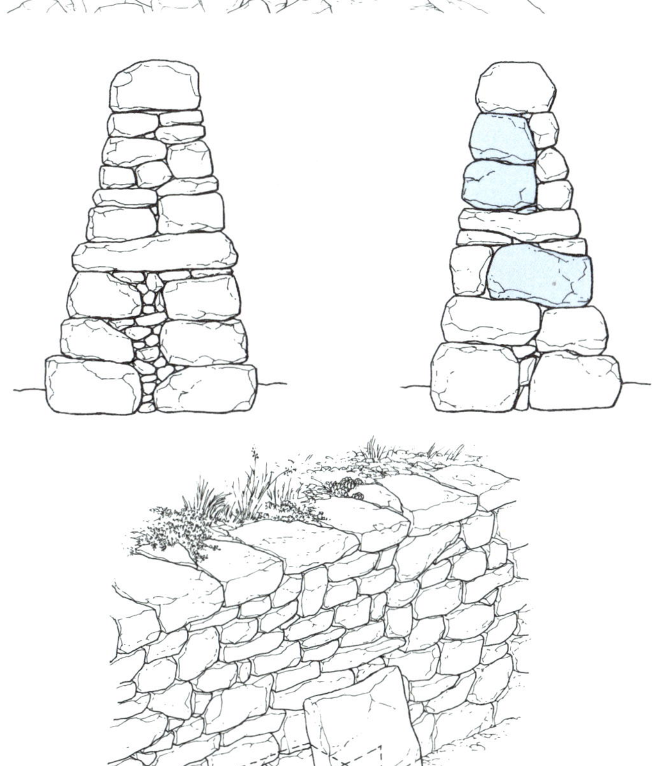

Figure 73. Correct stone placement (left); the largest stones are in the lower courses. The large blue stones (right) are incorrect. Because they are placed too high, they extend too far across the wall, forcing their adjacent facing stones to be too shallow and thus insecure. (Swiss Environmental Action Foundation, *Dry Stone Walls*, illustration by Dani Pelagatti, CC-BY-SA-4.0)

Figure 74. The gaps in drystone walls provide habitat for local wildlife such as toads, snakes, lizards, insects, bats, and birds. You can welcome them with tailored openings in the sunlit side of the wall. Here, one serves as a den for a family of hedgehogs. (Swiss Environmental Action Foundation, *Dry Stone Walls*, illustration by Dani Pelagatti, CC-BY-SA-4.0)

Sections of a stone wall can partially collapse over time due to subsiding soil, large animals, woody plant roots, reckless humans, or heavy machinery. As the book shows, repair is simple: Just rebuild.

All the stones are right there in the grass.

Figure 75. On slopes, the foundation stones and lower wall stones are laid horizontally, like stair steps. This wall is in England's Lake District National Park. (David C. Tomlinson/Getty)

2.5b Sub-Digression: Two Assault Rifles

Some of the most valued manuals focus on known weaknesses of the device in question. John Hall's musket manual did that. So did John Muir's VW manual. This digression-within-a-digression examines what was behind the most famous of all manuals dedicated solely to maintaining a flawed tool. It emerged from the Vietnam War and is one of the harshest maintenance dramas in history.

In the early years of the war, the mid-1960s, the North Vietnamese outgunned US forces on the ground. China had provided them with AK-47s, a cheap, highly effective firearm referred to as an "assault rifle," meaning a gun that can switch from semi-automatic (*bang bang bang*) to fully automatic (*braaaaaaaapp*). The US responded by fielding its own assault rifle, a brand-new, highly sophisticated weapon called the M16. It was extremely accurate, even out to 500 meters. It was light, with a distinctive carrying handle on top. The butt was in line with the barrel, so it didn't "climb" when fired on full auto. It was ergonomically brilliant—perfectly balanced and smooth-operating, with every control in easy, intuitive reach.

Old systems fail in familiar and prepared-for ways. New systems fail in unexpected and unprepared-for ways.

In the jungles of Vietnam, the M16 had a definitively fatal flaw: It was fatal to its users. The gun routinely jammed in the midst of a firefight, leaving the rifleman defenseless. In May 1967, one Marine wrote to his family, "We left with 250 men in

Figure 76. The maintenance-friendly AK-47 (top), designed in Russia from 1947–49. Length, 34 inches; weight, 10.5 pounds with fully loaded magazine (30 rounds); 73 parts. Note the cleaning rod mounted under the barrel, in handy reach. The maintenance-hostile M16 (bottom), designed in the US in 1957, originally as the ArmaLite AR-15. Length, 39 inches; weight, 7.9 pounds with fully loaded magazine (30 rounds); 144 parts. (Henrickson at the English Wikipedia, via Wikimedia Commons, CC BY-SA 3.0)

our company and came back with 107. We left with 72 men in our platoon and came back with 19. Believe it or not, you know what killed most of us? Our own rifle. We were all issued this new rifle, the M16. Practically every one of our dead was found with his rifle torn down next to him where he had been trying to fix it."[160]

Outrage like this was delivered directly from soldiers to their parents and hometown newspapers, and thence to their representatives in Congress. When the issue became a public scandal, senior leaders of the Army and Marines repeatedly declared that the M16 was a great weapon with no problems at all. But the enemy knew better. According to one report, "The only things that were left by the enemy after they had stripped the dead of our side were the rifles, which they considered worthless."[161] (The US military's pattern of denying problems and exaggerating successes continued for nine more years, until it culminated in its total defeat in 1975.)

A subcommittee of the House Armed Services Committee conducted a formal investigation in 1967. What they found in Vietnam shocked them. In the 1st Infantry Division (15,000 soldiers), for example, the state of maintenance of the M16s was "indescribable," according to one inspector. Kanemitsu Ito, a veteran of the Korean War, reported, "I have never seen such filthy, rusty, carboned, and corroded rifles, magazines, and ammunition. It is no wonder that these rifles will not function."[162] It turned out that the M16s, having been touted as

SLAPOUT9:
"At one time, the Army had ordered and distributed 85,000 M16 rifles but had not ordered a single bore brush for the new 5.56 (.223) calibre cartridge. Source: Eugene Stoner [who designed the M16]."

"self-cleaning," were being treated by some units as if they needed no maintenance. Cleaning kits and instruction weren't even provided to many of the soldiers.

But most of the problems were in the M16 itself. The Congressional inspectors found that the ammunition had the wrong powder, which fouled the rifle's mechanism. The unchromed barrel and chamber led to corrosion that would cause the cartridge case to jam in the chamber, dubbed "failure to extract." The rifles would jam no matter how surgically clean they were. The aluminum magazine carrying the cartridges was so flimsy it was easily damaged, and the cartridges wouldn't feed. Forty percent of the magazines in the field were too broken to use. (The steel magazines of the AK-47, by contrast, were so sturdy they could be used as a hammer and bottle opener.)

I take all of this personally. I was a professional rifleman in the early 1960s, serving for two years as an infantry officer teaching basic training. Some of the recruits I helped train went on to fight in Vietnam. Had I stayed in the Army, I might well have wound up as company commander of a line unit there, with total responsibility for the lives of 200 men. Sending them

Figure 77. A Viet Cong soldier with his robust AK-47 near Saigon in 1968. (Getty)

Figure 78. A US Marine cleaning his M16 during the Battle of Huế in February 1968. Even when perfectly cleaned, M16s were unreliable. (Photo by Gunnery Sergeant R.W. Thompson, US Marine Corps, via Wikimedia Commons, CC BY 2.0)

into combat with an unreliable weapon would have felt like fratricide, the unintentional killing of comrades in arms.

There's a famous series of combat photos from early in the Vietnam War whose full story is seldom told. They were taken at the end of April 1967, in what was called the Hill Fights or the First Battle of Khe Sanh. One hundred sixty-eight US Marines were killed and 436 wounded. It was the bloodiest battle of the war up to that point and the first in which American soldiers were armed solely with the new M16s. One Marine wounded in the battle limped to the rear using two hopelessly jammed M16s as crutches.[163] Some of the most intense fighting was on Hill 881N, a bunker complex manned by North Vietnamese. Embedded with the Marine attackers that afternoon was 22-year-old French photographer Catherine Leroy.

Leroy recalled, "I heard someone yelling, 'Corpsman, corpsman!' And I saw this other Marine rushing to the wounded man, and he put his ear on the man's heart. Then he looked up in total anguish."[164] The wounded man was Lance Corporal William Roldan, age 20. The corpsman, Vernon Wike, age 19, knew him as "Rock." Partway up Hill 881N, Roldan's M16 had jammed. When he crouched to try to clear it, a North

Figure 79. April 30, 1967, Hill 881N. Navy Corpsman Vernon Wike treats the chest wound of Marine Lance Corporal William "Rock" Roldan, shot while he was trying to clear his jammed M16. (Dotation Catherine Leroy)

Figure 80. After listening to Roldan's heartbeat slow to nothing, Wike reacts in anguish. (Dotation Catherine Leroy)

Vietnamese with an AK-47 in one of the bunkers shot him in the chest. In Edward Murphy's 2007 book *The Hill Fights*, Wike says,

> As soon as I reached him, I saw it was "Rock."... We'd just met that morning. He told me he had less than sixty days left in-country. I put my hand on his chest. It slipped in all the blood. Then I found the entrance wound on his left side. I put a bandage on it. I was talking to Rock, but he was unconscious. I then put my head on his chest. I could hear his heart, but it was getting fainter. Then I found the exit wound and knew he'd been hit in the lungs. Then Rock died.[165]

Two weeks later, in May 1967, Leroy's photos were published in *Life* and *Paris-Match* magazines to great acclaim. Neither article made any mention of jammed M16s. That same week, the letter from a survivor of the Hill Fights was read aloud in Congress. It ended: "Practically every one of our dead was found with his rifle torn down next to him where he had been trying to fix it." Thus began the Congressional investigation.

It takes a long time to make adjustments to a mass-manufactured complex tool. During the dangerous wait for better M16s, the Army decided to adjust the minds of the troops first. (Software fixes are quicker than hardware fixes.)

In the 1960s, combat soldiers in Vietnam were all young men, and nearly all were avid readers of comic books. That explains why, in 1969, the US Government Printing Office printed countless copies of DA Pamphlet 750-30, titled *The M16A1 Rifle: Operation and Preventive Maintenance.* They were distributed to every soldier in Vietnam or on the way there.

It was a jokey 32-page comic book drawn by the revered comic artist Will Eisner. Its first three pages, titled "How to Strip Your Baby," illustrated the 19 steps it took to disassemble the M16. The text began with flirty language: "You want to know her inside out, every contour and curve, every need and whim, what makes her tick."

A page titled "What to Do in a JAM" addressed the M16's most infamous weakness, illustrating the five rapid steps of "the procedure you'd best make second-nature" to clear the jam. Several pages were dedicated to the delicate magazine: how to adjust the magazine catch, get cartridges in and out without bending anything, and disassemble the magazine for

Figure 81. The M16 required assiduous maintenance to function at all, and its design made maintenance difficult. The famed cartoonist Will Eisner spent a month visiting troops in the field before writing and illustrating this 1969 comic book manual. (DA Pamphlet 750-30, illustration by Will Eisner)

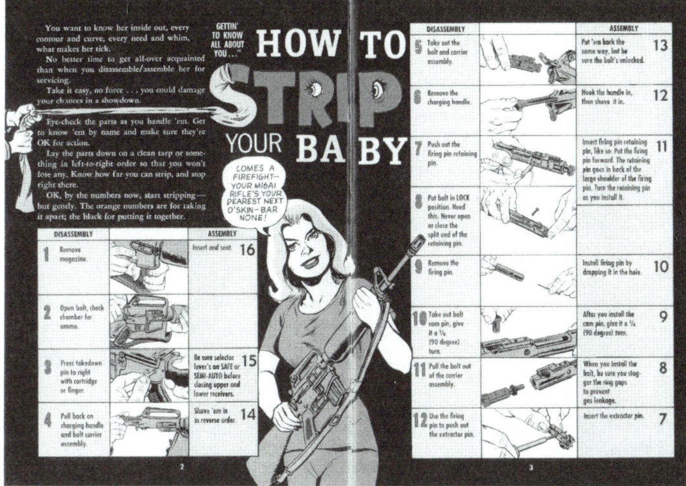

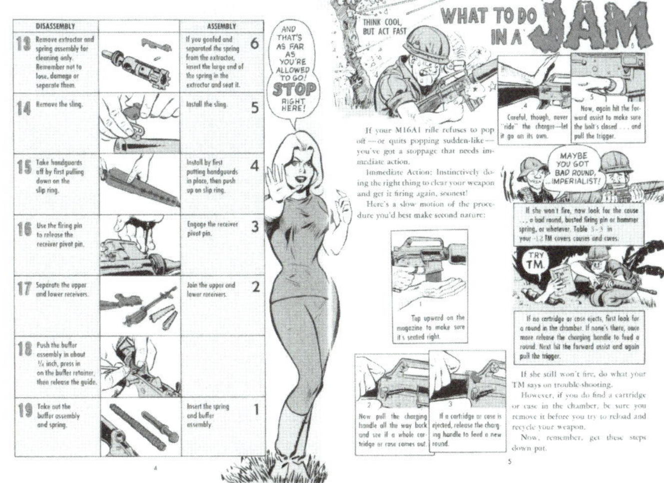

Figure 82. In the comic, the 19 steps of disassembly of the M16 are cleverly arranged as a caption column to read down on the left. Reassembly is guided by reading the caption column on the right upward. Unlike the AK-47, the M16 required intricate maintenance (and still does). Some vital details are easy to get wrong, such as inserting a certain small pin in its hole from the wrong side, guaranteeing the rifle will jam (Step 11). If you attempt the final step of reassembly (Step 15) with the selector switch set to "Auto" instead of "Safe," you will damage the parts. Eisner's comic has a whole page on the crucial task of clearing a jammed rifle, but it doesn't deal with the most frequent cause of jamming: a cartridge stuck in the chamber. The only cure for that is to run a cleaning rod down the barrel and push it out. (DA Pamphlet 750-30, illustration by Will Eisner)

cleaning. The soldiers were prohibited ("STOP right here!") from disassembling the complex lower receiver; any problem with it had to be sent to specialists. And no wonder—the mechanism had 31 parts, nine of which were tiny springs poised to spring away and hide. The price of the M16's beautifully smooth action was having to forbid the user from inspecting and cleaning the parts that made it smooth.

Fieldstripping the M16 was a pain. There were 15 disassembled components to keep track of, including four fiddly little pins that could easily be lost. A technical manual dryly explained that one of the smallest parts, the bolt cam pin, "must be installed or rifle will blow up while firing the first round. Doing so may result in injury, or death of, personnel." The manual added, "Do not interchange bolt assemblies from one rifle to another. Doing so may result in injury, or death of, personnel."[166]

So much for interchangeable parts. The enemy's AK-47s, in contrast, disassembled to just six components, all large, all interchangeable. And no mistake in reassembly could make the weapon blow up.

Eisner's comic detailed why and how to clean and lubricate the M16. It recommended, "Clean your rifle every chance you get—3–5 times a day's not too often in some cases."[167] So much for self-cleaning.

Will Eisner was so beloved as a teacher and exemplar of comic art that the annual prizes given "for creative achieve-

Do not exchange or switch bolt assemblies from one rifle to another. Doing so could result in *injury* or *death*.

Figure 83. A standard warning about disassembling and reassembling the M16 for cleaning. The rifle's design reversed the usual benefit of precision manufacturing, namely that parts are interchangeable. In the M16, the parts were—and still are—so precise in their fit that they are dangerously *non*interchangeable.

ment in American comic books"[168] are called the Eisner Awards in his honor. How did he come to pen a sexy, savvy maintenance manual for a troubled weapon in Vietnam? The story is worth telling as an example of how seriously the military takes maintenance.

When Eisner was drafted into the Army in 1942, he was already a recognized artist for his comic series *The Spirit*. He wrote later that he was assigned to work on Army publications for

> a new program called "preventive maintenance." This was a unique concept in military training, because it required a certain amount of voluntary participation. The army, more mechanized than it had ever been, was sensitive to the problem of equipment failure due to neglect. The desire to enlist troop enthusiasm for preventive maintenance became a major mission. It was obvious to me that comics would be the best way to publish information about field-fixes and to teach bootstrap repair under combat conditions. The concept was easy to sell; in wartime, the military is responsive to innovation.[169]

He was the founding artistic director of *PS: The Preventive Maintenance Monthly* and continued in the role as a civilian until 1971. That's why the Army called on him in 1967 to create the M16 manual. He wrote later that he spent a month in Vietnam researching for the comic: "My job was to visit field units

Figure 84. Long before Will Eisner was celebrated for his graphic novels, he was the founding artistic director of *PS: The Preventive Maintenance Monthly* for the US Army as it geared up for the Korean War. This was the cover of the premiere issue in June 1951. (*PS: The Preventive Maintenance Monthly*, illustration by Will Eisner)

and pick up maintenance stories from automotive and armament shops."[170]

Who allowed such a lemon as the M16 to become America's standard infantry weapon in Vietnam? According to former US Marine officer C.J. Chivers, author of the 2010 book *The Gun*, "The M16's journey was marked by salesmanship, sham science, cover-ups, chicanery, incompetence, and no small amount of dishonesty by a gun manufacturer and senior American military officers."[171] All of that fed the scandal of the gun's early failure in Vietnam, but the core problem was the misdirected design of the rifle itself.

The original design specs show why the M16 and the AK-47 went in opposite directions with regard to maintenance. Both weapons were invented by brilliant innovators operating outside the mainstream of government-supported gun designers. Neither was a formally trained engineer. The AK-47's inventor, Mikhail Kalashnikov, was a lifelong tinkerer, inventor, and poet. He had been wounded in action while serving in a Soviet tank unit in World War II. Eugene Stoner, who developed the rifle that became the M16, was an ex-Marine who had served in the Pacific. His employer was a private company called ArmaLite that pioneered using new materials such as aluminum and plastic for a lighter-weight gun.

For years, military researchers in the US had investigated the potential benefits of bullets smaller than the military world-standard .30 caliber (7.62 mm). A .22 caliber high-velocity round at half the weight had less recoil, which improved accuracy, and greater lethality on impact because of its extreme velocity. The lighter ammo meant a rifleman could carry twice as much. Accordingly, in 1957 a formal request came from the Army

> to develop a .223-inch caliber (5.56 mm) select-fire rifle weighing 6 lb (2.7 kg) when loaded with a 20-round magazine. The 5.56 mm round had to penetrate a standard U.S. helmet at 500 yards (460 meters) and retain a velocity over the speed of sound.[172]

Reliability and maintainability were not mentioned in the specifications.

At ArmaLite, Stoner designed the AR-15 to meet those specs. One early unofficial tester was Colonel David H. Hackworth, an officer so dedicated to troop effectiveness that he was known as "Mr. Infantry." He noted that the new rifle looked "small and light, with lightweight ammo—at first glance, exactly what was needed." He continued:

> I took the weapon out and pumped thousands of rounds through it in every conceivable situation an infantryman might find himself—in sand, mud, cold, rain, and dense foliage as close to "jungle" as I could get at Fort Campbell. I took it apart, put it together, fired it dirty, fired it clean. And whatever the situation, the AR-15 did one thing with consistency: it jammed. Far more than it fired. . . . The AR-15 would never be worth a pinch of salt as an infantry weapon. It just wasn't rugged enough. It wasn't GI-proof. The thing required almost surgical cleanliness (damn hard to achieve on a battlefield) and exacting maintenance that the average Airborne infantryman wasn't going to perform in a combat situation.[173]

SLAPOUT9:
"Very true. But elite troops who accepted the high level of maintenance came to like it. MACV-SOG (Special Forces) units loved the 11.5-inch-barrel carbine version of the M16."

Whereas the Ordnance Department of the 1820s had pushed hard for "practicability" in John Hall's muskets, the Ordnance Corps of the 1950s focused on rifle-range performance. They never conducted battle-realistic tests like Colonel Hackworth did. When Colt Firearms took on manufacturing the new rifle, which was renamed the M16, the Ordnance Corps introduced three additional features that Stoner said would degrade the gun's performance. They did. For spurious reasons, the Corps experts added a useless handle to the bolt, altered the rifling in the barrel in a way that reduced the gun's lethality, and, worst of all, changed the bullet's gunpowder in a way that created two additional causes of jamming. The new powder fouled the rifle and made it fire too rapidly on automatic and then jam.

Tens of thousands of the futuristic, unproven M16s were deployed to the American and South Vietnamese troops. The rifles corroded rapidly in Vietnam's tropical humidity, and their vaunted accuracy at 500 meters was of little use for fighting in jungle so dense that some soldiers wound up having to use their jammed M16s as clubs in hand-to-hand combat. The primitive-seeming AK-47 still had battlefield advantages over America's state-of-the-art assault rifle.

The AK-47 had a quite different design history. During the months in 1941 that Mikhail Kalashnikov spent recovering from his wounds in a military hospital, he overheard other soldiers complaining about the unreliability of the rifles they'd

Figure 85. In 1990, Eugene Stoner (left, with his M16) met Mikhail Kalashnikov (right, with his AK-47). They traveled together and became friends. In many of the world's wars since 1965, the two guns have been on opposite sides. (Chris Lawson, *Marines*)

been issued. As soon as he got out of the hospital, he set about designing a better gun. "His only goal," according to Larry Kahaner's 2007 book *AK-47*, "was to build a weapon that would work every time."[174]

Like the designers of the Lada three decades later, Kalashnikov and the engineers he worked with were realistic about their customers' situation. They knew that Soviet soldiers were mostly conscripts, many unable to read or write. There would be no manuals and probably no training in rifle maintenance. Fieldstripping and cleaning had to be easy and obvious. And manufacture had to be cheap, ideally with stamped rather than milled parts, because they were going to make a great many guns. No one cared what the gun looked like.

The answer to all these requirements was simplicity. Kalashnikov was guided by the words of Soviet gunsmith Georgy Shpagin: "Complexity is easy; simplicity is difficult." The route to simplicity was continuous paring down. Repeated field testing by soldiers led to hundreds of refinements, each enabling greater reliability and ease of use.

This was a case where *reducing* precision helped. Kahaner writes that Kalashnikov designed the "components with looser tolerances, more space between parts. Instead of dirt or sand clogging the gun, debris was thrown off in the firing process—like a dog shaking off water."[175] Unlike the M16, Kalashnikov's gun actually was self-cleaning.

Aside from being deliberately loose in their fit, some parts that looked unnecessarily large had a reason for their size. As C.J. Chivers explains in *The Gun*, "The combined bolt and gas piston were... massive, and by giving these parts heft, the designers provided the AK-47's operating system an abundance of energy every time a shot was fired... to push through any dirt or accumulated carbon inside the weapon."[176] The rifle could power through gunk that would paralyze the lighter, finely tuned M16. It had what engineers call "forgiveness." It forgave neglect. It forgave mud, sand, and ill usage.

The crude-looking but highly evolved AK-47 had just 73 parts. The snazzy M16 had 144 parts and required "surgical" care. It assumed a fully stocked supply line and skilled armorers with factory-level repair facilities nearby. It was—and is—a sophisticated weapon that depends on sophisticated support.

In Vietnam, the most common cause of jamming in both rifles—though far more common in the M16—was when a spent casing got stuck in the chamber instead of ejecting. There was no way to claw it out. The only way to remove it was to run a cleaning rod down the barrel and push it out. The AK-47 had its cleaning rod mounted under the barrel, in immediate reach. The early M16s had no cleaning rods. The later ones had a multipart screw-together rod stashed in a compartment in the butt of the gun. When your gun jams in a firefight, you're most likely flat on the ground or running, which is no place to be screwing together rod parts. "The experienced trooper tapes a cleaning rod to his M16 to unjam it when a cartridge sticks in the chamber," advised the *Army Information Digest*.[177] (In emergency situations, it's best to have the needed tool next to the task.)

After the Viet Cong triumphed over America, the AK-47 became world-renowned as the underdog's weapon of choice and was adopted, with Soviet largesse, throughout the developing world. In 2001, Secretary-General of the United Nations Kofi Annan wrote:

> The world is flooded with small arms and light weapons numbering at least 500 million, enough for one of every 12 people on earth.... When they fall into the hands of terrorists, criminals and irregular forces, small arms bring devastation. They exacerbate conflict, spark refugee flows, undermine the rule of law, and spawn a culture of violence and impunity...
>
> Small arms are easy to buy: In some places, an AK-47

Figure 86. An Afar man in Ethiopia with the long-traditional curved dagger called a *jile* and a now-traditional AK-47. (John Warburton-Lee Photography/Alamy)

Figure 87. "With minimal training, even a child can wield one," wrote Kofi Annan, Secretary-General of the UN. Here, in a Gaza refugee camp in 2000, a young girl is trained by a Palestinian policeman on how to disassemble and reassemble an AK-47 for cleaning. (Ahmed Jadallah/Bridgeman Images)

Figure 88. "Since they require little maintenance," Annan wrote, "they can last for decades." This AK-47, manufactured in 1954 in the Soviet Union, was still in use 55 years later in Afghanistan. The disassembled parts are (from top): receiver cover, recoil assembly, and bolt carrier with gas piston. (C.J. Chivers, *The Gun*)

assault rifle can be bought for as little as $15, or even for a bag of grain. They are easy to use: With minimal training, even a child can wield one. They are easy to conceal and transport. Since they require little maintenance, they can last for decades.[178]

(Meanwhile, in America, the civilian version of the M16 is the AR-15, a semi-automatic, magazine-fed assault rifle that differs from the M16 mainly in its legally required inability to fire in fully automatic mode. It is America's most popular gun for mass shootings. In my view, AR-15s are weapons of war that should, like hand grenades and mortars, be outlawed for civilians, but 20 million American civilians own them. In school shootings involving an AR-15, you seldom hear of a child surviving being shot. The high-velocity small bullet is designed to tumble when it hits flesh. It tears children apart.)

Fifty years after the Vietnam War, the M16 and AK-47 remain the world's standard assault rifles. Both, in their profoundly different ways, are brilliant designs. A total of some 8 million M16s in several variations have been sold for military use. AK-47s, in many variations, have sold over 100 million. An M16 costs $650; the official price of a later version of the AK-47 is $150.

As Ford's Model T and the Volkswagen bug showed, *cheap, clunky, sturdy, and maintainable* wins time after time. Russians sometimes excel at designing for those traits. It's there in the Lada car, in Kalashnikov's AK-47 rifle—and in the Soyuz rocket, as we'll see in a future chapter.

2.5c Two Assault Rifles Footnote: Corpsman Wike

After the Vietnam War, where Catherine Leroy was herself wounded just a week after the Hill Fights, she went on to a distinguished career as a war photographer, covering combat in Lebanon, Northern Ireland, Cyprus, Somalia, Afghanistan, Iraq, Iran, and Libya. In 2005, *Paris-Match* commissioned her to visit and photograph the subject of her most famous images, Vernon Wike.

Leroy found Wike in Prescott, Arizona, in bad shape but delighted to see her again. He looked much older than his 58 years. On his body were 19 warrior tattoos, including the names of comrades who had died in Vietnam. He had burned through four marriages and had two sons who wouldn't speak to him. Once, after he had collected a horde of weapons, he had an armed standoff with police at his remote cabin.

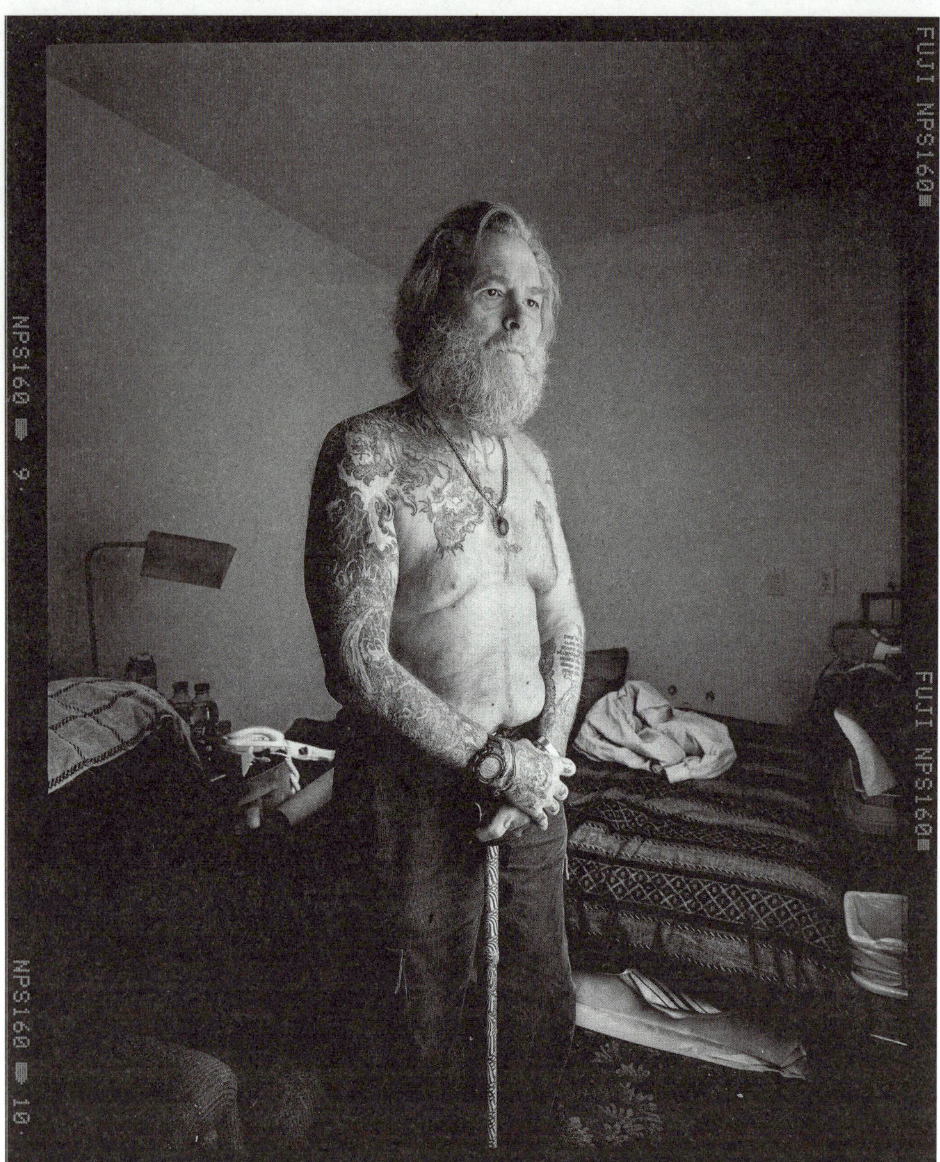

Figure 89. Former Corpsman Vernon Wike, March 1, 2005. (Dotation Catherine Leroy)

Later, the cabin burned down, and Wike lived alone in a tiny room in town when Leroy found him. Two days after she photographed him, he had a stroke that blinded him and paralyzed half his body. He died soon after. It was Catherine Leroy's last commission. She died a year later in California, age 61. Her life's work is collected online.[179]

It was her last public photograph, which, like her first public photograph of the same man, depicted suffering indelibly and honorably. The photos are honorable because, in the first case, she was in the same danger as Wike. It's not a telephoto shot.

The final image honors their friendship. She had visited him before. She was recording art he was proud of—his tattoos. There is so much craft in the image. The corners of the ceiling converge on his face. She had done professional fashion photography, and it's there in the window lighting and in her evoking of the room—of his situation. She photographed his dignity—the dignity of a ravaged man.

To my eye, it is a singularly great war photograph. It's better than iconic. Iconic is the Iwo Jima flag-raising photo—a marvel of composition. Leroy's photo of Wike is one you can study and study for its wealth of telling detail and its stark beauty.

2.5d YouTube Rules

In the olden days before the internet, when some device of yours had a problem, you had to seek out its manual—probably long misplaced—or some expert repair person. Now you just go online and enter a few search terms. Instantly, there's the manual for the make, model, and year of your device, even if the manufacturer no longer exists. It's probably worth having a look at the troubleshooting section in the back of the manual. More likely, though, you'll be drawn to a swarm of relevant YouTube videos begging for your attention. When you tell the search engine what kind of problem your device has, the videos offered become even more relevant. As soon as you pick one to sample, YouTube's recommendation engine shows you an array of related videos. After a bit of shopping among them, you'll probably find exactly the lore you need to figure out your device's problem and several demonstrations of how to fix it, all for free.

YouTube is a damn miracle. It's the most popular social medium in the world. Its website is the second most visited after Google. Of its 2.7 billion viewers worldwide in 2024, 239 million are in the United States—that's four-fifths of our adult population of 258 million. Pew Research reported in 2018 that two-thirds of American adults—188 million—declared that "the platform is important for helping them figure out how to do things they've never done before."[180]

YouTube's vast quantity of how-to-fix-everything videos is a small subset of the boundless cornucopia of how-to-*do*-everything videos on offer. You can find videos on any skill you want, at any depth you want—cook any food, learn the nuances of any musical instrument, study any language, upgrade your technique in any sport, and, indeed, fix any device.

No subject is too arcane or too common. Do you need to extract your own tooth without a dentist? There are several grotesque videos and, on a dental health site, one very sensible one. Want help repairing your Lionel model train? You'll find scores of videos on the subject. Fix a hole in Sheetrock? Scores of videos. Extract a splinter? Scores—including techniques that involve duct tape, glue, baking soda, a raisin, or sugar with soap. Restore an old vehicle or repair a current one? Thousands of videos.

A valuable element of many repair videos is the notes added by creators and commenters. They often provide links to resources such as other videos and sources of tools, materials, and parts.

Finding a spare part to replace something broken, worn down, or lost used to be an arcane quest that only specialists could manage. Auto junkyards littered the land as reservoirs of automobile parts. Now they're almost all gone, and the internet is the reservoir of parts for everything. Kevin Kelly, best known as a technology futurist, is also an avid do-it-yourself maker and fixer of things. In an email, he told me his approach to finding parts online:

MATISSE: "The McMaster online catalog is perhaps the best e-commerce site I have ever used—no flash BS marketing stuff and lots of great cross-referencing, categories, and detailed drawings and specifications. For example, I recently bought some tight-clearance long-nose pliers, and not only is there a detailed drawing showing how the tip thickness is measured, there is also a table showing compliance (or not) with various standards. If I search just for 'pliers,' I immediately see the categories: snap ring pliers, needle-nose pliers, retaining ring pliers, etc., and I can filter down to exactly what I want with ease. McMaster combines search and browse [functions] very effectively."

> I start with Amazon because it is shocking how often they will carry parts for all kinds of things you would not expect. I start with what I think a part is called and then hunt through the recommended alternatives to fine-tune what I want. For things I can't get on Amazon, I go to [McMaster-Carr]. They require that you know what a part is called, and they charge for shipping, but they ship fast. They have an incredibly vast catalog of things, particularly ones that come in huge diversity, like bolts, motors, hardware, etc., with more variations than Amazon. One advantage of the paper version of their catalog is that you can leaf through nearby pages looking for what you think the part is.
>
> I sometimes go to specific websites for things like spa covers, lamp parts, or vacuum cleaner parts, which offer a whole army of specialized brand-name device parts that neither Amazon nor McMaster has. Finally, for really obscure parts or materials, I will check eBay.
>
> I think the golden goose of maintenance is YouTube plus Amazon. This combo has revolutionized repair for the average person. Everyone I've met has a story of how they looked up a

broken thing on YouTube, saw how it was repaired, and then ordered the part on Amazon. I often use YouTube to uncover the part name or source I need, which is mentioned in the video or listed in the notes. The list of things I have repaired using YouTube and Amazon is long: repairing a car door handle, replacing a brake light case, fixing a garbage disposal, etc.

The relationship between a device's parts and the whole is illuminated by a popular genre called "teardowns." In teardown videos, manufactured things are taken completely apart to reveal their secrets: how everything functions, how the components fit together, and how they can be repaired. Many teardowns are the first step to completely restoring an old machine, part by corroded part. Many are for instruction. Many are just for the joy of exposing hidden things and demystifying a piece of the world.

Figure 90. Ryan Kluftinger shows how to get at the carburetor of a motorcycle in a seven-minute teardown video designed to spell out the function of every major component; Robert Pirsig of *Zen and the Art of Motorcycle Maintenance* would rejoice. Kluftinger explains, "Carbs just force gas through jets because a spritz mixes better with air."* His YouTube channel, FortNine, has over 2 million subscribers. (Ryan Kluftinger)

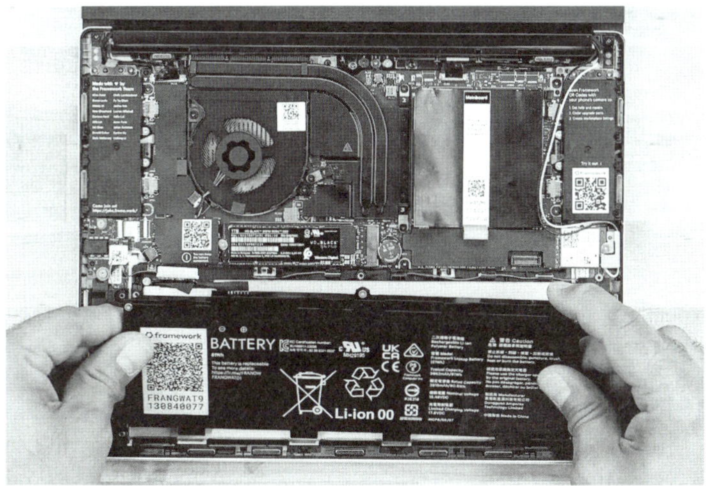

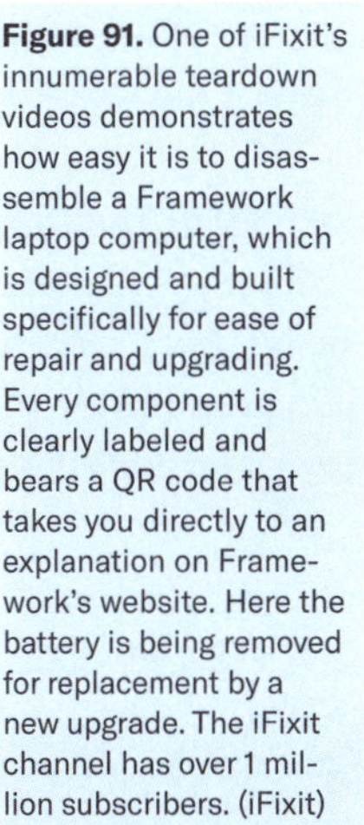

Figure 91. One of iFixit's innumerable teardown videos demonstrates how easy it is to disassemble a Framework laptop computer, which is designed and built specifically for ease of repair and upgrading. Every component is clearly labeled and bears a QR code that takes you directly to an explanation on Framework's website. Here the battery is being removed for replacement by a new upgrade. The iFixit channel has over 1 million subscribers. (iFixit)

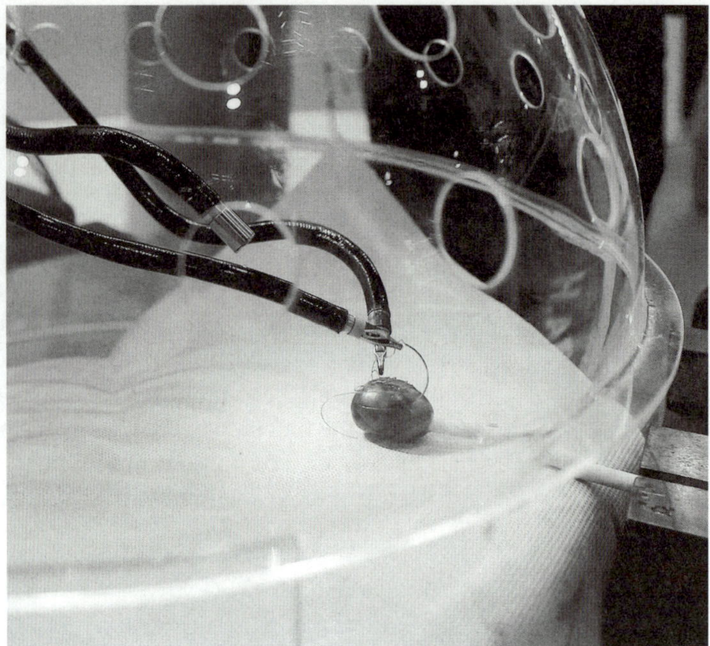

Figure 92. In 2011, over 10 million viewers studied a video showing a laparoscopic surgery robot peeling part of a grape and then suturing the bit of skin back in place. The maker of the surgery robot system, Intuitive Surgical, wouldn't let me use a still from their video, so this photo is from their Chinese competitor, Surgerii Robotics, performing the same feat at an entrepreneurship conference in Beijing in 2018. (Laparoscopic surgery, also called keyhole surgery, is minimally invasive, allowing even complex procedures to be done through a half-inch incision. A 2024 study by the US National Institutes of Health determined that the Intuitive and Surgerii systems had comparable effectiveness with human patients. And grapes.) (Imaginechina Limited/Alamy)

The primary value of YouTube how-to videos, though, is the easy acquisition of skills. This has unleashed ferocious democratization; now, even the most esoteric of nerds can find each other and up each other's game.

Consider the specialists who repair human bodies. "Surgeons are flocking to YouTube," Christina Farr reported on CNBC in 2019. A Dr. Justin Barad told her that during his medical education, "He'd often get prepped by watching a video before a procedure. Sometimes he'd even open a YouTube video in the operating theater when confronted with a particularly challenging surgery or unexpected complication. 'I don't know a surgeon who hasn't had a similar experience,' he said."[181] There are over 20,000 YouTube videos just for prostate surgery.

Professional plumbers are as keen to learn from YouTube as surgeons. A plumber stumped by a problem with your toilet will, right in front of you, scan for videos made by other plumbers about solving that particular problem. Us amateurs with plumbing problems can use the same videos. Here's a typical report I came across online:

> Our showerhead was leaking, even after I replaced the rubber washer. YouTube informed me that I had a scarred valve seat, which is the brass ring that is supposed to form a tight seal against the washer. I bought a reseating tool for about $10 on

> Amazon, which smoothens the surface of the valve seat. It worked and saved me a $150 plumber visit.[182]

When I posted a query on Twitter (later renamed X) about YouTube repair videos, I got responses like this:[183]

> I can't even begin to tell you how many things I've learned to do on YouTube! I redid the plumbing on my house myself, knowing nothing about plumbing… It was in the Caribbean, and the original copper pipes were eaten through because of the salt in the concrete. The standard there is PVC, so I replaced it all with that… I totally would not have pulled it off without videos of people doing it. There's some confidence that comes with seeing something vs. reading about it.[184]

In an online comment for an early draft of this section, Jonathan Owens wrote:

> Because the video medium is entertainment, a well-done video about even something as dry as a transmission service becomes something watched for fun. After a couple months of watching entertaining car maintenance videos, I find myself much more conversant in car maintenance than I ever would have [been] if I'd sat down to study it "on purpose" in books or otherwise… It's such a low-friction way to get familiar with something that I find myself learning without trying to.

One reply to my Twitter inquiry began "I have rebuilt my entire car using Timmy the Toolman and some manuals." I asked for details. The poster said he had acquired a 1996 Toyota 4Runner in pretty bad shape. He rebuilt it so it runs sweetly again, guided by Timmy the Toolman's channel (67,000 subscribers), which has a variety of well-made videos dedicated solely to Toyota vehicles. (Another person in the thread chimed in to praise The Car Care Nut's channel, with 497,000 subscribers, also dedicated to Toyota repair projects.) The 4Runner rebuilder added, "A major part of my success at repair has been the robust community of people that love Toyota 4Runners." He found them on Facebook. "I could post a video or picture of different problems. Or ponder possible solutions and have ten different people debating. Very specific advice. A secret/invisible kinship exists between the hobbyists and the original Japanese engineers."[185]

Several Twitter responders pointed me to Repair Clinic,

a site that offers full service on household appliances—every brand and model of dishwasher, refrigerator, stove, microwave, washing machine, drier, water heater, air conditioner, furnace, snowblower, lawn mower, and string trimmer. "Full service" means they stock all the parts and offer innumerable videos and brief articles on how to diagnose and fix your problem.

As for evaluating tools, no one can match the Project Farm channel (2.7 million subscribers). With a new video every week, Todd Osgood races tools against each other with exhaustive testing to determine which is best. For instance, he describes his 19-minute video on folding knives (2.5 million views) this way:

> 15 knife brands: Benchmade, Zero Tolerance, Spyderco Para 3, Cold Steel, Kershaw Link, Buck, Spyderco Tenacious, Civivi, SOG, CRKT Endorser, CJRB, Ontario, KA-BAR, Opinel, Smith & Wesson. Folding knives compared for initial sharpness, blade lock release pressure, corrosion resistance, and blade tip durability. Knives were then sharpened using the same sharpening system, then compared for blade edge durability.[186]

At the end of the video, Osgood declares a tie for best between the Zero Tolerance, the Benchmade, and the Spyderco, which all cost over $150, while the best deal is the surprisingly good Smith & Wesson at $13. A related Project Farm video on knife sharpeners (6.9 million views) compares nine sharpening systems. Osgood's winner, Wicked Edge, costs $900; the close second best, Lansky, costs $67.

Antique tool restoration videos abound on YouTube. One of the most intriguing, with 19 million views, concerns a forgotten "fractal vise" from the 1920s.[187] The jaws of the vise close around any irregular shape as 32 points of contact self-adjust to grip the object firmly. That something so ingenious and useful could be lost is alarming. That it can be rediscovered and revived is one of the countless benefits of the internet.

There are, of course, many compelling YouTube videos about how to make compelling YouTube videos. Along with the formal encouragement and advice that YouTube Help offers to creators, sundry volunteer experts spell out such things as the nuances of proper microphone use and how to create viral thumbnails. Making an effective how-to video requires three skills: knowing the subject well, explaining it well, and crafting a spiffy video. All three can be learned online.

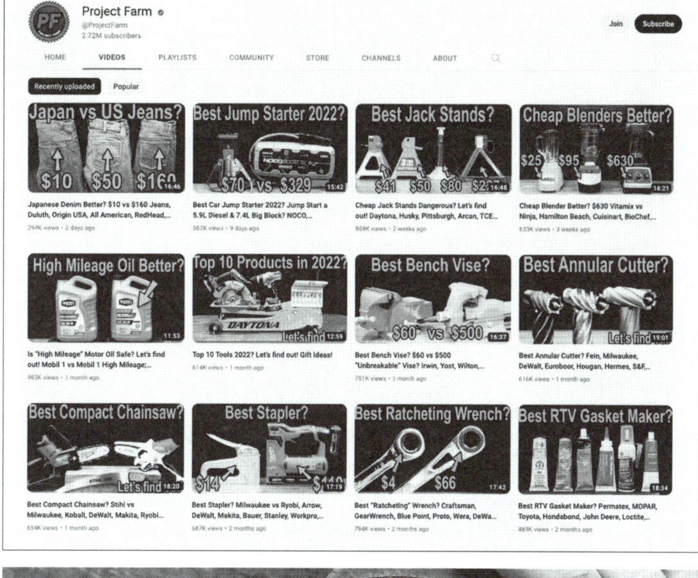

Figure 93. Which tools offer the best performance per dollar in a category, and which ones give the best overall performance? It takes extremely precise testing of every aspect of each tool to get a good answer, and that's what Todd Osgood delivers weekly to over 3.5 million subscribers of his Project Farm channel. These are a few of the video thumbnails from the last four months of 2022. (Todd Osgood)

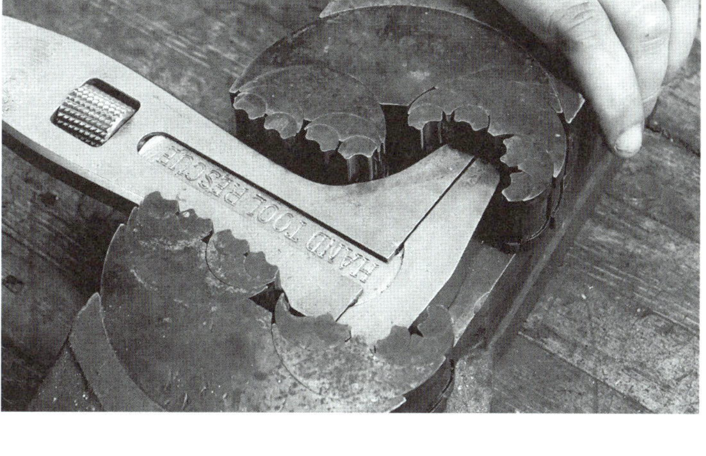

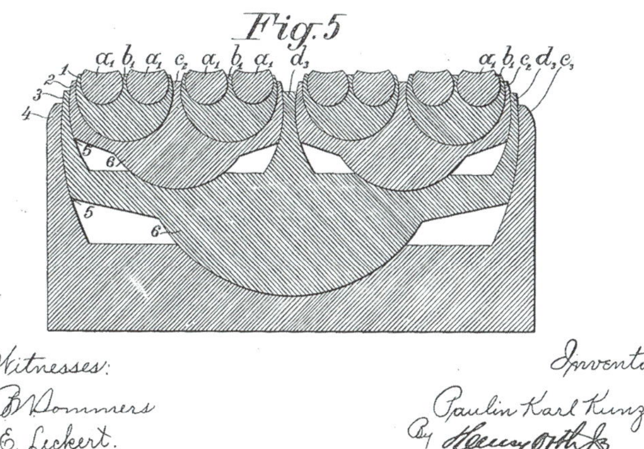

Figure 94. The restoration of a unique self-adjusting fractal vise on the Hand Tool Rescue channel has drawn over 23 million views (top). One of the top comments begins "This has blown up in the 3D-printing community. People are referencing this video and printing these out of plastic left and right!" In his video notes, the creator provides a link to the original 1913 patent for the device (bottom). The video lovingly details the disassembly, rust removal, repair with welding and brazing, fabrication of a missing part, and the japanning, sanding, and lapping it took to get the surfaces to mate properly. (Hand Tool Rescue)

Figure 95. The most common complaint about amateurish YouTube videos is their poor audio quality. On his Podcastage channel, Bandrew Scott offers "10 Tips for Better Sounding Vocal Recordings for Beginners." Tip #5 demonstrates that you don't need a pop filter in front of the microphone to defeat the distortion caused by plosives, the puff of air we blow when pronouncing Ps; you can get the same effect by moving the mic to point at your mouth from a 45-degree angle.

Here are Scott's other tips:

1. Shut off noisy devices.
2. Put anything unavoidably noisy *behind* the mic.
3. Have the mic close to your mouth.
4. Get the mic off your desk to avoid clunking sounds.
5. Record in your closet, or soften hard surfaces in the room where you're recording.
6. Set recording levels properly.
7. Stay stationary in relation to the mic.
8. Speak into the most sensitive part of the mic.
9. Confirm that you're using the right mic and that it is recording.
10. *Practice* before performing. (Bandrew Scott)

Figure 96. The wildly popular science explainer Derek Muller—his Veritasium channel has over 18 million subscribers—describes how to make the most effective thumbnail in a video titled "Clickbait Is Unreasonably Effective." Here, he shows the first thumbnail and title he used for his video about asteroids. It didn't perform very well; the trend in viewers looked like it might peak around 1.5 million views, far below his average. So, after trying a few alternatives, he adjusted the thumbnail and title to "These Are the Asteroids to Worry About." Immediately, the number of viewers soared past 14 million to become his most popular video ever. Two years later, views were at 73 million. Muller suggests that creators use the extensive data that YouTube provides them for comparison-testing thumbnails and titles, then go with the one that works best. You might wonder what thumbnail won out for his video about thumbnails. Here it is, with 6 million views and counting:

Clickbait is Unreasonably Effective

6.1M views • 1 year ago

INTJONATHAN: "Not just the existence of the videos but also their accessibility. In some ways, the undersold platform aspect of mass availability, discoverability, and being ad-supported at zero cost to access is an even bigger deal than the video format. Video's great, and often a much more effective learning tool than even an excellent repair manual, but it does no good if it's hard to discover and navigate to. YouTube's algorithm gets a lot of flak for surfacing clickbait, but for oddly specific maintenance stuff, man, it's great."

One of the greatest blessings of YouTube videos is how accessible they are. When you're flummoxed by something not working, it's short work to find some helpful videos. Pretty quickly you'll know whether you can fix the problem yourself or if it's beyond your skills and tools and you need to find professional help or replace the item.

The comfort that comes with knowing that advice is always at hand eases entry into adopting what I call "maintenance mind" in general. Instead of suppressing awareness about things going wrong with your devices, you become calmly vigilant for troubling signs and ready to act on them as needed. You take charge of your stuff.

How-to videos confer agency.

YouTube is a well-managed and innovative service operating at a global scale. (The most popular YouTube channel, with 261 *billion* views, is a music channel called T-Series, based in India and broadcast in Hindi.) YouTube is kept in business by advertising revenue. For me, the ads are a maddening interruption in the videos. A friend of mine, who had been using YouTube intensely for over a decade, was shocked to discover that if he paid $12 a month for YouTube Premium, the ads would disappear. I recommend it. Deriving value from YouTube involves perusing a lot of videos and studying some in depth. Get the ads out of your way.

What I've written in this book about manuals will probably stay relevant and useful for a good while. What I've written about YouTube videos is bound to be outdated instantly. That alone tells you where the action is.

2.6 Digression 3

Corrosion: Rust Never Sleeps

Defeating rust is an endless drudgery of oiling, greasing, brushing, scraping, cleansing, swabbing, painting, repainting, re-repainting, and finally discarding. All that hassle and expense is a strong incentive to devote a great deal of science and engineering to improving the situation. Thus maintenance issues are the force behind the anticorrosion part of technological progress. We want to make rust just go away, and it just won't. So we negotiate.

Later editions of John Muir's opus on Volkswagen repair include a section titled "How to Keep Your VW Alive Forever." The book emphasizes that the most crucial requirement is to "keep rust at bay."[188] Storing the car is no solution because it will suffer from what dealers call "lot rot." Since rust thrives in

Figure 97. Autumn in Pennsylvania at a Volkswagen graveyard. As soon as the snow flies, the Pennsylvania Department of Transportation will begin spreading its annual 1 million tons of rock salt on the roads to melt the snow and ice, thereby hastening the state's 8 million vehicles on their way to an early grave from rust. (Daniel Ashwood Photography)

moist conditions, humid climates are deadly. The most corrosive regions are near the salty moisture in ocean air or on icy roads strewn with salt to make driving safer. In America's humid southeast and freezing northern states, few old VWs can be found still running; they've all rusted out.

As John Jerome rants in his book *Truck*:

> Road salt makes a mushy, corrosive paste that is flung universally about the under- and over-sides of every vehicle. It fouls all the metal parts, pits windshields, scours paint, and reduces the useful life of north-country motor vehicles by several years. It also kills roadside trees, pollutes streams and wells, and destroys gardens.[189]

He wrote that in 1977. It's still true. There must be a way to ensure safe driving in snow that doesn't destroy every vehicle on the road, but so far all the less harmful substitutes for rock salt, such as sugar beet juice, cost four to 10 times more than rock salt's $70 a ton.

People have always agonized about their cars and trucks rusting out. It used to be said of Model Ts that "on a quiet night, you can hear a Ford rust." That's plausible, according to Jonathan Waldman's 2015 book *Rust*. He writes:

> Because corrosion is exothermic, the skin of a corroding Ford becomes hotter than the metal underlying it, and this thermal gradient generates local stress called electrostriction. Technically, with the right tools, you really could hear it.[190]

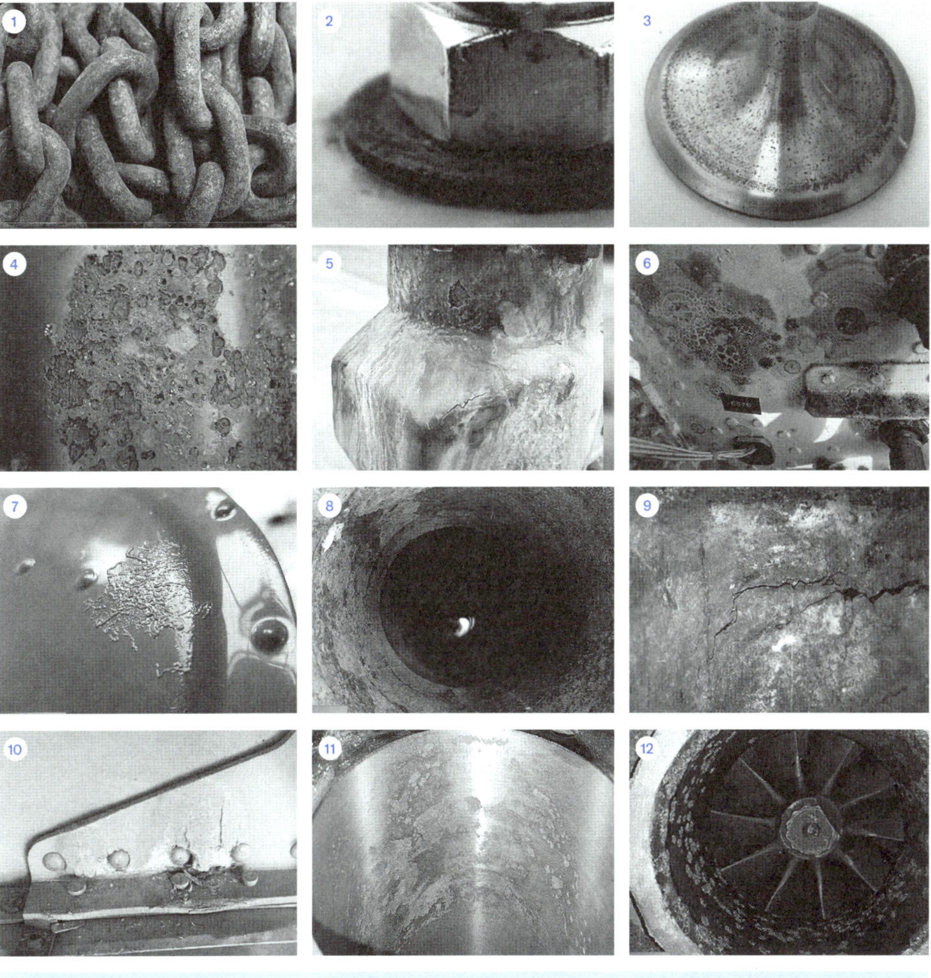

Figure 98. Twelve types of corrosion. Like cancer, corrosion comes in a variety of forms, each requiring a different mode of detection and treatment. Examples:

1. **Uniform surface corrosion**, where the lack of a protective coating causes the whole surface to corrode uniformly
2. **Galvanic corrosion** (also called bimetallic corrosion), caused by direct contact between incompatible metals
3. **Pitting corrosion**, caused by localized damage to a protective layer or by structural defects in the metal
4. **Intergranular corrosion**, which occurs at grain boundaries in the metal, caused by differential heating, such as in defective welding ("grain" refers to the tiny crystals in metal formed during cooling)
5. **Exfoliation corrosion**, a severe form of intergranular corrosion that raises the surface grains of metal formed by extrusion
6. **Crevice corrosion**, which occurs when fluid pools in tiny, hidden spaces between metal surfaces
7. **Filiform corrosion**, wormlike corrosion that forms beneath thin coatings on metal in a warm and humid environment
8. **Erosion corrosion**, caused by mechanical abrasion from corrosive fluids, common in piping
9. **Stress corrosion cracking**, caused by the effects of salty water or air on aluminum, titanium, or stainless steel under tension stress
10. **Corrosion fatigue**, where cracks form due to cyclic mechanical stress on corroding metal
11. **Fretting corrosion**, caused by rapid vibration between metal parts under load
12. **Hot corrosion**, oxidation of metal in extreme high-temperature conditions in the absence of water

Unsurprisingly, the most accurate imagery of corrosion types can be found in military sources. These diagnostic photos come from a nine-minute Navy video titled "Corrosion Identification" that accompanies the 52-page manual *NAVAIR 01-1A-509, Cleaning and Corrosion Control, Volume 1.* (Center for Naval Aviation Technical Training Control)*

"Exothermic" means it emits heat. Rusting is slow fire, an oxidation process that converts iron or steel exposed to air and moisture into iron oxide. Corrosion expert Zaki Ahmad describes it as "extractive metallurgy in reverse... Iron is made from hematite by heating it with carbon. Iron corrodes and reverts to rust, thus completing its life cycle. Hematite and rust have the same composition."[191]

From rust to rust, with civilization along the way.

Metallurgy and civilization ascended together. Because metals are hard, tough, dense, shiny, recyclable, and, most importantly, shapable, they proved perfect for making prized adornments, tools, and weapons, and defined what came to be called the Bronze Age (2300 to around 700 BCE) and the Iron Age (700 BCE to the early centuries of the Common Era).

Over the next two millennia, civilization burgeoned by mining and deploying vast quantities of metal in structures, machines, vehicles, and pipes for every kind of liquid and gas. Nearly everything made by humans has metal in it. So many billions of tons of metal are in use worldwide that its corrosion is a planet-scale expense. According to a 2016 report by the National Association of Corrosion Engineers, "The global cost of corrosion is estimated to be US $2.5 trillion a year, which is equivalent to 3.4 percent of the global gross domestic product." The report earnestly continues, "By using available corrosion control practices, it is estimated that savings of between 15 and 35 percent of the cost of corrosion could be realised, i.e., between US $375 and $875 billion annually on a global basis."[192]

That's the happy news. The hard news is what the engineers are admitting: Even if every one of their best practices is deployed worldwide, corrosion will *still* cost the world between 2.2 and 2.9 percent of global GDP—$1.6 to $2.1 trillion.

Civilization is in the same precarious situation as Sir Robin Knox-Johnston on his sailboat *Suhaili* in the stormy Southern Ocean. His engine rusted solid from just a bit of neglect. Constant vigilance, labor, and ingenuity are required to keep our engines from rusting solid, our bridges from collapsing, and our pipelines from failing catastrophically. Dealing with corrosion is such a massive and crucial undertaking that the search for new ways to do it better never stops. Most of the techniques discovered so far involve trying to make a protective coating so perfect that no combination of moisture and air, or any other corrosive material, can get at the metal.

Figure 99. "Rust Wedge" at San Francisco's Exploratorium demonstrates how rusting iron expands so powerfully it can crack concrete. This photo was taken in February 2012, just three years and four months after the museum put the concrete block and its iron plates out in the rain. ("Rust Wedge" was dismantled in 2015 when the Exploratorium moved; it was not recreated at the new site.) (Jim Heaphy)

Paint on steel is the commonest. Why steel? It's cheap and exceptionally sturdy. Its primary ingredient, iron, is abundant in the Earth's crust. Iron is relatively inexpensive to extract from ore and relatively inexpensive to smelt with enough carbon to make steel. Just since 1950, civilization has produced 36.8 billion tons of steel, according to the World Steel Association.[193] The US alone makes a quarter ton of steel per person per year, three-quarters of it recycled from scrap. The resources analyst Vaclav Smil rightly titles his 2016 book on steelmaking *Still the Iron Age*—we've been smelting iron for 3,000 years.[194]

Undermining the virtues of all that steel is one terrible flaw: Iron oxide is a bigger molecule than iron. When rust forms, it puffs up and flakes off, exposing ever more of the steel, which then rusts and flakes off in turn. When steel rebar rusts inside reinforced concrete, the puffing-up crumbles the concrete. Copper and aluminium corrode more benignly—their

Figure 100. Thin layers of paint, skillfully applied, are all that stand between the chaos of rust and the fragile order of a still-floating steel ship. The average large cargo ship requires 28 tons of paint, repainted every five to 10 years. If the ship carries 20,000 containers, the containers alone require 550 tons of paint. (Zay Yar Lin)

oxides protect the metal by bonding tightly to it—but they're so much weaker and more expensive than steel that the endless hassle of painting steel is the better choice most of the time.

Bernard Moitessier's obsession with getting the best possible layering of specialized paints to protect his steel sailboat *Joshua* exemplifies the pains people take to seal off steel from an oxidizing world. It is an ultraspecialized field. In the course of researching his book *Rust*, author Jonathan Waldman found the most thorough appreciation of the arcana of paint in an organization that estimates its annual corrosion costs at $20 billion: the US military.

The lore Waldman discovered at the Pentagon inspired him to write litanies worth reciting aloud. The Corrosion Office, he reported,

> has funded the development of coatings for aircraft, decks, fire systems, jet fuel tanks, water tanks, air-conditioning coils, pump impellers, vehicle underbodies, bilges, magnesium parts, and cold environments. They're single coats or multiple coats, primers or topcoats, designed to cure quickly or at high temperatures or low temperatures, for spraying or rolling or powder coating or depositing by laser. Some are magnesium rich, or zinc rich, or vinyl based, or epoxy based, or nickel titanium based, or specifically chrome free. Some are fluorescent, stealth, sticky, thick, long-lasting, flexible, fire-resistant,

> chip-resistant, thermally insulating, or nonskid. The office has put more than $3 million toward paints that are self-priming, self-inspecting, self-cleaning, or self-healing.[195]

Engineers at the Naval Research Laboratory composed an ode to the paint on their nuclear submarines:

> The purpose of the hull is to protect the paint.
> The purpose of the reactor is to drive the paint around.
> The purpose of the SUBSAFE program is to ensure the paint comes to the surface and will not be lost.
> The purpose of the cathodic protection system is to back up the paint.
> The purpose of the weapons is to defend the paint.
> The purpose of the Special Hull Treatment is to protect the paint.
> The purpose of the Vertical Launch System is to destroy those who would do the paint harm.[196]

A high degree of expertise is required to find the right paint for a job and then apply it in exactly the right way. When it goes wrong, you need further expertise to analyze the problem and correct it. The best guide is a publication from the National Association of Corrosion Engineers titled *Fritz's Atlas of Coating Defects*. Waldman's *Rust* recites the variety of defects Fritz covers:

> A coating may be cheesy, checked, rippled, wrinkled, peppery, seedy, saponified, crocodiled (or alligatored), cratered, crazed, cobwebbed, crow's-footed, or cracked, like mud or stars. It may look, technically, like an orange peel. It may appear flocculated, or have fish eyes, or be flaking. It may be blistering, bubbling, cissing, disbonded, delaminated, pinholed, peeling, or just plain undercured.[197]

No wonder everyone longs for a single, comprehensive protective coating that can last indefinitely with no need for maintenance at all, please. A coating that comes close to that ideal is hot-dip galvanized steel. The magic ingredient is zinc. When you dip ordinary steel into an ultrahot bath of molten zinc (840 degrees Fahrenheit), you get an inexpensive product with impressive properties. The inner surface of the thin zinc layer bonds tightly with the steel as an alloy, and the exterior reacts with air to form noncorroding zinc carbonate.

Figure 101. A hot-dip galvanized steel wall remains intact while the ordinary steel letterbox mounted on it rusts away. The crystalline shapes on the galvanized surface, called spangles, are formed when the molten zinc cools. (Chianti, via Wikimedia Commons, FAL)

Painted steel is a little cheaper than galvanized at first, but over time it costs three times more because it must be periodically repainted whereas galvanized steel doesn't. Of the roughly 2 billion tons of steel produced annually in the world, as much as one-fifth is galvanized steel, used primarily in construction.

For the billion people who live in shantytowns throughout the developing world, sheets of galvanized corrugated steel are their most treasured building material. In *Machete Season*, a book about the 1994 genocide in Rwanda published in 2006, author Jean Hatzfeld has a section titled "Some Thoughts on Corrugated Metal." He notes, "Of all the elements of the house... the corrugated metal sheet is the only one the villager cannot make with his own hands—hence its commercial value."[198] The sheets don't just have value; they *are* value. With

Figure 102. Entirely clad in galvanized corrugated steel sheets, Migingo Island is in Kenya's Lake Victoria. Over 130 Kenyan and Ugandan fishermen occupy the half-acre island, served by four pubs, several brothels, a hotel, and a pharmacy. This photo was taken in 2016. (Carl De Souze/AFP via Getty)

two sheets you can buy a goat, with 20 an Ankole cow. Sheeting that is worn out from use as roofing and walls, writes Hatzfeld, "serves secondhand to build kitchen shelters, toilets, animal pens, and silos in the courtyard. It also enters into the making of doors, shutters, cabaret terraces, chests, and coffins for the poor."[199]

Galvanized steel is really good for a while, but only a while. Its zinc layer gradually erodes over decades, especially in polluted or ocean air. If the coating is bruised physically, rust quickly invades through any break, and it needs to be cleaned off and resurfaced with specialized paint, just like ordinary steel. Isn't there anything better?

Enter stainless steel. For 2,300 years, starting in ancient China, the alchemists of steel alloys have sought a version that would never rust. European metallurgists finally began to succeed in the 19th century. These days, of the 3,500 steel alloys manufactured for various purposes, some 180 are called stainless. The term is "stainless" instead of "rustless" because the first widely known usage was for kitchen knives that would not stain from the acids in fruit and vegetables. In 1915, the *New York Times* broke the news that a firm in Sheffield, England,

> has introduced a stainless steel, which is claimed to be non-rusting, unstainable, and untarnishable... The initial cost of articles made from this new discovery, it is estimated, will be about double the present cost; but it is considered that the saving of labor to the customer will more than cover the total cost of the cutlery in the first twelve month.[200]

The magic ingredient this time is the metal chromium. When it makes up more than 11 percent of the alloy, the chromium forms a microthin layer of chromium oxide that is stable and highly resistant to corrosion. The protective coating has the ultimate in self-healing properties because it forms instantly whenever the underlying steel is exposed to the air. Thus stainless steel requires even less maintenance than galvanized steel.

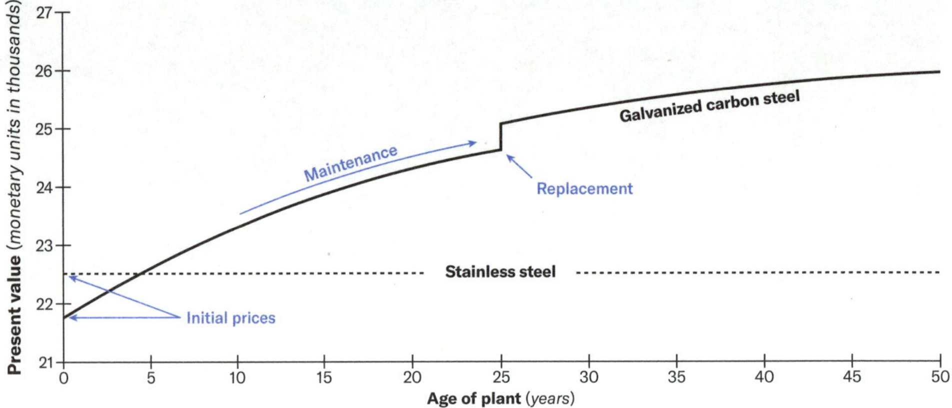

Figure 103. Galvanized steel is cheaper to buy than stainless steel, but as soon as a few years go by, the maintenance costs for galvanized add up, making stainless the less expensive option over time. This diagram compares the life cycle costs of two manhole covers for water storage over 50 years. (Data from Huber Technology)

Comparing stainless to galvanized steel, stainless is more expensive, stronger, and far more resistant to corrosion over time. It is usually the best choice for particularly corrosive environments such as salt water, and for uses that must be highly sanitary, such as medicine and food handling. The shininess of stainless is considered a feature both for its appearance and its ability to be cleaned as perfectly as glass.

However, stainless steel still requires some maintenance, even in ordinary use. Experts advise that dirt and other contaminants that accumulate on the surface can lead to corrosion, so it is vital to keep it clean. But detergents, alcohol-based cleaners, and steel wool scrubbers can damage the chromium oxide protective coating, so stick with soap and water. And don't let stainless have direct contact with certain other metals such as aluminum or galvanized steel, because it will cause them to weaken from galvanic corrosion. (Metals corrode by losing electrons to "nobler" metals in the galvanic series. Zinc loses electrons to iron, which loses electrons to copper, and so on.)

Only gold and platinum are corrosion-free. All other metals require nuanced techniques to protect them. To meet the specialized needs of customers looking to protect their vehicles, boats, buildings, machinery, tools, or weapons, the online Rust Store offers over 3,000 different products dedicated to preventing or removing rust.[201]

Figure 104. This galvanized steel pipe rusted so badly in only seven years that it blocked the water supply at a site in Texas. It was attached to a brass valve that caused the pipe to lose its protective zinc coat through galvanic corrosion, and the exposed steel rusted rapidly. If the stainless-steel pipe shown above it had been used instead, the problem would not have occurred. The short piece of galvanized pipe cost $3.26. The identical piece of stainless pipe would have cost $3.69. (Terry Raines)

What makes corrosion so pernicious is that the process is slow, incessant, usually out of sight, and it metastasizes like cancer. How that plays out over time can be observed in the saga of the Statue of Liberty.

The 150-foot statue in New York Harbor was a gift from the French in 1886. It was made of 80 tons of copper sheets riveted to 135 tons of wrought iron armature. Gustav Eiffel, who designed the Eiffel Tower as well as the iron skeleton for the Statue of Liberty, knew that galvanic corrosion would attack the iron anywhere it touched the copper.[202] His design kept the metals separate with a layer of asbestos soaked in shellac. But that solution only made the problem worse because over time the asbestos layer became a sponge, soaking up highly conductive salt water from the marine environment around the statue, accelerating the galvanic corrosion. The rusting iron put so much stress on the rivets that many popped out.

Eiffel's misuse of asbestos was just the first in a century-long procession of maintenance mistakes.

The core problem was administrative. The statue was first placed in the care of the US Lighthouse Board (part of the Treasury Department), then the War Department in 1901, then the National Park Service in 1933. The directorship of the site

Figure 105. Popped and corroded rivets were visible in the toes of Lady Liberty's right foot in 1984. Each open rivet hole let more salt-laden water into the spots where the copper skin was attached to the iron armature, hastening galvanic corrosion of the iron. (Jet Lowe, Library of Congress)

was a hardship post that few would suffer for long, so management kept changing. When there is no continuity of custody, continuity of scrutiny and maintenance is nearly impossible. Neglect becomes the norm.

Attempts to deal with the popped rivet holes and the destructive moisture they let in led to a series of stopgap measures. In 1911, a coating of coal tar was applied everywhere on the interior to fill in the leaks. Some of it leaked through the rivet holes and discolored the outside of the statue. Over the years, eight additional layers of various kinds of paint trapped moisture between the copper and iron and concealed the escalating corrosion.

Never paint rust.

The extent of the damage only became apparent in 1981, when the findings of a comprehensive investigation were reported. According to Jonathan Waldman's *Rust*, the engineers found that "one-third of the statue's twelve thousand rivets were loose, damaged, or missing, and more or less half of the iron frame had corroded."[203] The painted-over problems were so extensive that parts of the statue, such as the upraised arm, were in danger of collapsing. The statue that was regarded as a symbol of America was now a symbol of decay. And its centennial celebration, in 1986, was just five years away.

Restoring the statue became a matter of national honor. Committees of public-spirited citizens raised $277 million (about $1.5 billion these days) for the effort. Committees of preservation engineers devised schemes to repair the corrosion damage at a scale never before attempted, and they laid out strategies to keep the statue corrosion-free in the future. Since the goal was historic preservation, the original copper skin of the statue had to be treated as inviolate. Scaffolding on the exterior wasn't allowed even to touch the skin at any point.

So they built the world's tallest free-standing scaffolding—305 feet from the pedestal's base to the tip of the torch. When removing the eight layers of paint on the inside of the copper skin proved to be impossible with traditional techniques, the engineers invented a cryogenic solution. Thirty-five hundred gallons of liquid nitrogen was sprayed on the paint to make it so cold that it lost its grip and came off in sheets. Getting the coal tar off, however, required something even more drastic. The eventual solution was a combination sandblaster and vacuum cleaner to scour all the copper with 40 tons of baking soda, followed by a complete rinse with vinegar.

As for the colossal iron frame, it was too far gone. Every one of the 1,825 six-foot armature bars uniquely shaped to the curves of the sculpture's skin had to be replaced with an identically shaped bar of stainless steel. The process of heating, twisting, and pounding each replacement stainless-steel bar into its correct shape made the metal so brittle that it had to be annealed to make it as supple as the wrought iron had been. (The statue's copper skin moves in the wind, and the armature metal has to move with it.) Annealing required heating each bar to 2,000 degrees Fahrenheit, then quenching it in water and sandblasting it. But annealing destroys the chromium oxide layer that makes stainless steel rustproof. To get the layer back, each annealed bar had to be scrubbed with detergent, rinsed, bathed in nitric acid for 30 minutes, rinsed again, boiled in deionized water, air dried, and tested in a copper sulfate solution before it could be wrestled to its unique place high up in the sculpture, taped with Teflon for protection against galvanic corrosion, and refastened to the skin. Molecule by molecule, the statue's giant metal skeleton was refreshed.

The process was so labor intensive that it took six months of 24-hour workdays to complete.[204] (The ongoing maintenance budget for the statue these days, I'm told, is about $6

Figure 106. By 1983, engineers recommended 12 major projects to fully restore the Statue of Liberty in time for its centennial in 1986. Nine of the 12 projects were to solve corrosion problems. The work had to repair all the past corrosion damage in the statue and prevent corrosion in the future.

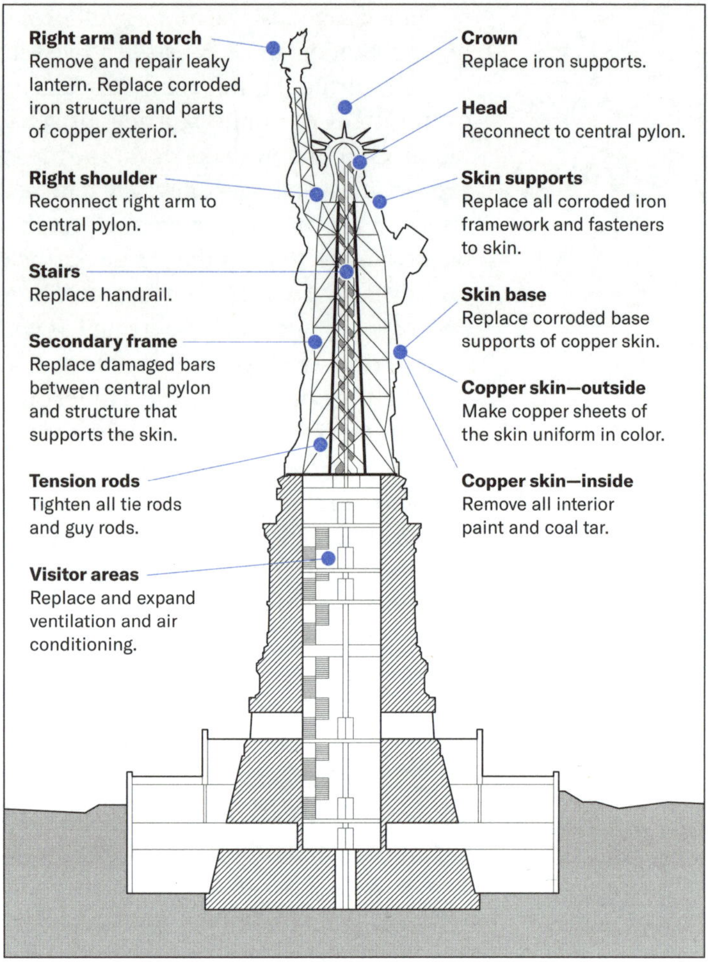

Right arm and torch
Remove and repair leaky lantern. Replace corroded iron structure and parts of copper exterior.

Right shoulder
Reconnect right arm to central pylon.

Stairs
Replace handrail.

Secondary frame
Replace damaged bars between central pylon and structure that supports the skin.

Tension rods
Tighten all tie rods and guy rods.

Visitor areas
Replace and expand ventilation and air conditioning.

Crown
Replace iron supports.

Head
Reconnect to central pylon.

Skin supports
Replace all corroded iron framework and fasteners to skin.

Skin base
Replace corroded base supports of copper skin.

Copper skin—outside
Make copper sheets of the skin uniform in color.

Copper skin—inside
Remove all interior paint and coal tar.

Figure 107. Looking down the folds of the statue's toga, the uniqueness of each of the 1,825 iron armature bars bracing the copper skin is readily apparent. Replacing every single bar with a perfect stainless-steel replica was a gargantuan task. (Jet Lowe, Library of Congress)

Figure 108. July 4, 1986, New York Harbor. The Statue of Liberty has been rebuilt from within with stainless steel. Because of a blunder in the original construction followed by a century of botched maintenance, the repair cost $1.5 billion. (Thananit, Adobe Stock)

million a year: $5 million for managing public access and $1 million for physical maintenance. And any year the $1 million is not entirely spent, the remainder is banked so that the fund will become sufficient over time to pay for a major overhaul.)

Having a hard, extremely public deadline forced the project to finish on schedule. On July 4, 1986, the centennial celebration was attended by millions of people, 40,000 boats, and two presidents—Ronald Reagan of the US and François Mitterand of France—while a third of the world's population watched on TV. Twenty tons of fireworks, the largest display in history at that time, lit up the night. They provided a thundering light show for the US Marine Band playing "The Stars and Stripes Forever" and a chorus roaring "Glory, glory, hallelujah."

It was just a maintenance project.

2.7 Digression 4: Sustainment

2.7a How Poor Maintenance Loses Wars: 1973, Israel Maintains

Is there such a thing as maintenance mind? If so, what are its features, and what is its underlying character? What hinders it? Can it be cultivated? Can it be institutionalized? This digression about the role of maintenance in two wars may have some clues.

War one: 1973. On October 6, Israel was attacked by Egypt and Syria simultaneously. The conflict was variously named the Yom Kippur War, the Ramadan War, and—the non-sectarian option—the October War.

The assault by Egypt and Syria arose directly from what had happened six years before in the Six-Day War of 1967. After a crushing victory over Egypt, Israel took possession of the Sinai Peninsula and fortified its new border with Egypt on the eastern bank of the Suez Canal with elaborate defenses called the Bar-Lev Line. Behind a continuous berm of sand and concrete 75 feet high, the Bar-Lev Line stretched 93 miles long and 19 miles deep, comprising three layers of roads connecting 22 forts, 35 strongpoints, and 11 strongholds. Supporting it from nearby was an armored division of 8,000 soldiers and 350 tanks. The defenders knew they could count on at least 48 hours' warning before an attack, and it would take any attacker another 48 hours to breach the high berm by the canal with explosives or tractors—plenty of time for additional Israeli armored divisions to arrive.

Egypt's surprise attack across the Suez Canal on October 6 nullified all that. It took only an hour for 40 engineer battalions using water cannons to blast through the sand berms. In the opening phase of the attack 32,000 Egyptian troops, followed by 200 tanks, crossed the canal, first in boats and ferries, then on 20 floating bridges. Israel's vaunted Air Force could not

Figure 109. October 6, 1973. A day of triumph and glory for Egypt is depicted in a circular mural at a military museum near Cairo called the 6th of October War Panorama. This section of the panorama shows two of Egypt's 20 floating bridges across the Suez Canal. In the foreground, Israel's supposedly impregnable sand berms are being blasted away with water cannons. The stunning success of Egypt's surprise attack was the product of six years of meticulous planning and rehearsal. (October War Panorama, via Wikimedia Commons, public domain)

stop the crossing because of an overwhelming barrage from Soviet-made surface-to-air missiles on the Egyptian side of the canal. Also, to divide Israel's forces, Egypt's offensive was synchronized with a massive tank attack by Syria in the north to seize Israel's Golan Heights.

By October 8, Egypt had another 60,000 troops and 600 tanks across the canal, setting up long-planned defensive positions. When Israel hastily counterattacked with 640 tanks in three armored divisions, they were met by Egyptian infantry ready for them, armed with Soviet wire-guided anti-tank missiles and rocket-propelled grenades. At the end of a bloody day, 400 of Israel's tanks were destroyed, the counterattack had failed, and Egypt controlled the entire former Bar-Lev Line. Israel was in shock.

SLAPOUT9:
"They were indeed in shock. I remember that day well since I was a member of the 82nd Airborne Division at the time, and President Nixon alerted my unit to help prevent Israel's near destruction. The following is what I remember from that time, and how maintenance was very much an issue."

Egypt's triumph was a retaliation six years in the making. In 1967, Egypt responded to the humiliation of its defeat in the Six-Day War by devising a plan to recapture the Sinai. The government invited assistance from the Soviet Union. By the early 1970s, Egypt was fully armed with Soviet tanks, fighter jets, surface-to-air missiles, anti-tank missiles, and as many as 20,000 military trainers and specialists.

The invasion across the Suez Canal was planned in elaborate detail. Half of the engineers in Egypt—some 15,000, deployed in 40 combat engineer battalions—were tasked with designing the crossing and carrying it out. When experiments showed how long it would take to blow up or bulldoze through the high sand berms of the Bar-Lev Line, a junior officer named Baki Zaki Youssef came up with the idea of using water cannons.

Every detail of making the crossing and establishing multiple bridgeheads on the other side was rehearsed exhaustively for years before the attack. In a report on the October War, analyst and US Army Colonel James Powell writes:

> Squads and platoons trained on mockups of Bar-Lev Line fortifications. "Tank-hunting teams" of infantry familiarized themselves with Sagger wire-guided antitank missiles repeatedly over the course of several months, firing up to 25 per day on special ranges. The dissemination of explicit, detailed instructions enabled soldiers across the armed forces to hone the specific skills that would be required of them during the anticipated assault.[205]

It paid off. Military historians regard Egypt's so-called Operation Badr offensive as a masterpiece of deception, strategy, training, coordination, and logistics.

Then it went sour. On October 14, Egypt launched 1,000 tanks in an immense but disorganized attack toward the Sinai passes 20 miles away. It was a catastrophe. The following day, Israel launched a counterattack with three divisions across the Suez Canal into Egypt, threatening cities north and south of their bridgehead. The Israeli forces destroyed enough of Egypt's surface-to-air missile sites on the west side of the canal to regain air dominance.

Egypt's spectacular victory had capsized into defeat. What happened?

Figure 110. In the Golan Heights battles against Syria, as in the Sinai Peninsula against Egypt, Israeli tank crews and ordnance technicians worked 24 hours a day to get their battle-damaged Centurion tanks back into combat immediately. On October 10, 1973, the group in the foreground is fixing the idler wheel that maintains the track tension on a tank. The mobile crane in the back is swapping out a tank's diesel engine. Neither the Syrian nor Egyptian armies recovered and repaired their own tanks. According to one report on the Golan Heights battle, "just 177 Israeli tanks resisted the concerted offensive of 1,400 Syrian tanks over a period of 81 hours without reinforcement and with hardly any sleep or respite under the incessant artillery bombardment."* With the arrival of Israeli reinforcements, the Syrian forces were swept from the Golan Heights, leaving 867 disabled tanks behind—many of which were repaired and put to use by Israel. (Azure Menashe, Israel Government Print Office)

SLAPOUT9:
"This is true, but it was also due to the massive airlift of spare parts by the US Air Force. This airlift basically kept the 82nd from being deployed. It lasted over 30 days. The Air Force lifted over 20,000 tons of equipment, including M60 tanks, artillery, and ammunition; also aircraft spare parts and weapons. (On Wikipedia, just type in 'Operation Nickel Grass.')"

One answer is spelled out in Powell's 2019 paper, titled "Taking a Look Under the Hood: The October War and What Maintenance Approaches Reveal about Military Operations." I'm drawing on his paper and other analyses to see what the conduct on both sides of the October War might reveal about maintenance mind—because apparently the Israeli troops had it and the Egyptian troops didn't, and it turned out to be pivotal.

The shocking statistic is that of the 840 tanks Israel lost to battle damage in the war with Egypt, fully half were recovered, repaired, and returned to the fight. Powell credits the Israeli military with

> a mindset that naturally viewed damaged tanks as *soon-to-be-repaired tanks*, rather than the irredeemable flotsam of battle. The fact that [Israeli] commanders thought in these terms gave purpose and direction to the maintenance-related technical and tactical skill their crews possessed.[206]

Each tank crew of four had the tools and ability to do minor repairs, and ordnance teams in the rear were equipped to repair major damage and return disabled tanks to action quickly. Division Commander General Avraham "Bren" Adan was moved to devise a tactical innovation in the thick of the fighting after he noticed that some of his tanks were inexplicably moving to the rear. When he learned they were bringing wounded crew members and other problems back to be dealt with, he established a checkpoint just behind the front to provide fuel, ammunition, medics, and ordnance technicians. Adan recounts in his memoir:

Our procedure was to halt a tank at the checkpoint, and the crew would report their problems. The officers there would see to the evacuation of the wounded, then combine crews from two tanks that had been hit. After giving them a "pep talk," they would send the men back to the front. Malfunctioning tanks would either be repaired on the spot by mechanics or the crew given another tank so they could get back to the battlefield. There was considerable improvisation at the checkpoint, and many tanks and crews were able to be sent back into battle quickly.[207]

In Powell's paper, he proposes that innovation like Adan's reflects "the productive relationship between Israel's military and scientific communities and the country's underlying culture of improvisation." He adds:

> In the Israeli way of war, skilled tactical leaders and technically proficient weapon crews were top commodities. The challenges of maneuver warfare were best handled by officers and men accustomed to exercising initiative in the midst of fast-paced, decentralized operations. What is more, against a numerically superior foe, these qualities applied also to the realm of maintenance in the sense that every armored vehicle counted.[208]

Most of Israel's main battle tanks in the October War were British Centurions that had been upgraded. Egypt's enormous inventory of tanks was made up largely of Soviet T-55s. The Soviet Union had designed the tank on the same principles

Figure 111. Israeli tanks counterattack across the Suez Canal into Egypt on October 15, 1973. Egypt's Soviet T-55 tanks were considered evenly matched with Israel's upgraded British Centurions, but their crews were not. Israeli tank crews had the skills and tools to maintain and repair their tanks; the Egyptian crews didn't. Most of Egypt's tank repair was done by foreigners in depots far from the fighting. (Israel Defense Forces)

Figure 112. Israeli troops in an armored personnel carrier advance past one of Egypt's Soviet T-55 tanks abandoned on the battlefield. A little smaller than Israel's Centurion tanks, the T-55s presented a smaller target, but inside they were cramped for the crew of four. There is no evidence that any of the damaged or abandoned T-55s were recovered and repaired by Egyptian forces. (Terry Fincher)

as their AK-47 assault rifle: simple, rugged, reliable, and cheap to manufacture. Between 1952 and 1977, nearly 100,000 T-55s were produced and used in combat worldwide, more than any other tank in history. Its simplicity and reliability should have made the T-55 easy for Egyptian troops to maintain and repair. But it didn't work out that way, for reasons that had nothing to do with the tank.

A trait the Egyptian army and its Soviet trainers had in common was that they discouraged soldiers below the level of general from taking initiative of any kind. The job of everyone in the military, especially the junior officers, was to follow orders without deviation. "Soviet commanders considered 'improvisation' a pejorative term," writes Powell, "since it seemed to indicate, above all, a lack of preparation."[209]

Family life in Egypt's villages has the same structure. The patriarch decides nearly everything for everyone in his extended family. They are kept in line with the powerful culture of shame common throughout Arab countries.[210] In his 2019 book *Armies of Sand*, analyst Kenneth M. Pollack states that "because shaming is the primary instrument by which Arab society enforces conformity, and because shame is considered an unbearable punishment, 'worry about external dignity is [the Arab's] continual concern.'"[211] He adds:

> Fear of dishonor also contributes to tendencies toward secrecy and compartmentalization of knowledge. Shame attaches only when the sin becomes public...
>
> In order to conceal mistakes that would result in shame, features of Arab culture encourage the individual to exaggerate, lie, and/or remain secretive.[212]

Norvell De Atkine, a retired US Army colonel who got his graduate degree in Arab studies and spent eight years training soldiers in Egypt, Lebanon, and Jordan, has this account:

> Arabs husband information and hold it especially tightly... Having learned to perform some complicated procedure, an Arab technician knows that he is invaluable so long as he is the only one in a unit to have that knowledge; once he dispenses it to others he no longer is the only font of knowledge and his power dissipates... On one occasion, an American mobile training team working with armor in Egypt at long last received the operators' manuals that had laboriously been translated into Arabic. The American trainers took the newly minted manuals straight to the tank park and distributed them to the tank crews. Right behind them, the company commander... collected the manuals from those crews... He did not want enlisted men to have an independent source of knowledge. Being the only person who could explain the fire control instrumentation or boresight artillery weapons brought prestige and attention.[213]

The avoidance of public dishonor was partially responsible for the chaos of Egypt's massive tank attack on October 14, which cost Egypt 265 tanks to Israel's 40. (Israel quickly repaired all but six of that 40.) Until that day, every action of Egypt's forces had been tightly scripted and rehearsed. The moment they went off script, they floundered. Junior officers had no training in taking initiative in rapid-maneuver warfare, and the dread of making a mistake hobbled them. "In Arab society," writes Pollack, "to do something wrong generally is much worse than to do nothing at all."[214] So Egypt's tank formations attacked whatever was directly in front of them and were shredded by Israel's fast, impromptu maneuvering.

When things began to go badly on the battlefield, Egypt's generals didn't know what was happening and were unable to redirect their forces, because the officers in the field couldn't bear to report bad news and instead proclaimed fictional successes. "Starting on October 14," writes Pollack, "the combat reports... coming in from tactical commanders spiraled off into fantasy."[215] Egypt's defeat that day was the turning point of the war.

Most damaging of all for maintenance in Arab militaries is the officers' disdain for manual labor and their caste-like distance from enlisted men. By one scholarly account, "There is a common and very deep-seated feeling that manual or rural forms of work mean drudgery and nothing more; that furthermore, there is an element of degradation in them, so that they must be avoided by all and any means."[216] De Atkine reports:

> Officers refuse to get their hands dirty and prefer to ignore the more practical aspects of their subject matter, believing this below their social station. A dramatic example of this occurred during the Gulf War when a severe windstorm blew down the tents of Iraqi officer prisoners of war. For three days they stayed in the wind and rain rather than be observed by enlisted prisoners in a nearby camp working with their hands.[217]

"Most Arab officers treat enlisted soldiers like subhumans," De Akine adds. Consequently, "the young draftees who make up the vast bulk of the Egyptian army hate military service for good reason and will do almost anything, including self-mutilation, to avoid it." A vital missing element, he argues, is that "most of the Arab world either has no NCO corps or it is non-functional."[218]

NCOs are noncommissioned officers—the sergeants. In effective military forces, they provide the bridge of trust between officers and enlisted troops, conduct most of the training, and oversee maintenance and repair work. Typically, an NCO is the most experienced soldier in a unit and is

Figure 113. At an Israeli ordnance depot, Soviet T-55 tanks abandoned on the battlefield by Egyptian and Syrian soldiers are repaired and refitted for use as Israeli tanks. (Alamy)

respected accordingly. "Without the cohesion supplied by NCOs," De Atkine observes, "units tend to disintegrate in the stress of combat."[219]

Desert warfare is maintenance-intensive. A US Army manual warns that "sand mixed with oil forms an abrasive paste."[220] American tank crews fighting in desert conditions are required to constantly inspect and replace all oil, fuel, and air filters, check lube fittings and Teflon bearings, and change the engine oil frequently.[221] Powell points out that in 1973,

> despite their reputed ruggedness, the Soviet-made tanks in Egypt's arsenal were not immune to the effects of inadequate maintenance under conditions of sustained combat—particularly in the desert. Ten days into the war, about 80 percent had broken down.[222]

The Egyptian attitude toward maintenance was so "abysmal," reports Pollack in his book *Arabs at War*, that "crews abandoned vehicles on the field of battle because of relatively minor problems."[223] In Powell's account, this presented an opportunity for Israel's ordnance teams. They

> recovered and went on to employ about 300 repairable Arab tanks during the conflict...
>
> ... Familiar enough with their own equipment, Israeli soldiers could transfer that knowledge and apply it to the maintenance and operation of analogous weapon systems—even ones that began the war on the opposite shore.[224]

Some of Egypt's T-55 tanks became part of Israel's counteroffensive across the Suez Canal.

The maintenance disparity I've described here was duplicated in Israel's victory over Syria in the Golan Heights and its air war with Egypt above the Suez Canal. It was a different story, however, with the Egyptian engineer battalions that bridged the canal. Israel's Air Force, reports Powell, "targeted pontoon bridges as a way of disrupting the crossing, but they soon found that Egyptian engineers repaired the damage so quickly as to render bombing and strafing runs nearly fruitless."[225] It should also be noted that throughout Egypt's forces, "unit cohesion and personal bravery... were high points for the Egyptians during the October War," Pollack writes.[226]

The fighting ended when a ceasefire was declared on October 25, brokered by the United Nations, the United States,

Figure 114. Arab armies often excel at handling logistics operations. The most impressive was Egypt's assault across the Suez Canal that overwhelmed Israeli defenses on October 6, 1973. Here, the soldier on the Soviet T-55 tank is brandishing a Soviet AK-47 assault rifle. (Egyptian Government Information Office)

and the Soviet Union. Israel had once again prevailed on the battlefield, but you would never know it from the way the two countries behaved after the war. Egypt celebrated the first four days of the war as a famous victory over Israel and forgot the rest. Israel acted as if its forces had lost. In his 2012 book on the conflict, historian Simon Dunstan describes the reaction:

> The Israeli people were staggered by the early successes of the Arab armies that smashed the myth of IDF [Israeli Defense Force] invincibility and the scale of their casualties was beyond comprehension... That anger was reflected in the ballot box when the Labour Party [led by Prime Minister Golda Meir] that had held office for almost 30 years was voted out of office and replaced by the right-wing Likud government of Menachem Begin in 1977... Israel's faith in her leaders, both political and military, was shaken, leading to the factionalised and polarised society that exists today.[227]

Geopolitically, the war's outcome was treated as a draw. It led directly to the Egypt–Israel peace treaty of 1979, which normalized relations between the two countries.

Every major military in the world has studied the October War to see how its lessons might apply to them. Colonel Powell's paper draws attention to what China's military analysts learned. In a People's Liberation Army publication on military strategy, analysts wrote:

> In the Middle East War of 1973... it was only when the Israeli army enhanced its technical support... that 80 percent of the damaged tanks in the war could be recovered and sent back to the battlefields... The equipment support ability of the Israelis... contributed a great deal to the reversal of their disadvantageous posture and changed the process and outcome of the war.[228]

Powell himself concludes:

> An understanding of how a military regards and conducts maintenance... sheds light on the extent to which it will be able to improvise in wartime. Maintenance proficiency serves as an indicator for how fast and how frequent new techniques can be developed and implemented and whether the expertise exists to apply them widely across the force as it fights.[229]

In other words, maintenance prowess is core to rapid adaptivity under duress. Israel had institutionalized it. Egypt never tried, apparently for reasons embedded culture-deep.

2.7b Sustainment: The Concept

Who studies, tests, and institutionalizes maintenance mind best? I find that the most active frontiers of maintenance theory and practice are in four domains: manufacturing, aerospace, software, and the military.

The US Army has lately introduced a new term, "sustainment," that signals a seismic shift in its doctrine. It was formally introduced in 2009 with a new edition of *Field Manual FM 4-0*, previously titled *Combat Service Support*. The new *FM 4-0* was titled *Sustainment Operations*. For the Army, the manual has the semi-Biblical status of what the military calls a "doctrinal publication," spelling out official principles, guidance, and best practices. The 2019 edition defines the subject this way: "Sustainment is the provision of logistics, financial management, personnel services, and health service support necessary to maintain operations until successful mission completion."[230]

That sounds like no more than a bureaucratic nuance, but it is a major redirection for the military. Some of the supporting concepts are particularly interesting. The stated goal is

Figure 115. A US Army magazine on logistics was renamed *Army Sustainment* in 2009. This 2022 cover (left) shows the M88 armored recovery vehicle hoisting a truck out of trouble. The Army built 1,000 M88s for battlefield rescue and recovery, especially in support of tanks. Meanwhile, the magazine founded by Will Eisner in 1951, *PS: The Preventive Maintenance Monthly*, continues to be published monthly, often illustrated with comic book art (right). (*Army Sustainment, PS: The Preventive Maintenance Monthly*)

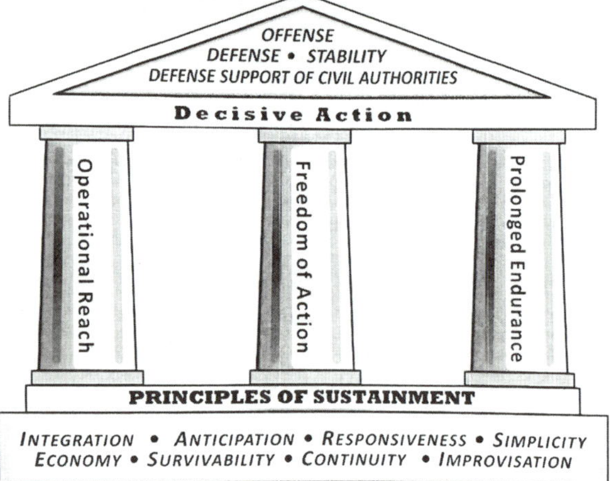

Figure 116. The US Army's new doctrine portrayed in institutional mode—as sound as a bank, as informative as a library—with signifying words and catchphrases shown in architectural relationship. The illustration and the concept point toward the crucial outcome: decisive action. (*FM 4-0*)

The appearance of US Department of Defense (DoD) visual information does not imply or constitute DoD endorsement.

"decisive action," achieved by "operational reach," "freedom of action," and "prolonged endurance," also referred to as "unrelenting endurance." Sustainment never lets up.

The manual describes what is meant by "freedom of action":

> The proper application of the mission command philosophy to sustainment operations encourages the greatest possible freedom of action from subordinates… [It] equips subordinate commanders with the authority and flexibility to act boldly and achieve desired support effects in the absence of continuous direction from higher headquarters.[231]

The principle of mission command (as distinct from "detailed command") is a profound improvement on how I was trained as a young Army lieutenant in 1961. My instructors said that American soldiers won't follow orders they think are meaningless; they insist on knowing *why* a particular mission is important. That's fine, but it's just about motivation. Mission command goes way beyond that to *distributed empowerment*. A paper on the subject explains that "mission command provides the means through commander's intent, mission-type orders, and decentralized execution to operate at the speed of the problem." It quotes General George Patton, who said, "Never tell people how to do things. Tell them what to do and they will surprise you with their ingenuity."[232]

The idea has a rich history. On October 14, 1806, the fabled Prussian army was vanquished on two battlefields simultaneously by Napoleon's forces. In a 2005 paper titled "The Road to Mission Command," historian Stephen Bungay explains how it happened:

> Napoleon introduced mini-armies called Corps, containing a balance of infantry, cavalry and artillery, and so able to operate independently of each other. Each was commanded by a Marshal, a man picked on merit by Napoleon himself. In conducting the campaign, Napoleon was able to communicate very rapidly with the Marshals because they shared a basic operating doctrine, and he explained his intentions as well as what he wanted them to do. He expected them to use their initiative and act without orders in line with his intentions. They did. The result was an operational tempo which left the incredulous Prussians bewildered.[233]

SLAPOUT9:
"When I was a young buck sergeant, I was taught to never make a decision that someone at a lower level could make. This took some getting used to, but I had a patient senior NCO leadership cadre who was dedicated to seeing it was done. This is more important in airborne divisions then regular line units because of the extreme likelihood you will have to fight independently."

Stung by the humiliation, the Prussian military studied how Napoleon had beat them and created their own doctrine of decentralized command called *Auftragstaktik*—"mission-type tactics." The doctrine stated that "senior commanders should 'not order more than is absolutely necessary' but should ensure that the goal was clear. In case of doubt, subordinate commanders should seize the initiative."[234] The next time the Prussian and French armies met on the battlefield, in the Franco-Prussian War of 1870, the French commanders had forgotten Napoleon's practice and were defeated by the Prussian commanders who had studied and improved upon it.

When Prussia followed up its victory by launching the highly militarized German Empire, *Auftragstaktik* was the core philosophy for training its officer corps. They were taught that the army that could act and react with the greatest speed would prevail in battle, and to expect chaos on the battlefield and take charge of it. Chaos they created would be transparent to them while it blinded the enemy. Since trust between levels of command was essential, "all NCOs were trained as officers and officers were expected to master the tasks of two ranks higher up the hierarchy and to take their place if needs be."[235] As a result, Nazi Germany's Wehrmacht was the ablest military force in the Second World War. A 1977 study by US Army Colonel Trevor Dupuy declared:

> On a man-for-man basis, the German ground soldiers consistently inflicted casualties at about a 50 percent higher rate than they incurred from the opposing British and American troops under all circumstances. This was true when they were attacking and when they were defending, when they had a local numerical superiority and when, as was usually the case, they were outnumbered, when they had air superiority and when they did not, when they won and when they lost.[236]

In 1977, the American military was figuring out how to recover from Vietnam, a conflict it had lost despite—or perhaps partly because of—a combination of superb communications and data collection and complete air superiority, all of which intensified top-down control. It had got to the point that Commander-in-Chief Lyndon Johnson was selecting bombing targets. The search for a better theory of battlefield command led to investigation of the Wehrmacht's *Auftragstaktik* and its eventual translation into Yank: mission command.

The idea took hold formally in 2010, when mission command was made part of official Army doctrine in *Field Manual FM 3-0*. In this philosophy of command,

> commanders focus on the purpose of the operation rather than on the details of how to perform assigned tasks. Doing this minimizes detailed control and allows subordinates the greatest possible freedom of action.[237]

Figure 117. Mission command stars in the new editions of the US Army's 362-page *Field Manual 3-0*, which expounds "the fundamental principles and overarching doctrinal guidance for conducting operations" and "applies to all members of the Army Profession."* (*FM 3-0*)

Sustainment providers in particular are now expected to be able to act without direct orders in support of whatever unit they are responsible for. In a combat situation, they must not wait for a supported commander to tell them, "I need ammunition (or fuel, or food, or repair, or medical help) *now*." They have to understand the commander's intent well enough to anticipate the needs of the supported unit and, on their own initiative, keep the right support flowing to the right places at the right time. When speed is essential and information is limited, sustainers understand that "a decent plan carried out immediately is superior to a superb plan carried out much later."[238]

Fundamental to all of this is maintenance. The operators and crew of a weapons system, vehicle, or other equipment are encouraged to assume ownership of their machine and take pride in how well they can make it perform. Their manuals declare, "Operator/crew maintenance is the most critical operation of the Army maintenance system. Preventive maintenance checks and services (PMCS) is the foundation of field level maintenance."[239]

Some of the maintenance training is so specialized that commanders worry about the requisite skills being "one deep" in the crew, so "the commander must ensure that multiple individuals are cross-trained and cross-supportive."[240] (Cross-training was a decisive element in the October War of 1973. What would happen if a tank's gunner was incapacitated? For the Egyptians, it would put the tank out of action because the gunner's skills were jealously concealed from everyone else. In the Israeli forces, every tank commander had been trained as a fully qualified gunner and thus could see the battlefield with a gunner's eye, direct the tank accordingly, and aim and fire the gun if necessary.) Cross-training builds mutual respect and sharp teamwork, and it makes training lively when team members' roles are suddenly swapped.

For weapons systems in combat, where hard use and battle damage can take a weapon down, the focus is "on returning systems to operational status as quickly and as near as possible to the point of failure or damage."[241] On the battlefield, units of Ordnance School-trained maintainers with specialized tools and skills are deployed as far forward as possible to back up the combat units. The combat crews are trained "to move the [damaged] vehicle at least one terrain feature or one kilometer away from enemy contact"[242] and to recognize the "distinct colors and odors" of leaking fluids to help the ordnance specialists diagnose problems. Battle damage and repair (called BDAR) emphasizes expediency. One manual spells it out:

> BDAR is accomplished by bypassing components or safety devices, cannibalizing parts from like or lower-priority equipment, fabricating repair parts, jury-rigging, taking shortcuts to standard maintenance, and using substitute fluids, materials,

> or components. Depending on the repairs required and the amount of time available, repairs may or may not return the vehicle to a fully mission-capable status.[243]

In other words, do whatever is necessary to get the system back in action. The acronym ASAP, for "as soon as possible," was invented by the military.

The idea of sustainment has uses far beyond the realm of the military, and happily there is a good book published in 2023 that expands the concept and formalizes it. Its title is *System Sustainment: Acquisition and Engineering Processes for the Sustainment of Critical and Legacy Systems*, by Peter Sandborn and William Lucyshyn. They define sustainment as follows:

> "Sustainment" (as commonly defined by industry and government) is comprised of maintenance, support, and upgrade practices that maintain or improve the performance of a system and maximize the availability of goods and services while minimizing their cost and footprint or, more simply, the capacity of a system to endure. System sustainment is a multi-trillion-dollar enterprise, in government (infrastructure and defense) and industry (transportation, industrial controls, data centers, energy generation and others).[244]

They refer to legacy systems such as infrastructure, transportation, and power generation as "critical systems," noting that "these systems are rarely adequately resourced for their long-term sustainment, and even when they are, the sustainment budgets are the first thing raided when funds are needed for other more pressing matters." Indeed, they write, "One defining attribute of sustainment-dominated systems is that they always end up having to be supported longer than anyone anticipated... In fact, the title of this book could have been 'support of legacy systems.'"[245]

"The most common modern synonym for *sustain*," they note, "is *maintain*. *Sustain* and *maintain* may be used interchangeably, however, maintaining most often refers to actions taken to correct or avoid problems, while sustaining is a more general strategic term referring to the management of the evolution of a system." A footnote on the definition of "repair" adds that "'Repair' represents a subset of maintenance activities that occurs after a failure. Maintenance includes repair, but also activities associated with keeping the system from failing."[246]

Sustainment, then, is seen as embracing a larger time frame than maintenance, and it supports system evolution. A worrying condition worldwide is that civilization's critical systems are rarely adequately resourced for long-term sustainment. The authors draw attention to the related concept of sustainability:

> The best-known socio-ecological definition of sustainability (attributed to the "Brundtland Report") is commonly paraphrased as "development that meets the needs of present generations without compromising the ability of future generations to meet their own needs."[247]

The distinction is that sustainability is merely a goal, whereas sustainment is a plan, a program, a set of actions. The one says, "Aspire"; the other says, "Here's how to get it done."

And keep it done. Unrelenting endurance is the commitment.

Charles C. Mann, a science journalist, expands on the distinction. He wrote me:

> "Sustainability" has become, all too often, a vaguely invoked goal of reaching some steady-state situation in the indefinite future. "Sustainment" calls for a course of present-day action, iterative and constantly adjusted.[248]

He's right to emphasize iteration. It means the sustainment process never stops learning, and that's inviting. Also, the process can, if necessary, start small and uncertain and find its way. Sustainability says almost nothing about how to begin. Sustainment says, "Get to work."

The sustainment concept might help us think pragmatically about humanity's role in taking increasing responsibility for the health of our largest and oldest legacy system, Earth's biosphere. I will come back to these matters in future chapters on system repair, cities, software, and the planet.

2.7c How Poor Maintenance Loses Wars: 2022, Ukraine Maintains

The Ukraine war that began in 2022 turned dramatically on sustainment issues, amid surprising echoes of the 1973 October War.

When Russian forces invaded Ukraine on February 24, 2022, they were confident that they could conquer the capital city of Kyiv and overthrow the government quickly with a massive show of force. Just eight years earlier, in 2014, they had crushed the Ukrainian army in the Donbas region of eastern Ukraine. Senior officers in the invading force were told to pack their parade dress uniforms for the victory celebration in Kyiv.

Some outspoken American intelligence officers told the media they had the same expectation. The day after the invasion, American news outlets were full of grim predictions such as, "Three US officials have told Newsweek they expect Ukraine's capital Kyiv to fall to incoming Russian forces within days, and the country's resistance to be effectively neutralized soon thereafter."[249]

Figure 118. One photo, two different captions, two days apart. Taken on February 28, 2022, this satellite photo showed part of a 40-mile-long Russian convoy of trucks headed toward Kyiv. The caption in Britain's *Metro* tabloid on March 1 read: "The sheer numbers of Russian troops are likely to crush the impressive Ukrainian resistance, officials have warned."* On March 3, the headline for the same photo in America's *AP News* was a question: "Is stuck convoy in Ukraine a setback for Russia?"† (Maxar Technologies)

The predictions were wrong. The experts had overestimated Russia's competence and underestimated Ukraine's. Not only was the war still going on a year later, but Ukraine was winning. One assessment the following February declared:

> Russia's overwhelming power was anything but; instead of unleashing modern war on the Ukrainians, Russia relied on antiquated weaponry and command structures. Instead of taking Kyiv within weeks, Russian forces experienced major system breakdowns. Since then, Russia's problems seem to have gotten worse. Putin has changed commanders like socks, equipment quality has degraded, and the number of casualties has skyrocketed.[250]

Even more than in the October War of 1973, maintenance practices in the opposing armies were pivotal to the outcome. I'll focus on two of Ukraine's early victories: their successful defense of Kyiv in February and March 2022, and their Kharkiv counteroffensive against the Russian forces in eastern Ukraine five months later in September 2022.

Feb.–Mar. 2022
Russia invades Ukraine

Apr.–Aug. 2022
Russia stalls outside Kyiv, withdraws to the east

Figure 119. Ukraine's first victory over Russia's forces occurred in the north. The map (left) shows the area controlled by the Russian invaders in early March 2022. By midsummer, Ukraine's military had recovered all the area shown in blue (right). Ukraine is large: 800 miles west to east, 550 miles north to south. It spreads an invader vulnerably thin on the ground.

The first sign of something deeply wrong with the Russian military came in early March, when widely publicized satellite photos showed a Russian convoy of trucks 40 miles long permanently stalled on its way south from Belarus to Kyiv. A month later, the Russian forces were all gone, and Kyiv was safe from attack except by long-distance missiles. What happened?

Since mud season had begun, Russia's trucks had to stay on the road. Ukrainian troops attacked vehicles at the head of the column to block the road, and the whole convoy came to a halt—sitting targets for further attack. Meanwhile, the trucks themselves were deteriorating.

A useful source to follow on Twitter was Trent Telenko, some of whose comments were quoted by the *Economist*, the *Wall Street Journal*, and CNN. He was described as an expert "who spent 33 years at the Pentagon's Defense Contract Management Agency and has studied Russian military logistics."[251] To CNN, Telenko explained, "Everything that an army needs to do its thing comes from a truck... The weapon isn't the tank; it's the shell the tank fires. That shell travels by a truck... Trucks are the backbone of any modern mechanized military force, and if you don't have them, you walk."[252]

Doubts about the competence of Russia's ground forces deepened with Telenko's analysis of a photo of a multimillion-dollar, state-of-the-art Russian surface-to-air missile vehicle. It was stuck in the mud and had been abandoned by its crew. The photo appeared in a tweet by Telenko on March 2. He wrote: "This is a thread that will explain the implied poor Russian army truck maintenance practices based on this photo of a Pantsir-S1 wheeled gun-missile system's right rear pair of

Figure 120. Note the shredded tire (top photo, lower left). Consider that it is on a vehicle carrying one of Russia's most advanced and expensive weapons systems, left abandoned on the battlefield in the first week of the war in Ukraine. What does that say about the state of maintenance in Russia's army? An intact Pantsir S-1 missile system (bottom photo). (Source unknown)

tires and the operational implications during the Ukrainian mud season." In this thread, Telenko wrote:

> Military trucks need to be [started] and moved once a month for preventative maintenance reasons. In particular you want to exercise the central tire air inflation system (CTIS) to see if lines have leaks or had insect/vermin nests blocking the system... and [keep] the tire sidewalls supple [because direct sunlight ages truck tires]. When you leave military truck tires in one place for months on end, the side walls get rotted/brittle such that using low tire pressure setting for any appreciable distance [such as for better traction in mud] will cause the tires to fail catastrophically via rips.
>
> Now look at the same Pantsir-S1 tire sidewalls after the Ukrainians tried to tow or drive it out of the mud. The right rear tire fell apart because the rips in it were too big for the CTIS to keep aired up. No one exercised that vehicle for [a] year. There is a huge operational-level implication in this. If the Russian army was too corrupt to exercise a Pantsir-S1, they were too corrupt to exercise the trucks and wheeled AFVs [armored fighting vehicles] now in Ukraine.[253]

In a related thread, he added:

> Each mile traveled by a military truck in war is between 10 and 20 miles [of normal] wear... Truck drivers abuse trucks because they don't want to die...
>
> [The US Army] has professional NCOs that lived, breathed, and ate preventive maintenance as a religious catechism. And the US Army enforced rest periods for its truck drivers because it cared enough about having men and equipment [for] future operations. None of that is true for the Russian Army. Most of the time between 2012 and 2022 the Russian army did not maintain their trucks. The Russians don't have a professional NCO Corps so they ARE NOT DOING IT NOW.
>
> Every truck is being sent out in whatever condition, overloaded with ammunition. The engines are running white hot and no one has checked the oil or other fluid levels, let alone does an oil change, in these last three weeks... The cumulative effects of all these factors leads to horrendous levels of Russian army truck fleet operational attrition.[254]

Several sources on Twitter identified the tires in the photo as cheap Chinese imitations of military-grade Michelin tires. How could so sophisticated a weapons system have such crappy tires? In a CNN article, professor of strategic studies Phillips O'Brien observed, "Often glamorous dictator militaries are good at the showy weapons, they buy the fancy aircraft and the fancy tanks, but they don't actually buy the less glamorous stuff."[255] And an article in *Foreign Affairs* spelled out how corruption had drained Russia's military:

> During the economic collapse in the 1990s, Russian President Boris Yeltsin's government often proved unable to pay officers and soldiers alike, and corruption became institutionalized. Conscripts were frequently on the edge of starvation because their rations were sold off; theft, bullying, and ill discipline became rampant. Spare parts from vehicles, as well as anything from fuel to light bulbs, boots, and especially any cold weather kit, disappeared onto the black market.
>
> Corruption became even worse following Russia's chaotic invasion of Georgia in 2008. Putin began throwing money at the armed forces. The waste on prestige projects encouraged contractors and generals alike to pad their bank accounts.[256]

It wasn't just shoddy equipment; the whole invasion was based on a wrong theory. Putin and his military advisors made the mistake of assuming that the Ukrainian army they faced in 2022 was the same army they had defeated so quickly in 2014. They were shocked to discover on the battlefield that Ukraine had accomplished a radical military metamorphosis in just eight years. Books will be written about what *Foreign Policy* magazine called "the Ukrainian military's slow-burn transformation from a Soviet army to a NATO-style outfit able to outfight, outfox, and out-equip its Russian foes."[257]

In the years between Ukraine's declaration of independence in 1991 and its failure to defend the Donbas and Crimea in 2014, its military had been systematically hollowed out by a series of presidents, ending with the pro-Russian president Viktor Yanukovych. His successor in 2014, Petro Poroshenko, was provoked by the Russian victories in Crimea and the Donbas to set in motion a sweeping overhaul of Ukraine's armed forces. The reforms were accelerated in 2019 by President Volodymyr Zelenskyy, who elevated mid-rank General Valerii Zaluzhnyi to be Ukraine's first commander-in-chief of its

Figure 121. A Ukrainian soldier (left) trains to repair a US-donated M109 self-propelled howitzer, a long-distance cannon riding on tracks like a tank. He and his US Army trainer were photographed at an American training area in Germany, May 2022. (Nicko Bryant)

Figure 122. The M109 in action in eastern Ukraine, February 2023. The pile of spent shells shows how intensely the weapons are being used and why they require constant maintenance and frequent repair. (Mustafa Ciftci, Anadalou Agency/Getty)

armed forces. Zaluzhnyi was a convert to the West's mission command philosophy, which empowers subordinates to act with initiative and flexibility. It had become standard doctrine throughout NATO, which Ukraine was eager to join. By deploying it, Zaluzhnyi made Ukraine's military capable of instant adaptivity on the battlefield, which led to the stunning successes in 2022.

After the events of 2014, Ukraine and NATO opened up to each other. Former Commanding General of US Army Europe Mark Hertling recalls, "In December 2015, [we] formally established Joint Multinational Training Group–Ukraine, where a multinational team of Americans, Poles, Canadians, Lithuanians, and Brits began training Ukrainian battalions as combined arms teams." According to the senior enlisted man in America's military, Chief Master Sergeant Ramón Colón-López, at that time

> the NCOs [in Ukraine]... were not empowered, they were not entrusted, and they were not properly trained or educated to be autonomous on the battlefield... The government of Ukraine decided to go all in on an NCO development model.[258]

Ukraine created three NCO training centers. The program scaled up quickly because the graduates were trained to train others in leadership and combat skills. The eight NATO countries that participated also introduced practices such as civilian control of the military, inspectors to root out corrupt officers, and proper sustainment for battlefield success.

As the fighting against Russians in the Donbas continued sporadically for eight years after 2014, promotion in Ukraine's military was increasingly driven by merit—proven competence in battle—and Ukraine was developing the most combat-hardened troops in Europe. The NATO trainers discovered that they were learning as much from the experienced Ukrainians about modern warfare as they were teaching.

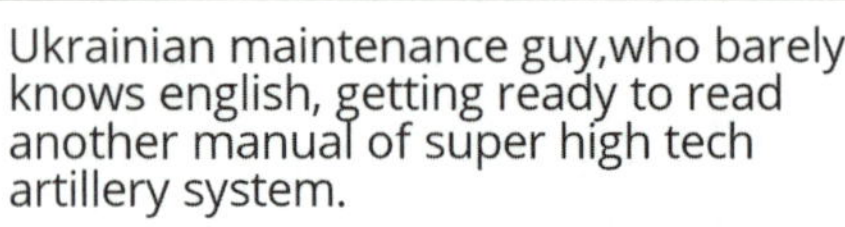

Figure 123. A meme that emerged among Ukraine's devoted fans on Twitter. (Source unknown)

America's military aid to Ukraine between 2014 and 2024 amounted to $55 billion. That included, the Defense Department reported, weapons systems such as

> the Javelin anti-armor system, the Stinger anti-aircraft weapon, unmanned aerial systems, grenade launchers, howitzers, helicopters, tactical vehicles, counter-artillery radars, armored personnel carriers, high-mobility artillery rocket systems, and millions of rounds of ammunition.[259]

Ukrainian soldiers had to learn how to operate, maintain, and repair every one of these exotic systems, along with a variety of weapons donated by other NATO nations, and they had to do it fast. Some critics thought that was asking too much. The deputy chief of the US Army Materiel Command responded, "The Ukrainian maintainers are very, very resourceful, and they are very good at keeping the weapons systems that we provide them in the fight."[260]

Part of their resourcefulness was skillful use of the web for "telemaintenance." For every weapons system, a team of American experts in Poland advised the Ukrainian soldiers via an encrypted chat line, with the manufacturers on call when needed. The same went for other nations contributing weapons. One report noted:

> Certain hard-to-get parts require the full spectrum of Ukrainian ingenuity. They use computer-assisted design to draw up designs, run them past US specialists for guidance, and make the parts themselves.[261]

Figure 124. What does it take to make artillery effective? Photos of artillery always show the big gun being fired—*boom!* They seldom show the elaborate choreography of sustainment behind the boom. How did this howitzer, a British-designed American M777 firing 155 mm projectiles, get to the front for Ukraine's counteroffensive in Kharkiv in September 2022? How did it get to Ukraine from overseas? What about the ammunition? Who trained the crew? Who maintains and repairs the weapon? (Sergey Bobok, AFP/Getty)

Figure 125. Projectiles for the M777 are loaded by hand and are so heavy, at 90 pounds, that the propelling charges, being prepared here, are loaded separately. (Sergey Bobok, AFP/Getty)

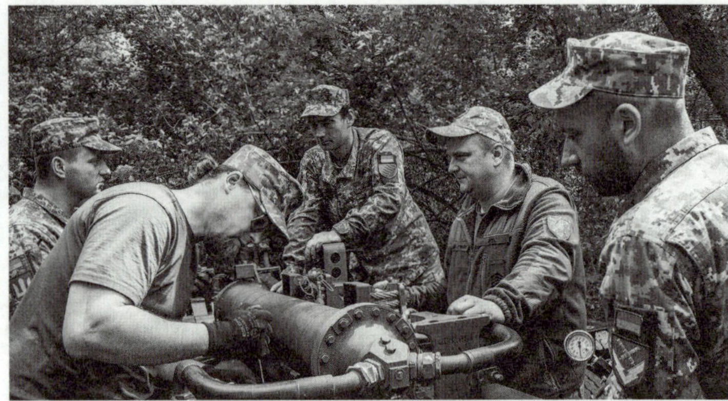

Figure 126. An M777 crew works on their gun. If a thing is used hard, it has to be maintained hard. The howitzers in Ukraine were fired so constantly that at any given time about a third were out of action for repairs or to replace their barrels after firing 2,500 rounds. (Ivor Prickett)

Figure 127. M777s are built partly of titanium, so they are light enough to be towed rapidly, and the 20-foot barrel has a convenient tow hook on the muzzle. (Arsen Fedosenko, via Wikimedia Commons, CC BY-SA 4.0)

Figure 128. Long-distance sustainment is an American military specialty in part because all of America's deployments in the 150 years since the Civil War have been expeditionary forces to distant continents. At March Air Reserve Base in California in early 2022, M777s are loaded onto a C-17 Globemaster III for delivery to Ukraine. (Shawn White)

Figure 129. On another Globemaster at Travis Air Force Base in California, palletized munitions are loaded to be flown to Ukraine. The US promised a million rounds for the M777s and other weapons. (Chustine Minoda)

Figure 130. Artillery is about two *booms*: one from the gun, one at the target. The point of the whole exercise is what happens at the target. In this case, a Russian armored personnel carrier was carrying troops to attack Ukrainian forces in Kharkiv. A quadcopter drone pinpointed it for Ukraine's artillery and recorded the result in August 2022. (Militarnyi, 45th Artillery Brigade)

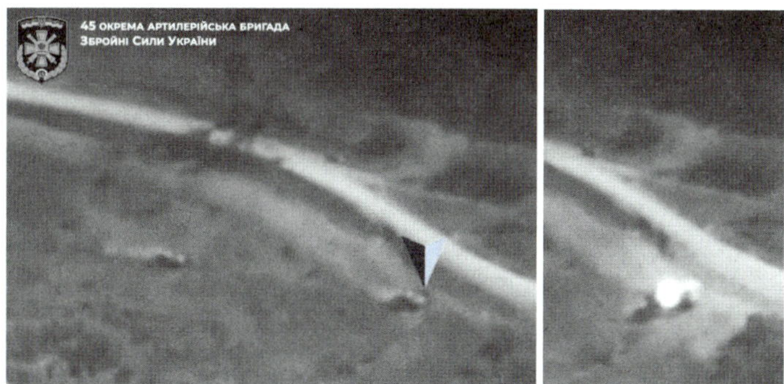

By September 2022, enough powerful long-distance artillery provided by America and NATO allies was deployed at the front to be crucial to the success of Ukraine's second major victory: its spectacular counteroffensive in the city of Kharkiv, which began on September 6. Ukraine's 170 howitzers, along with 16 M142 HIMARS (high mobility artillery rocket systems), were capable of precise strikes on targets such as ammunition depots, fuel storage tanks, and command centers up to 25 miles behind enemy lines. *Bloomberg News* reported, "Ukraine's gunners had learned to rapidly dismantle and reassemble the US M777 howitzers. In its drive east from Kharkiv... Ukraine could bring its heavy guns forward in real time to perform the role of air cover."[262]

Ukraine's multiple breakthroughs and rapid advance bypassed so many enemy strongpoints that the Russian troops fled in panic, leaving their military hardware behind. Within a month, Ukraine had recaptured an astonishing 4,600 square miles of its northeastern territory, and its military had proved it could be as effective with a large-scale offensive as it had been in defending Kyiv.

Figure 131. Ukraine's second victory was in the east (right). It was a one-two punch. Ukraine announced and initiated its Kherson counteroffensive toward Crimea in the south to draw Russian troops away from their northern defense lines. Once that was accomplished, Ukraine's massive surprise attack in Kharkiv broke through easily.

Apr.–Aug. 2022
Russia stalls outside Kyiv,

Sep.–Nov. 2022
Ukraine's lightning breakthrough

A military analyst told the *New York Times* that it was "a very effective combined arms operation with tanks, mechanized infantry, Special Operations forces, air defenses, artillery, and other systems."[263] That level of coordination was made possible by Ukraine's sophisticated battle-awareness platform called Delta. Projects of this sort were routine for a government dedicated to computerizing the whole nation. The effort was led by the newly created Ministry of Digital Transformation, headed by a 33-year-old named Mykhailo Fedorov. In a post on Facebook, Federov described some of the platform's features:

> Delta provides comprehensive real-time battlefield understanding, integrating enemy information from a variety of sensors and sources, including digital map intelligence. Situational awareness tools, data processing centers, instant communication on the battlefield, cloud environments, and the mass use of drone armies... are the Army of the future.[264]

The user end of the system is accessible from laptops and smartphones; the back end is described as cloud native and zero-trust secure. The Wikipedia entry says Delta "integrates information from... troops, civilian officials, and vetted bystanders [as well as] sensors, intelligence sources, surveillance satellites, and drones—especially geolocated data, which it maps in real time, along with pictures of enemy assets."[265]

Delta almost didn't happen. When the Russians first attacked in February 2022, they jammed Ukraine's satellite communications. On Twitter, Minister Federov publicly asked Elon Musk to have his company, SpaceX, provide Starlink satellite services and terminals to restore Ukraine's access to the internet. Five hundred terminals arrived two days later, followed in short order by 2,000 more, along with solar panels and battery kits for use in places where electricity was down because of the war.

Fifteen thousand Starlink terminals were in Ukraine by July, uniquely immune to Russian jamming technology. SpaceX provided the terminals and service for free or at a discount, and further funding came from various governments and private individuals. (Starlink usually charges $500 for a terminal and $120 a month for the service.) A Ukraine platoon leader on the southern front told the *Wall Street Journal*, "Without Starlink, we would have been losing the war already."[266] By early 2023, SpaceX's chief operating officer, Gwynne Shotwell, had worked

Figure 132. Communications sustainment was provided to Ukraine through SpaceX's donation of tens of thousands of Starlink terminals and services. Terminals like this one can be small and mobile because the thousands of Starlink satellites are in low Earth orbit, 340 miles up instead of the usual 22,000 miles. This photo shows a mechanized brigade soldier on training exercises in northern Ukraine in June 2023. (Maxym Marusenko, NurPhoto/Getty)

out a deal with the US Defense Department and CIA to provide 100,000 more Starlink terminals to Ukraine, along with military-grade service called Starshield for use by the US and allies such as Ukraine.[267]

Ukraine has a world-class, world-serving tech sector adept at solving problems with whatever resources come to hand, at digital speed. An article in the *Wall Street Journal* titled “Ukraine Has Digitized Its Fighting Forces on a Shoestring” noted that

> volunteer soldiers are using their private-sector experience developing enterprise resource-management software for multinationals to automate payroll on the front lines… One element of Ukraine's success in innovation is how different military units and Ukrainian tech companies are working on their own new military technologies—a bottom-up approach that at times… resembles a string of Silicon Valley garages.[268]

Managing payroll is a classic sustainment task.

Ukraine repaired its armored vehicles—and Russia's—in a similar fashion. Tanks are so heavily built that even severe battle damage is fixable. “Every tank could be repaired, as long as it's not been cut in half,” said an official at Ukraine's tank factory.[269] As with the Israelis in the October War, Ukrainian repair facilities were highly mobile and operated close to the front, with depots capable of major overhauling further in the rear or over the western border in Poland. Most were staffed by volunteer civilian mechanics. "A host of private companies," reported *The Guardian*,

> have set aside their usual business to get in the game of refurbishing killing machines: the tanks, armoured vehicles, missile systems and other lethal hardware left behind.
>
> These operations are often funded through donations [to military aid groups such as] the Prytula Foundation.[270]

A year into the war, Russia had lost over half the 3,000 tanks it started with. According to Oryx, the Dutch chronicler of battlefield statistics, the Russians lost 1,688 tanks.[271] Of those, Ukraine captured 544, which meant that more than half of Ukraine's operational 1,000-tank fleet was made up of battlefield donations from Russia. Many were found astonishingly intact. The *Washington Post* reported that after the rout of Russian forces in Kharkiv,

> [Ukrainian] troops were dumbfounded at what lay before them: Tanks in working order, ready to be driven. Abandoned artillery pieces, ready to be fired. Fuel tankers "filled up to the eyeballs." Tons of ammunition and light weapons.[272]

The Russian crews were especially eager to ditch a line of dangerously obsolete tanks fielded in desperation—relics from the 1960s called T-62s.

Ukraine captured at least 43 of the old T-62s. Then the question was what to do with them. The optics and gun were useless against modern tanks, but the well-armored hull and engine worked fine. A headline in *Forbes* magazine announced, "The Ukrainians Are Converting Worthless Russian Tanks into Priceless Engineering Vehicles" and noted,

> A pitched fight between armored forces more often than not litters the terrain with recoverable tanks. So the army with the most responsive ARVs [armored recovery vehicles] collects the spoils: damaged tanks that the army can repair and send back into battle.[273]

By converting the obsolete T-62s into armored recovery vehicles, Ukraine transformed an outdated killing tool into a critical sustainment tool.

(A reminder of the human cost of these battles. A reporter asked a Ukrainian mechanic working on a damaged Russian

Figure 133. In February 2023, a captured Russian T-62 tank is converted to an armored recovery vehicle for Ukraine's use. The eight-ton turret and gun were hoisted off to be replaced by an armored winch—and sometimes a crane—to recover disabled tanks on the battlefield, including more Russian ones. (John Moore/Getty)

tank if Russians died in it. The mechanic replied, "There were arms and legs in it. Lots of blood.")[274]

Ukraine's tech-forward sustainment mindset extends to the citizenry as well. In 2020, Ukraine began building an e-government tool called Diia, a web platform and mobile app promoted as "the state in a smartphone." By 2023, fully half of Ukraine's 36 million residents were using the system. After Russia's invasion in 2022, it was used as a tool for citizens in the occupied parts of Ukraine to report the precise location and nature of enemy activity, which fed into the Delta battle-awareness system.

Just as Ukraine's Delta platform was showing the world how to manage warfare digitally, the Diia system was doing the same for running a government. With Diia, Ukrainians have the world's first wholly digital passports, driver's licenses, car registration, and vaccination records. They have direct access to 70 government services, free of paperwork. Registering a new company can be done in half an hour. To further enrich the process, Ukraine created a special legal and tax domain for information technology companies in a virtual hub called Diia City.

What can be learned about maintenance mind from all this? One thing that seems clear is the need to examine its opposite: neglect mind. Examples of both were evident in individuals in my tale of the 1968 Golden Globe Race of single-handed around-the-world sailors. The formal winner, Sir Robin Knox-Johnston, had maintenance discipline and skills trained into him by England's Merchant Navy. The informal winner,

Bernard Moitessier, gained his discipline and skill from extensive single-handing experience, including getting wrecked twice. The race's biggest loser, Donald Crowhurst, had neither maintenance training nor much sailboat experience, and he was delusionally optimistic. His neglect mind was part laziness and ignorance, part surrender to fantasy.

Maintainers are realists.

My accounts of the two wars in this digression show maintenance mind versus neglect mind at the level of institutions and societies. Ukraine's army and culture were defending against Russia's army and culture in 2022, just as Israel's army and culture defended against the Egyptian army and culture in 1973. The 2022 war demonstrated a rare case of rapid institutional and cultural change. Ukraine's military in 2014 was basically Soviet, with Soviet-style neglect of its equipment. By 2023, Ukraine's military was teaching NATO how to be modern.

History shows that many battles are won by the side that can act and respond with the greatest speed. Wars, however, are only sometimes won by speed. More often, they are won by whichever side can doggedly outlast the other. Combat support helps win battles, but full-on sustainment is required to win a war. Sustainment comprises everything it takes to ensure prolonged endurance of capability. Thus the war in Ukraine is, in part, a contest between Russian sustainment and NATO-supplied sustainment.

Maintenance is so pervasive and labor-intensive in all armed forces that enlisted soldiers do it, not officers. If there is too much social distance between officers and troops with nobody connecting them, maintenance will always be low-status and poorly supervised—a perfect formula for institutional neglect mind. Egypt had it in 1973 and reportedly has it still. Russia, with its doctrine of treating equipment and soldiers as expendable, has it on a vast scale. The proven solution is a cadre of highly experienced NCOs who have the respect of both officers and troops and are empowered within the mission-command philosophy to take a strong leadership role. They are the ones charged with overseeing and enforcing maintenance. They teach the whole armed forces to take maintenance seriously.

MAKERJAK: "Important point. This concept of maintenance being low status is a definite risk. I worked in a quality assurance role for manufacturers early in my career. In almost every plant I worked at, QA was seen as a hindrance to hitting productivity metrics. We never got credit for a well-maintained manufacturing capability, but QA almost always got blamed when things went wrong. It's the main reason I didn't stay in that function for long."

In both Israel and Ukraine, the civilian population and the military were closely linked. The resulting national coherence was crucial for defending their homelands against invasion. In both wars, Israel's and Ukraine's forces were greatly outnumbered and outgunned. To defend their country, each had to innovate rapidly while mending all the equipment they had and everything they could capture.

That they did.

2.8 The End of Combustion Vehicles

By 2011, the world's automobile industry was enormous, intensely competitive, and asleep. Car manufacturing, inspired by Toyota's lean production system, had become highly efficient and perfectionist but also conservative. Innovations came piecemeal from all over the map: stability control from one company, GPS navigation from another, Bluetooth integration from somewhere else. That's the norm in a mature industry with many players in prolonged close competition. Progress comes in distributed increments rather than concentrated leaps.

Then, in 2012, a brash new company introduced a glamorous version of an ancient kind of car, and everything changed. *MotorTrend* magazine gave the new vehicle their Car of the Year award in 2013 with an unprecedented unanimous vote. *Consumer Reports* declared that it was probably the best car ever built and assigned it their highest rating in history, 99 out of 100.[275]

The car could accelerate from 0 to 60 mph in a whiplash 4.2 seconds. It was rated the safest car in history. It seated five, with luxurious features controlled from a huge touch screen next to the driver. Its motor was twice as efficient as anything else on the road. And, most importantly, its exhaust was free of greenhouse gases because there was no exhaust at all.

The new company was Tesla. The new kind of car, Tesla's all-electric Model S, was also the oldest kind of car: a battery-driven horseless carriage. Internal combustion engines had so dominated the world for a century that they contributed to destabilizing Earth's climate; that was one reason they were

Figure 134. Released in 2012, Tesla's Model S luxury sedan combined panache with a new kind of utility as a mass-marketed all-electric car with dazzling features and surprisingly low maintenance costs. (Tesla)

about to become history. Tesla's ambition was to replace fossil-fuel vehicles with something cleaner, and it would do that by building a car that was better than the old petrol burners in nearly every way.

(I won't try to write about the ongoing industry-wide shift to electric vehicles because it would be out of date almost immediately. All I'm attempting here is to recount the sudden transition that occurred when one company set about converting what people thought of as glorified golf carts into the ultimate in irresistible cool.)

Tesla's competitors were initially puzzled, then worried by a peculiarity in Tesla's business model. There were no Tesla dealerships; the cars were sold directly to customers online. How could Tesla give up the highly profitable stream of revenue car companies got from the service centers at their dealerships? Every auto company counted on the fact that when a car needed maintenance or repair, customers nearly always took it to the dealership they'd bought it from to take advantage of expert knowledge and the ready supply of specialized parts.

Analysts began to notice the ways in which electric vehicles, known as EVs, were going to be deeply disruptive. In a 2018 essay titled "Will Car Dealerships Survive the EV Revolution?" the online billing service Aria wrote:

> Car dealers today make the biggest chunk of income—44 percent, according to *Forbes*—from parts and service. When it comes to EVs, that's a real problem, because they require very little in the way of traditional auto maintenance. Their electric motors and single-speed drive trains eliminate the need for oil changes, transmission fluid and radiator coolant checks, drive belt and air filter replacements, and many other income-generating services dealerships now take for granted.[276]

Few remembered the similar attractions of the first electric vehicles a century earlier. In terms of the four sources of most problems in machines—moving parts, flowing fluids, flowing electricity, and temperature stresses—electric vehicles are easier to maintain in every respect. The only fluid the customer puts in is for the windshield wipers—no gasoline, no oil to change, and no engine coolant. While a gas engine and drivetrain have many hundreds of moving parts, an electric vehicle's motor and drivetrain have just 17 to 20. There's no starter, no distributor, no carburetor, no spark plugs, no gaskets, no valves, in fact no engine at all; also no fuel pump, no

Figure 135. The motors, drivetrain, and fuel tank of the Tesla Model S in 2023. The two electric motors between the wheels provide 670 horsepower, capable of accelerating the car from a dead stop to 60 miles per hour in 3.1 seconds (a second faster than the original 2012 Model S). The low-slung battery array gives the car a very low center of gravity and thus exceptionally good handling. (Tesla)

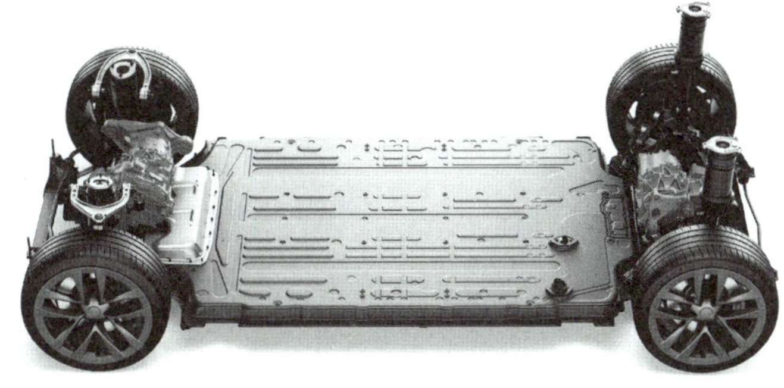

water pump, no hoses, no clutch, no muffler, no exhaust pipe, and no catalytic converter. All the hard-won lore of how to deal with those things was headed toward irrelevance, good only for maintaining antiques.

The 12 moving parts of the electric motor and drivetrain provide power to the wheels at approximately 90 to 95 percent efficiency. A combustion engine is lucky to get 30 to 35 percent, meaning that 65 to 70 percent of its energy is wasted as heat, vibration, friction, and noise. The high temperature caused by all that thrashing metal, added to the inherent heat of combustion, increases wear and tear on all the moving parts, so an elaborate liquid cooling system and fan is required to keep the system functioning at all. By contrast, the superefficient electric motor generates so little heat that it can be air-cooled. (The electric car's battery pack, however, can generate a lot of heat, especially when rapidly charging or discharging. For that reason, most electric cars have their own integral liquid cooling system with a pump and radiator, but the fluid almost never needs replacement.)

Comparing a Tesla Model S's electric motor to a Land Rover Defender's standard combustion engine, mechanic Richard Morgan explains how they differ:

> So, essentially, this [Tesla Model S rear motor] is one complete drive unit. It's the equivalent of an engine, a gearbox, and an ECU [electronic control unit] and everything, all in one. Look how small it is—I mean, it's 84 kilos [185 pounds]... That is about 330 newton meters of torque... compared to this beast [the Land Rover Defender internal combustion engine] here, which is also around about 300 newton meters of torque... Just look at the size... and the complexity of it... [With] the gearbox... and all the things to keep it alive...

Figure 136. In a YouTube video, mechanic Richard Morgan compares the Tesla Model S's electric motor (left) to a Land Rover Defender's standard combustion engine (right). (Electric Classic Cars Ltd.)

Figure 137. In another YouTube video, Morgan compares the energy density of petrol versus batteries. (Electric Classic Cars Ltd.)

> you're up to around about 350 kilos of weight [700 pounds]... This [Tesla engine] is 90 percent efficient; that [Land Rover engine] is 35 percent efficient at turning energy into motion.[277]

Richard Morgan converts classic vintage cars—such as a DeLorean or a 1967 Maserati Ghibli—into powerful, better-handling electric vehicles at his shop in Powys, Wales. He owns a 1972 Volkswagen Beetle with a Tesla motor that accelerates it from 0 to 60 mph in 2.6 seconds. His YouTube channel, Electric Classic Cars, has 138,000 subscribers.

Morgan again, in a video comparing the energy density of petrol and batteries:

> This five-liter can of petrol contains 45 kilowatt hours of energy, but it only weighs 3.7 kilos. That makes 12.2 kilo[watt] hours per kilogram... That is very energy dense... [This lead-acid battery] weighs 16 kilos, and it's got 0.84 kilowatt hours of energy in it, which gives it an energy density of 0.05 kilowatt hours per kilogram. So compare the 0.05 kilowatt hours

per kilogram to the 12.2 [kilowatt hours per kilogram], and you can see why petrol won that race for so long… [The Tesla P100 lithium-based battery technology gets] 0.22 kilowatt hours per kilogram… But it's still nowhere near the 12.2 kilowatt hours per kilogram of petrol.

Comparing the efficiency of petrol versus batteries, Morgan notes:

> What I've laid out down here is your typical average battery size in an electric car—it's a 58 kilowatt-hour battery pack… My wife's Tesla Model 3 is around about the same kilowatt-hour battery size as this…
>
> Now, as we already discussed, 95 percent of that is turned into motion, so [you get] about 55 kilowatt-hours of usable energy… Now, 20 liters of petrol equates to around about 180 kilowatt-hours of energy, but don't forget, only 30 percent of that is turned into motion. So that means 54 kilowatt-hours of this [petrol] is turned into motion… This is a very fair comparison of the amount of energy to make a car go forward, so if you put this [petrol] into a similar-sized car… like a BMW Series 3, for instance, compared to a Tesla Model 3, they should in theory go the same distance down the road.
>
> But obviously, this [battery] weighs 280 kilos [617 pounds] and this [petrol] weighs 14.8 kilos [32 pounds]. And that's the rub with batteries versus petrol… My wife's Tesla Model 3, for instance, is 40 kilos heavier than an equivalent BMW Series 3… [But] it's great to have weight distribution really low down in a car. So again, my wife's Tesla Model 3, it handles fantastic because all the weight is underneath you.[278]

In another video, Morgan takes on the argument that electric cars are impractical because of the time it takes to charge them:

> One of the most common questions we get asked… is "How long does it take to charge up?"… I've come to realize that actually that wasn't the most pertinent of questions to ask, and here's why… Coming from Petrol World, we're all used to… filling up en route… But electric vehicle ownership is completely different. You're setting off, usually, with a full tank of electrons from home, because that's where 95 percent of charging is done—at home… Very little charging is actually done en route…

> The other thing that I normally say to people when they say "How long does it take to charge up?" is "Two seconds"... As soon as I get out of my car, I plug it in and go in the house and get on with the rest of my life... While your car is sitting there, parked up, which it is for 99 percent of the time anyway, you may as well get it to do some work.[279]

One lauded feature of Tesla cars is the way the brake calipers are prevented from wearing down because the regenerative braking that feeds power back into the batteries does most of the slowing. (Roads that are salted for winter driving override that feature, however. Teslas in those areas are required to have their brake calipers lubricated every year or every 12,500 miles.) Windshield wipers are usually replaced at the same rate and cost as nonelectric vehicles. Tires, however, may need to be swapped out more often because of the extra wear from battery weight and the high-torque acceleration. The exact amount of fuel cost reduction depends on local prices of electricity and gas, but generally the cost of fuel from a plug is about half the cost of fuel from a pump.[280] An analysis by *Consumer Reports* in 2022 declared that "EV owners could save between $1,800 and $2,600 in operating and maintenance costs for every 15,000 miles they drive... compared to drivers of gas-powered vehicles."[281]

The most startling thing for early Tesla owners—I was one of them—was the way new features and improvements for the car would show up overnight via its connection with the internet.

Figure 138. Dog Mode is one of Tesla's many features that arrive magically as software upgrades over the internet. The car improves while you own it, at no extra cost. (Tesla)

Some were software fixes. One day, my automatic windows wouldn't close properly. News of the problem must have been noticed and fixed by Tesla-in-the-sky because the windows worked fine the next day.

Software upgrades for owners are frequent and often dramatic. Unexpectedly one morning, your car might have more power or faster charging or greater range or better traction on hills or a feature that vibrates the steering wheel when you cross a lane divider on the highway. There are luxuries like Dog Mode, which keeps the parked Tesla at a comfortable temperature for the driver's pet and displays a message on the video console for passersby—"My owner will be back soon. Don't worry!"—along with a readout of the temperature in the car.

Conveniently, the new features come with matching updates in the digital onboard manual. There are no printed Tesla manuals. On Tesla's website for my car, the "Do It Yourself" maintenance instructions include a catalog of the various signaling sounds the car makes (such as the chime that tells you Autosteer is enabled) as well as all the car's mysterious normal operating sounds (such as the clunks and thumps that occur during supercharging due to temperature changes in the battery system).

2.9 Digression 5: Elon Musk

Walter Isaacson's 2023 biography of Elon Musk is worth reading. Much of its quality comes from the fact that Isaacson shadowed Musk in person for all his subject's pivotal moments during 2021 and 2022. By the end of that period, Musk was CEO of six companies: Tesla, SpaceX, The Boring Company, Neuralink, xAI, and X (formerly Twitter).

Musk's innovations at the leading edge of software design and artificial intelligence are rivaled by other companies, but when it comes to designing and manufacturing hardware, he has unique mastery. His cars, batteries, solar gear, rockets, and satellites have all proven to be game changers in part because they combine ingenious design with surprisingly low cost.

His hardware companies range from successful to extremely successful because of his foundational altering of manufacturing practice. He requires that his design engineers do their work next to the people and machines fabricating the car, battery array, rocket, or other device. In a ferocious cycle of iteration, they design and redesign the device and its manufacture simultaneously. The ferocity of the iteration cycle comes from what Musk calls "the algorithm." Isaacson quotes his five commandments to the design teams:

1. Question every requirement. Each should come with the name of the person who made it....
2. Delete any part or process you can. You may have to add them back later. In fact, if you do not end up adding back at least 10 percent of them, then you didn't delete enough.
3. Simplify and optimize. This should come after step two. A common mistake is to simplify and optimize a part or a process that should not exist.
4. Accelerate cycle time. Every process can be speeded up. But only do this after you have followed the first three steps. In the Tesla factory, I mistakenly spent a lot of time accelerating processes that I later realised should have been deleted.
5. Automate. That comes last. The big mistake in Nevada and at Fremont was that I began by trying to automate every step. We should have waited until all the requirements had been questioned, parts and processes deleted, and the bugs were shaken out.[282]

By 2023, Tesla had the world's best-selling car of any kind with its Model Y. Priced at $40,000, it outsold even the $22,000 Toyota Corolla. Meanwhile, SpaceX's reusable rockets were so efficiently manufactured that by 2022, according to Isaacson, the company was launching "twice as much mass into orbit as all the other companies and countries combined."[283] SpaceX rockets, such as the "absurdly low-cost"[284] Falcon Heavy, had lowered the cost of getting payload to orbit to one-tenth of what it had been just 10 years before.[285]

Isaacson's biography of Musk was published at the same time as a surprisingly parallel biography by Michael Lewis of Sam Bankman-Fried titled *Going Infinite*. Both are skilled accounts, based partly on direct observation, of brilliant billionaires dedicated to saving the world. Bankman-Fried, inspired by the earn-to-give strategy that was part of the effective altruism movement, accumulated $26 billion in three years by building a cryptocurrency exchange named FTX. The giving part of his scheme was relatively thin—$130 million to effective altruism-approved charities, $70 million to US political campaigns—before FTX collapsed in November 2022, and he was arrested and charged with fraud. Through Tesla and SpaceX, Musk initiated and directly led a new, accelerated regime in climate-friendly electric vehicles *and* a new, accelerated regime in providing access to Earth orbit. With the success of these projects, Musk may have done more practical world saving than any other business leader of his time. Bankman-Fried couldn't even save himself from prison.

In Isaacson's book, there's a choice encounter between Musk and another noted world saver, Bill Gates, founding CEO of Microsoft and prodigious philanthropist. In early 2022, they met in Austin, Texas, to discuss philanthropy, particularly in relation to climate change. Musk declared that Gates would do the most good for the climate by investing in Tesla. He then berated Gates for having made a huge investment in shorting Tesla stock—betting that its price would go down—and thereby devaluing the stock in the market. Gates apologized. At which point "Elon was super-mean to me," Gates later told Isaacson.

When Isaacson asked Gates why he had shorted Tesla stock,

> he explained that he had calculated that the supply of electric cars would get ahead of demand, causing prices to fall. I nodded but still had the same question: Why had he shorted the stock? Gates looked at me as if I had not understood what he just explained and then replied as if the answer was obvious: he thought that by shorting Tesla he could make money.[286]

As it turned out, Gates lost $1.5 billion in the deal. Tesla stock kept going up. "Earn to give" as a strategy for doing good has a way of scrambling the giver's incentives.

Electric cars did have to sacrifice a few things. So much weight is in their batteries that the rest of the vehicle has to be made as light as possible to retain reasonable range and mileage, and that leads to some maintenance issues. Spare tires add a lot of weight and are seldom used, so they are left out of many electric cars. Tesla owners never change a tire anymore. When you get a flat, you call Tesla's road service, they come and replace the flat with a temporary spare, and you take the tire to a Tesla service center for repair or replacement. It's a nuisance. (Tesla did eventually have to create service centers. By 2023, when they had 4 million cars on the road, their earnings report declared, "Body shop and part sales are core drivers of profit growth.")

More serious is the matter of damage to the car's body.

To save weight, the frame and skin of a Tesla are made of aluminum. It is much lighter than steel, but unlike steel, "aluminum has no memory," as they say. Rather than bouncing back from light impact, it crumples and stays crumpled. Replacing body parts on a Tesla typically costs tens of thousands of dollars and can take weeks.

After some wrangling with right-to-repair advocates and laws, the company decided to provide free access to its Service Mode on every Tesla. (The Tesla website shows how to access Service Mode via the touch screen and describes the ways it can be used to service your car.) Access to full diagnostic software is available for $3,000 a year. In 2014, Musk declared that all of Tesla's patents would be open source. He wrote:

> Tesla Motors was created to accelerate the advent of sustainable transport… Tesla will not initiate patent lawsuits against anyone who, in good faith, wants to use our technology… We believe that Tesla, other companies making electric cars, and the world would all benefit from a common, rapidly evolving technology platform.[287]

Since they were starting from scratch as an all-electric automobile manufacturer, Tesla had the advantage of clarity of purpose. The company was making only one kind of car, and it was so radically different from combustion vehicles that Tesla was free to rethink everything from the ground up. With fewer parts, the car was simpler to manufacture. Its hardware and software could be tightly integrated, making it easy to continuously upgrade the software for the owner.

There was also the advantage of conferring an approved public benefit. US federal and state governments, eager to reduce fossil-fuel use, stepped in with substantial loans and tax credits. In 2010, as part of a Department of Energy stimulus package, Tesla got a vital $465 million loan. As soon as the company showed a profit in 2013, the loan and interest were paid off ahead of schedule. The company's stunning success, combined with government pressure on all auto companies to replace dirty fuels with clean electricity, forced the entire industry into a new era. Just a decade after Tesla's introduction, every major auto company in the world was either offering an all-electric model or publicizing plans to do so.

The industry at large increasingly began to follow practices created by Tesla. In 2023, Tesla's charging port standard was adopted by its leading competitors, Ford and General

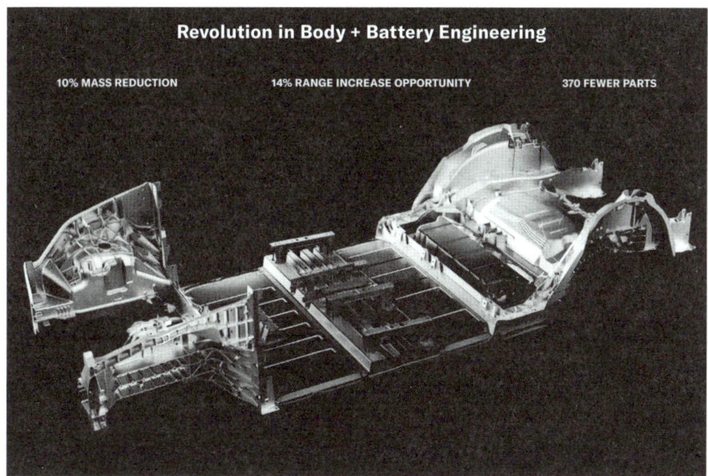

Figure 139. In 2021, Tesla introduced megacasting as a way to fabricate the whole underbody of its Model Y in just two pieces. In his biography of Musk, Walter Isaacson describes the process: "The machines inject bursts of molten aluminum into a cold casting mold, which can spit out in just eighty seconds an entire chassis that used to contain more than a hundred parts that had to be welded, riveted, or bonded together. The old process produced gaps, rattles, and leaks. 'So it went from a horrible nightmare to something that is crazy cheap and easy and fast,' Musk says."* (Tesla)

Motors, followed by Audi, BMW, Hyundai, Kia, Porsche, Rivian, Volkswagen, Volvo, Nissan, Toyota, Honda, Mercedes-Benz, Jaguar, Mini, and Rolls-Royce, whose cars were welcomed at Tesla's thousands of supercharging stations. When Musk challenged his engineers to find a way to "single-piece megacast" most of the underbody of their cars, they developed giant presses to do so, and in 2021 Tesla began applying the technique in all their factories. Megacasting had so many advantages that six automakers in China as well as Volvo in Europe immediately copied the practice.

Along the way, just as it did for Henry Ford, manufacturing a desirable new kind of car made Elon Musk the richest man in the world.

The world is still waiting, however, for an all-electric equivalent of the Model T or Volkswagen Bug—something dirt cheap, brilliantly simple and durable, that invites embellishment and repair by the owner.

Before Tesla revolutionized automobiles, other consumer products began switching to battery power—even chainsaws and leaf blowers. The most rapid transitions came with every form of two-wheeled vehicle: bicycles, motorcycles, motor scooters, and stand-up scooters, also known as kick scooters. Back when bicycles preceded automobiles on the world's roads, one early proposal, in 1897, was for an electric bike. It failed back then, but in the 2000s, thanks to far more efficient batteries, e-bikes and other electric two-wheelers took off, especially in the densely inhabited cities of Asia.

China led the way with electric two-wheelers thanks to a convergence of government fiat and entrepreneurial zest.

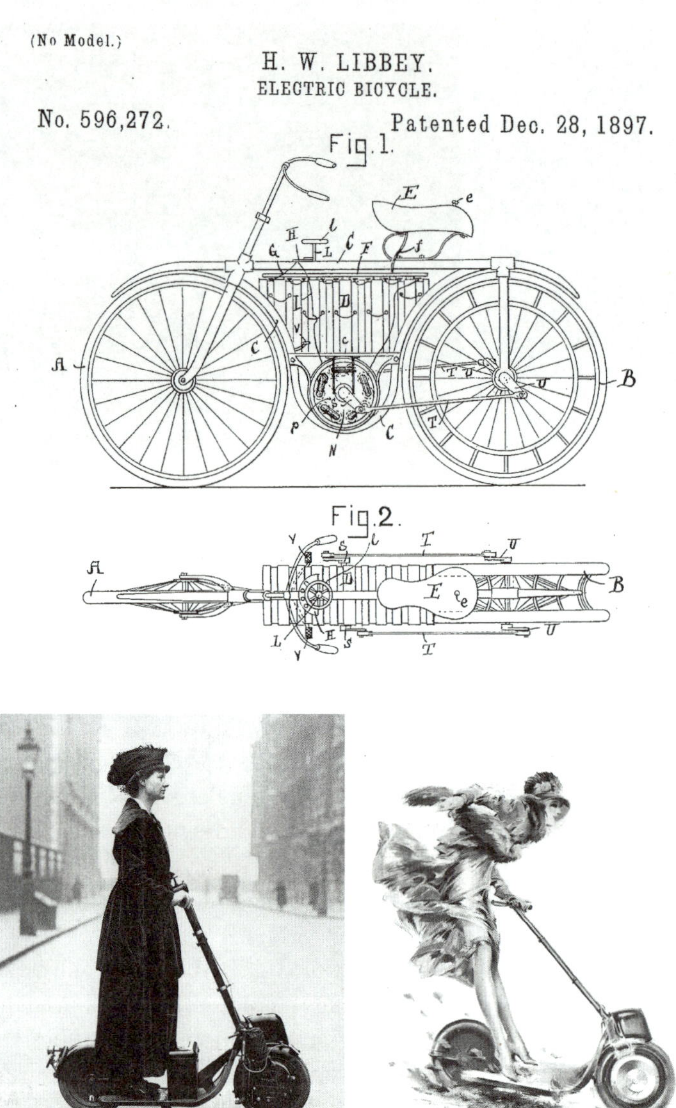

Figure 140. H.W. Libbey's 1897 patent for an electric bicycle declared that "the batteries are supplied with the exciting fluid, such as diluted sulfuric acid, from a tank, reservoir, or hollow seat *E*, of saddle form, said fluid being conducted to the tube *F*, supplying the batteries by a flexible tube *f*. A small nozzle *e* is fitted at the rear of the seat, through which the tank or reservoir is filled with the exciting fluid." The battery had two independent sides, and "thus only one half of said battery may be used on level roads and both halves employed when climbing a hill, and by employing the rear double-treaded wheel for the driving-wheel a double amount of traction is obtained."* (H.W. Libbey, via Wikimedia Commons, public domain)

Figure 141. The Autoped, seen here in 1916 in London (left), was a motorized stand-up scooter. There was an electric version, but most had a tiny 1.5-horsepower gas engine. Lady Florence Priscilla Norman, an activist and suffragette, used her Autoped to get to her office in downtown London. New York's *Puck* magazine ran an ad titled "Look out for the Autoped girl!" with this illustration by Everett Shinn (right). Autopeds were manufactured from 1915 to 1922. (Wikimedia Commons, public domain, and Smithsonian)

By 2010, the country had 100 million e-bikes in use—four times the number of automobiles—and the government built an extensive infrastructure of charging facilities. The general manager of a leading manufacturer told *Time* magazine, "Motorcycles are too dangerous, cars are too expensive, public transportation is too crowded, and pedal bikes leave you too tired. So people buy e-bikes."[288] Chinese cities have abundant bike lanes, and bikes can be charged overnight with an ordinary household plug. By 2020, there were well over 200 million e-bikes in China as well as 51,600 e-bike manufacturers, many of them exporting to the growing world market. India and

Figure 142. Taiwan has 23 million people and 14 million motor scooters. (PeiXuan/Shutterstock)

Figure 143. Gogoro's 2,500 battery-swapping stations serve 90 percent of the 1.7 million electric motor scooters in Taiwan. Some cities have more battery stations than gas stations. (Gogoro)

Vietnam became massive early adopters, followed by the rest of Asia and much of Africa.

A problem for electric vehicles from the very beginning was the time it takes to recharge your batteries while traveling. One solution was battery-swapping stations, but they never worked for electric cars and still don't. With two-wheeled electric vehicles, however, it may be a different story. In Taiwan, a company called Gogoro pioneered battery-swapping networks for scooters and motorcycles. It quickly developed partnerships and networks in China, India, Indonesia, Singapore, and the Philippines, as well as in Israel, France, and Germany. A monthly subscription gets the customer access to unlimited fresh batteries.

Electric two-wheelers took off in the developing world much as cell phones did, and for the same reasons: low-cost personal empowerment that can be home brewed.

Meanwhile, in America, the Harley-Davidson LiveWire ONE electric motorcycle burst onto the scene in 2019. There's

Figure 144. The Harley-Davidson LiveWire electric motorcycle. (Harley-Davidson)

no violent kickstart; you just turn it on. The engine roar is gone, and so is the intricate dance of throttle and gearshift to accelerate. In complete silence, a simple twist of the wrist takes the 500-pound bike—and you—from 0 to 60 miles per hour in 3.1 seconds. Reviewers use words like "addictive sheer exhilaration" to describe the ride. The range on a charge is about 140 miles in town. The price is $20,000 (with tax rebates).

If electrics replace combustion-powered motorcycles, does that mean that the motorcycle maintenance books that began this chapter are about to be obsolete? In some ways, yes. The practice of prying off "shit-colored chunks of bike cheese" to track down an oil leak will be a yarn from yesteryear. But the wisdom in the books—gumption traps and the like—will hold their value. And motorcycle worship ("Live to ride!") is likely to continue. Electricity-powered or not, you still wrap your delicate body around heavy, unstable high-velocity propulsion.

At every speed on every kind of electric two-wheeled vehicle, the sweetest thing about the ride is the quiet—both for the rider and for everybody nearby. It's another reason for cities to find ways to encourage two-wheeled traffic. Cities with good mass transit and bike lanes have a distinct advantage because the electric mini-vehicles foster new ease with what city planners call micromobility. Folding stand-up scooters and some e-bikes can be carried on mass transit or picked up at public scooter- and bike-share spots near the transit stations.

The properties of electric two-wheelers enhance the ambiance of urban life. Everyone on the street can see and hear each other. You can stroll on foot, zip on wheels, or sit and watch the show. With the rumble and rattle of combustion traffic gone, the town feels more congenial, and the air is better.

2.10 Postscript 1: Unreliability Incorporated

GLENNMERCER: "Fun fact: Almost every Formula 1 car is made here in Britain. As the joke goes, the Brits are superb at volumes under 100 per year, but over that number, they fall apart."

In the 1950s, Britain was the world's second-largest manufacturer of cars after the US, boasting renowned marques such as Rolls-Royce, Mini, Jaguar, Land Rover, MG, and Bentley. All that went away in the ensuing 40 years because the British automotive industry lost its version of the maintenance race to Japan, Germany, and the US.

Cars made in England acquired a fatal reputation for unreliability. Rainwater leaked in and oil leaked out. They were noisy. They rusted. They wouldn't start in cold weather. The heaters were feeble. The bearings wore out. The paint wore off. The electrical wiring was so fluky that the provider, Lucas Industries, was universally known as "the prince of darkness" and inspired a genre of jokes and stories such as:

- Lucas is the patent holder for the short circuit.
- Lucas is an acronym for Loose Unsoldered Connections and Splices.
- Lucas—inventor of the self-dimming headlamp.
- The Lucas motto: "Get home before dark."

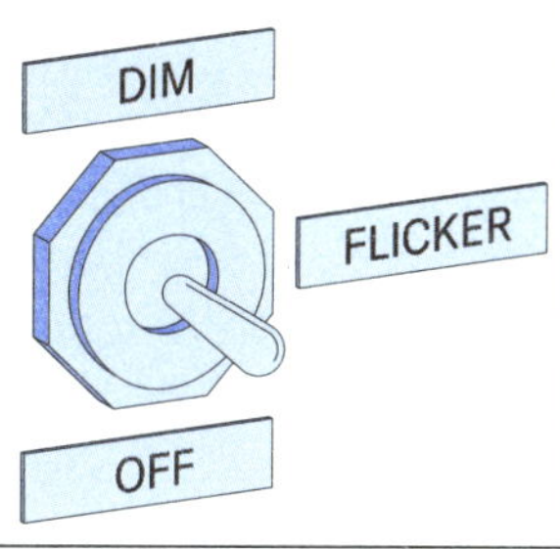

Figure 145. Imagine running a company that becomes famous primarily for the shoddiness of its product.

And there's this report:

> I have firsthand experience with Mr. Lucas's legendary vintage British electrical products, due to a disastrous but fairly typical experience with a 1970 Triumph GT6+ I bought after high school and owned from 1976–78. The car was a rolling Lucas joke (that is, when it was capable of rolling). I was particularly fond of the wipers that quit working in the rain and the headlights that magically shut off at night. It was so bad that it cured me of British cars for 37 years.[289]

Among the many theories of what went wrong—the damn unions, the damn government, the oblivious engineers—is one from Brian Eno, the British musician and composer, that focuses on management. He wrote me that his wife bought a used Aston Martin that, once she tired of having it repaired, wound up as a "beautiful ornament to have in the drive, but not a practical proposition for transport." He added:

> My feeling is that one reason for this was that there was a complete absence of communication between management and workers. Totally different from Germany, where there are always workers' representatives on the board, and Japan, where there are streamlined ways for workers' observations and comments to reach management. People who own car companies in England come straight out of the public (i.e., private) school system and have never had, or sought, any contact with the people who work for them.

Whatever the cause, manufacturers who make products deemed unmaintainable are ripe for takeover. Rolls-Royce and Mini were bought by BMW in Germany, MG by SAIC in China, Jaguar and Land Rover by Tata in India, and Bentley by Volkswagen in Germany. All of them recovered under their new ownership.

What Rolls-Royce did with its reputation for opulence is interesting. It now specializes in crafting individually storied cars. Each one is extravagantly bespoke, customized to whatever the buyer fancies amid a near-infinity of expensive options, which are added on to the base price of $460,000 for the sedan or $650,000 for the Phantom Platino. Every Rolls has an umbrella hidden in the driver's door. Every Rolls has 330 pounds of acoustic insulation and double-layer windows to shut out exterior noise. Every Rolls flaunts the Spirit of Ecstasy hood ornament (which disappears into the hood when you park) and self-righting wheel centers to make sure the RR logo on all four wheels stays upright and readable.

Options are the main attraction. No other Rolls will look like yours. The palette you select from 44,000 available colors is registered uniquely to you and named by you. The dashboard art can be whatever you desire; one owner wanted a gold-plated, 3D-printed, stainless-steel replica of his DNA profile.[290] And so on through a wealth of luxurious options in leathers, upholstery, wood trim, detailing, entertainment devices, food and drink service, and communications gear. Each car takes three to six months to build and embellish to your specifications. In the old days, the whole vehicle was handcrafted by mechanics; these days, 50 specialists handcraft the amenities.

In 2022, 6,021 such vehicles were sold. Thanks to German ownership, maintenance of the whole machine and all that fussiness is also bespoke. To quote the authoritative Kelley Blue Book:

> All modern Rolls-Royce vehicles incorporate parent company BMW's Condition Based Servicing System which uses sensors and algorithms to determine when the car's oil lifespan has been reached. It also tracks other vehicle parameters, such as brake pads, fluids, and more to keep you ahead of the curve as far as Rolls-Royce vehicle maintenance is concerned. Using Rolls-Royce TeleService, data will be transmitted to Rolls-Royce, and your local dealership will call to arrange an appointment.[291]

The downside is that Rolls-Royce charges heart-attack prices to fix your car once the four-year warranty runs out. You might be better off leasing instead of purchasing, or you could follow the advice of some experienced owners and take your Rolls that needs work to a BMW dealer first. Many of the parts are now BMW-standard and can be replaced at BMW rates.

Way back in 1900, Charles Rolls reportedly said, "The electric car is perfectly noiseless and clean. There is no smell or vibration. They should become very useful when fixed charging stations can be arranged."[292] Apparently, that has now happened. One hundred and twenty-three years later, the all-electric Rolls-Royce Spectre can be yours for $420,000. It is said to "drive sublimely."[293] For over half of the buyers, it is their second or third Rolls-Royce.

2.11 Postscript 2: First Vehicle

For 6,000 years before 1900, humanity's primary land vehicle was the horse. It ran on one horsepower, multiples of which became the measure of power in all of the motorized vehicles that replaced horses after 1900. City dwellers rejoiced to have their streets free of dung and no longer hazardous from runaway half-ton animals, but something was lost.

Maintaining a horse is different from maintaining a car or a bicycle. A horse is no small project, what with tending to its stall, its paddock, the hay and grain, the water, the tack, the training, the grooming, the farrier, the vet. All that is a form of caring, a relationship with another sentience. The philosopher Albert Borgmann once wrote:

> You cannot remain unmoved by the gentleness and conformation of a well-bred and well-trained horse—more than a thousand pounds of big-boned, well-muscled animal, slick of coat and sweet of smell, obedient and mannerly, and yet forever a menace with its innocent power and ineradicable inclination to seek refuge in flight; and always a burden with its need to be fed, wormed, and shod, with its liability to cuts and infections, to laming and heaves. But when it greets you with a nicker, nuzzles your chest, and regards you with a large and liquid eye, the question of where you want to be and what you want to do has been answered.[294]

I wonder if that might come again someday—a vehicle that cares back.

Recommended Reading

Of all the books I used, these are the ones with the most news and soul.

Chapter 1: The Maintenance Race

A World of My Own
by Robin Knox-Johnston
Intrepid nonstop maintenance.

The Long Way
by Bernard Moitessier
The right way.

The Strange Last Voyage of Donald Crowhurst
by Nicholas Tomalin and Ron Hall
An optimist's lies; death's honesty.

Chapter 2: Vehicles (and Weapons)

Zen and the Art of Motorcycle Maintenance: An Inquiry into Values
by Robert M. Pirsig
Philosophy via attentive maintenance.

Shop Class as Soulcraft: An Inquiry into the Value of Work
by Matthew B. Crawford
Maintenance embodies intelligence.

The Perfectionists: How Precision Engineers Created the Modern World
by Simon Winchester
The driver of technical progress.

Farewell to Model T: From Sea to Shining Sea
by E.B. White
Adventurous car, young joy.

"Faster, Better, Cheaper" in the History of Manufacturing: From the Stone Age to Lean Manufacturing and Beyond
by Christoph Roser
From hand-axe to Lean.

From the American System to Mass Production, 1800–1932: The Development of Manufacturing Technology in the United States
by David A. Hounshell
The definitive account.

Harpers Ferry Armory and the New Technology: The Challenge of Change
by Merritt Roe Smith
John Hall's heroic mechanization.

Military Enterprise and Technological Change: Perspectives on the American Experience
edited by Merritt Roe Smith
The deep roots of DARPA.

60 Years with Men and Machines: An Autobiography
by Fred H. Colvin
The ascent of American machine tools, personified.

How to Keep Your Volkswagen Alive: A Manual of Step-by-Step Procedures for the Compleat Idiot
by John Muir and Tosh Gregg
The most revered user manual ever.

The Merck Manual of Medical Information: Home Edition
edited by Mark H. Beers
The shop manual for your body.

Enlightening the World: Encyclopédie, the Book that Changed the Course of History
by Philipp Blom
The *Encyclopédie* was the real French Revolution.

A Diderot Pictorial Encyclopedia of Trades and Industry
by Denis Diderot
Four hundred and eighty-five astounding engravings from the *Encyclopédie.*

Dream Babies: Childcare Advice from John Locke to Gina Ford
by Christina Hardyment
The history of child-care manuals.

The Medieval Art of Swordsmanship: Royal Armouries MS I.33
by Jeffrey L. Forgeng
A medieval masterpiece.

Dry Stone Walls: Basics, Construction, Significance
by the Swiss Environmental Action Foundation
Inspirational how-to.

American Gun: The True Story of the AR-15
by Cameron McWhirter and Zusha Elinson
The AR-15 story.

The Gun
by C.J. Chivers
The scandal of the M16 assault rifle.

About Face: The Odyssey of an American Warrior
by David H. Hackworth and Julie Sherman
The scandal of the Vietnam War by its most decorated veteran.

Rust: The Longest War
by Jonathan Waldman
Tales of the war on corrosion.

Armies of Sand: The Past, Present, and Future of Arab Military Effectiveness
by Kenneth M. Pollack
Why Arab militaries fail.

Mission Command: The Who, What, Where, When, and Why; An Anthology
edited by Donald Vandergriff and Stephen Webber
What makes mission command work.

System Sustainment: Acquisition and Engineering Processes for the Sustainment of Critical and Legacy Systems
by Peter Sandborn and William Lucyshyn
Sustainment as a way to think.

Endnotes

1. Peter Nichols, *A Voyage for Madmen* (Harper Collins, 2009), 35.
2. Robin Knox-Johnston, *A World of My Own: The First Ever Non-Stop Solo Round the World Voyage* (Adlard Coles Nautical, 1969), v.
3. Knox-Johnston, *World of My Own*, 5.
4. *Sir Robin Knox-Johnston: Sailing Legend*, documentary, directed by Clifford Webb, posted May 14, 2020, by Clipper Round the World Yacht Race, YouTube, 56 min., 34 sec., https://youtu.be/WdIlYr1GdIs.
5. Nichols, *Voyage for Madmen*, 93.
6. Knox-Johnston, *World of My Own*, 168–69.
7. Knox-Johnston, *World of My Own*, 106.
8. Knox-Johnston, *World of My Own*, 78.
9. Knox-Johnston, *World of My Own*, 133.
10. "A Golden Anniversary," Royal National Lifeboat Institution, March 13, 2019, https://rnli.org/magazine/magazine-featured-list/2019/march/a-golden-anniversary.
11. Knox-Johnston, *World of My Own*, 222.
12. Knox-Johnston, *World of My Own*, 4.
13. Nicholas Tomalin and Ron Hall, *The Strange Last Voyage of Donald Crowhurst* (Quercus, 1970), 22.
14. Tomalin and Hall, *Donald Crowhurst*, 102.
15. Tomalin and Hall, *Donald Crowhurst*, 272.
16. Tomalin and Hall, *Donald Crowhurst*, 282.
17. Tomalin and Hall, *Donald Crowhurst*, 312.
18. Tomalin and Hall, *Donald Crowhurst*, 264.
19. Bernard Moitessier, *The Long Way* (Sheridan House, 1971), 49.
20. Bernard Moitessier, *A Sea Vagabond's World* (Sheridan House, 1995), 18.
21. Moitessier, *Sea Vagabond's World*, 157.
22. Knox-Johnston, *World of My Own*, 179.
23. Moitessier, *Long Way*, 27.
24. "Bernard Moitessier," video, produced by Fabrice Florin, posted August 31, 2012, by Videowest TV, YouTube, 8 min., 1 sec., https://www.youtube.com/watch?v=Ptmn0L-LSqE.
25. Moitessier, *Sea Vagabond's World*, 13.
26. Moitessier, *Long Way*, 38.
27. Moitessier, *Long Way*, 53.
28. Moitessier, *Long Way*, 70.
29. Moitessier, *Long Way*, 116.
30. Moitessier, *Long Way*, 163.
31. Moitessier, *Long Way*, 116–17.
32. Nichols, *Voyage for Madmen*, 237.
33. Glin Bennet, "Psychological Breakdown at Sea: Hazards of Singlehanded Ocean Sailing," *British Journal of Medical Psychology* 47 (1974): 189, https://doi.org/10.1111/j.2044-8341.1974.tb02284.x.
34. "Moitessier, Bernard," *Encyclopedia of World Biography*, Encyclopedia.com. https://www.encyclopedia.com/history/encyclopedias-almanacs-transcripts-and-maps/moitessier-bernard.
35. This quote is widely credited to the *Telegraph*.
36. Matthew B. Crawford, *Shop Class as Soulcraft: An Inquiry into the Value of Work* (Penguin, 2009), 27.
37. Crawford, *Soulcraft*, 115.
38. Crawford, *Soulcraft*, 116.
39. Crawford, *Soulcraft*, 118.
40. Crawford, *Soulcraft*, 117.
41. Crawford, *Soulcraft*, 118.
42. Crawford, *Soulcraft*, 26–27.
43. John Jerome, *Truck: On Rebuilding a Worn-Out Pickup and Other Post-Technological Adventures* (University Press of New England, 2014), 134.
44. Robert M. Pirsig, *Zen and the Art of Motorcycle Maintenance: An Inquiry into Values* (Harper Collins, 2009), 391.
45. Pirsig, *Motorcycle Maintenance*, 400.
46. Pirsig, *Motorcycle Maintenance*, 399.
47. Tomalin and Hall, *Donald Crowhurst*, 99.
48. Pirsig, *Motorcycle Maintenance*, 391.
49. Pirsig, *Motorcycle Maintenance*, 407.
50. Pirsig, *Motorcycle Maintenance*, 392.
51. Pirsig, *Motorcycle Maintenance*, 395.
52. Pirsig, *Motorcycle Maintenance*, 30–32.
53. Pirsig, *Motorcycle Maintenance*, 361.
54. Pirsig, *Motorcycle Maintenance*, 89–90.
55. Crawford, *Soulcraft*, 55.
56. Crawford, *Soulcraft*, 205.
57. Pirsig, *Motorcycle Maintenance*, 51.
58. Pirsig, *Motorcycle Maintenance*, 52.
59. Pirsig, *Motorcycle Maintenance*, 386.
60. "'Zen Motorcycle' Takes Final Journey into the Smithsonian's Collections," Smithsonian, December 17, 2019, https://www.si.edu/newsdesk/releases/zen-motorcycle-takes-final-journey-smithsonians-collections.
61. Crawford, *Soulcraft*, 196.
62. Benjamin Carr, "Motorcycle vs. Car Accident Statistics (2024)," AutoInsurance.org, last updated April 18, 2024, https://www.autoinsurance.org/motorcycle-vs-car-accidents/.
63. George Dyson, email to author, 2021.
64. George Basalla, *The Evolution of Technology* (Cambridge University Press, 1989), 198.
65. "1916 Rauch and Lang Electric Brougham," Marshall Steam Museum at Auburn Heights, https://auburnheights.org/automobile/1916-rauch-and-lang-electric-brougham/.
66. Michael Brian Schiffer, *Taking Charge: The Electric Automobile in America* (Smithsonian Institution Scholarly Press, 1994), 136–37.
67. Simon Winchester, *The Perfectionists: How Precision Engineers Created the Modern World* (HarperCollins, 2018), 149–50.
68. "Rolls-Royce Silver Ghost (1909 to 1926)," Classic.com. https://www.classic.com/m/rolls-royce/silver-ghost/.
69. Winchester, *Perfectionists*, 146.
70. Winchester, *Perfectionists*, 154.
71. David A. Hounshell, *From the American System to Mass Production, 1800–1932: The Development of Manufacturing Technology in the United States* (Johns Hopkins University Press, 1984), 220.
72. Henry Ford and Samuel Crowther, *My Life and Work*, Project Gutenberg, January 2005, https://www.gutenberg.org/ebooks/7213.

73 Wikipedia, "Ford Model T," last updated June 20, 2025, https://en.wikipedia.org/wiki/Ford_Model_T.
74 E.B. White, *Farewell to Model T: From Sea to Shining Sea* (New York Review Books, 2003), 13, 16.
75 *Model T Ford Service* (Ford Motor Company, 1927), 231–44.
76 Winchester, *Perfectionists*, 37.
77 Jeremy Norman, "John Wilkinson Invents the First Machine Tool: A Boring Machine for Cylinders and Cannons," Jeremy Norman's HistoryofInformation.com, last updated July 15, 2024, https://historyofinformation.com/detail.php?id=4755.
78 Christoph Roser, *"Faster, Better, Cheaper" in the History of Manufacturing: From the Stone Age to Lean Manufacturing and Beyond* (CRC Press, 2016), 120–21.
79 Hounshell, *Mass Production*, 25.
80 Hounshell, *Mass Production*, 26.
81 Winchester, *Perfectionists*, 92.
82 Ken Alder, *Engineering the Revolution: Arms and Enlightenment in France, 1763–1815* (University of Chicago Press, 2010), 7.
83 Hounshell, *Mass Production*, 27.
84 Hounshell, *Mass Production*, 33.
85 Merritt Roe Smith, *Harpers Ferry Armory and the New Technology: The Challenge of Change* (Cornell University Press, 1977), 107.
86 "Thomas Blanchard," National Park Service, last updated March 25, 2023, https://www.nps.gov/spar/learn/historyculture/thomas-blanchard-and-his-lathe.htm.
87 Hounshell, *Mass Production*, 38.
88 Winchester, *Perfectionists*, 100.
89 Hounshell, *Mass Production*, 43.
90 Smith, *Harpers Ferry*, 201.
91 Smith, *Harpers Ferry*, 206–7.
92 Peter A. Schmidt, *Hall's Military Breechloaders* (Andrew Mowbray Pub, 1995), 28.
93 Schmidt, *Breechloaders*, 211.
94 Schmidt, *Breechloaders*, 213.
95 Merritt Roe Smith, ed., *Military Enterprise and Technological Change: Perspectives on the American Experience* (MIT Press, 1985), 52, 86.
96 Alder, *Engineering the Revolution*, 324.
97 Smith, *Military Enterprise*, 64.
98 Smith, *Harpers Ferry*, 219.
99 Smith, *Military Enterprise*, 78.
100 Hounshell, *Mass Production*, 15.
101 Hounshell, *Mass Production*, 48–49.
102 "Samuel Colt," Wikipedia, last updated April 2, 2024, https://en.wikipedia.org/wiki/Samuel_Colt.
103 "Samuel Colt's Manufacturing Company," Wikipedia, last updated April 13, 2024, https://en.wikipedia.org/wiki/Colt's_Manufacturing_Company.
104 Richard Kurin, *The Smithsonian's History of America in 101 Objects* (Penguin, 2013), 176.
105 Hounshell, *Mass Production*, 121.
106 John S. Reid, "A Tale of Invention: The Birth of the Modern Bicycle," University of Aberdeen, 2012, 14, https://homepages.abdn.ac.uk/nph120/meteo/Bicycles.pdf.
107 Hounshell, *Mass Production*, 208.
108 Fred H. Colvin, *60 Years with Men and Machines: An Autobiography*, (McGraw-Hill, 1947), 84, 88–9.
109 David V. Herlihy, *Bicycle: The History* (Yale University Press, 2004), 280.
110 Carlton Reid, "Reclaiming the Roads," Works in Progress, July 21, 2022, https://worksinprogress.co/issue/reclaiming-the-roads.
111 "Nellie Bly Interview with Susan B. Anthony," Timothy Hughes Rare & Early Newspapers, https://www.rarenewspapers.com/view/621269?acl=851761768&imagelist=1.
112 Henry Ford and Samuel Crowther, *Moving Forward* (Doubleday, 1930), 213.
113 Hounshell, *Mass Production*, 260.
114 Smith, *Military Enterprise*, 4.
115 Winchester, *Perfectionists*, 297.
116 "List of Best-Selling Automobiles," Wikipedia, last updated May 3, 2024, https://en.wikipedia.org/wiki/List_of_best-selling_automobiles.
117 Peter Hamilton, "The Lada: A Cultural Icon," in *Autopia: Cars and Culture*, ed. Peter Wollen and Joe Kerr (Reaktion Books, 2002), 193.
118 Taylor Martin, "The Infamously Terrible Lada Riva Is Also One of the Best-Selling Cars of All Time," MotorBiscuit, November 15, 2021, https://www.motorbiscuit.com/terrible-lada-riva-sixth-best-selling-car/.
119 John Muir and Tosh Gregg, *How to Keep Your Volkswagen Alive: A Manual of Step-by-Step Procedures for the Compleat Idiot* (Avalon Publishing, 2001), 96.
120 Muir and Gregg, *Volkswagen*, 441.
121 Muir and Gregg, *Volkswagen*, 37.
122 Muir and Gregg, *Volkswagen*, 95.
123 "RTFM," Wikipedia, last updated June 28, 2024, https://en.wikipedia.org/wiki/RTFM.
124 "John Muir (engineer)," Wikipedia, last updated January 18, 2024, https://en.wikipedia.org/wiki/John_Muir_(engineer).
125 Crawford, *Soulcraft*, 177.
126 The automotive repair site Mechanic Base reviews all the best auto manuals: https://mechanicbase.com/reviews/best-auto-repair-manual.
127 *Model T Ford Service*, 1.
128 *Model T Ford Service*, 260.
129 Philip Nicholas Furbank, *Diderot: A Critical Biography* (Knopf, 1992), 459.
130 Furbank, *Diderot*, 38–39.
131 Richard Sennett, *The Craftsman* (Yale University Press, 2008), 97.
132 Furbank, *Diderot*, 39–40.
133 Furbank, *Diderot*, 76.
134 Furbank, *Diderot*, 40.
135 Sennett, *Craftsman*, 90.
136 Philipp Blom, *Enlightening the World: Encyclopédie, the Book that Changed the Course of History* (Macmillan, 2005), 251.
137 Blom, *Encyclopédie*, 224.
138 Maximilien Robespierre, "On the Principles of Political Morality," Marxists.org, http://marxists.org/history/france/revolution/robespierre/1794/political-morality.htm.

139 Jean-Jacques Rousseau, *The Confessions of Jean-Jacques Rousseau, Book VI*, Project Gutenberg, September 5, 2015, https://gutenberg.org/files/3913/3913-h/3913-h.htm#link2H_4_0007.
140 Friedrich Nietzsche, *The Will to Power* (Dover Publications, 2019), 68.
141 Blom, *Encyclopédie*, 312.
142 "Scottish Enlightenment," Wikipedia, last updated July 29, 2024, https://en.wikipedia.org/wiki/Scottish_Enlightenment.
143 "Scottish Enlightenment," Wikipedia.
144 Alistair MacDonald, "Scottish Enlightenment," British Council, July 2016, https://www.britishcouncil.org/research-insight/scottish-enlightenment.
145 "Nicholas Culpeper," Wikipedia, last updated April 13, 2024, https://en.wikipedia.org/wiki/Nicholas_Culpeper.
146 Benjamin Woolley, *Heal Thyself: Nicholas Culpeper and the Seventeenth-Century Struggle to Bring Medicine to the People* (HarperCollins, 2004), jacket.
147 Woolley, *Heal Thyself*, 316.
148 Woolley, *Heal Thyself*, 314.
149 Nicholas Culpeper, *A Directory for Midwives: Or, a Guide for Women, in Their Conception, Bearing, and Suckling Their Children* (John Streater, 1651), 21.
150 Culpeper, *Directory for Midwives*, iv.
151 Joseph Moxon, *Mechanick Exercises: Or, The Doctrine of Handy-Works* (D. Midwinter and T. Leigh, 1703), 62.
152 Moxon, *Mechanick Exercises*, 124.
153 Jocelyn E. Hargrave, "Joseph Moxon: A Re-Fashioned Appraisal," *Script & Print: Bulletin of the Bibliographical Society of Australia and New Zealand* 39, no. 3 (2015), 163–81, https://search.informit.org/doi/10.3316/INFORMIT.473337499287786.
154 Joseph Moxon, *Mechanick Exercises: Or, the Doctrine of Handy-works Applied to the Art of Printing* (J. Moxon, 1683), 7.
155 Derek Albert Long, *At the Sign of Atlas: The Life and Work of Joseph Moxon, a Restoration Polymath* (Shaun Tyas, 2013), 96.
156 Jeffrey L. Forgeng, *The Medieval Art of Swordsmanship: Royal Armouries MS I.33* (Royal Armouries Museum, 2018), 19.
157 Gary Snyder, "Riprap," Poetry Foundation, https://www.poetryfoundation.org/poems/47178/riprap.
158 Swiss Environmental Action Foundation, *Dry Stone Walls: Basics, Construction, Significance* (Scheidegger and Spiess, 2018), 311.
159 Swiss Environmental Action Foundation, *Dry Stone Walls*, 179.
160 Edward F. Murphy, *The Hill Fights: The First Battle of Khe Sanh* (Presidio Press, 2007), 289.
161 James Fallows, "M-16: A Bureaucratic Horror Story," *The Atlantic*, June 1, 1981, https://www.theatlantic.com/magazine/archive/1981/06/m-16-a-bureaucratic-horror-story/545153/.
162 Edward Clinton Ezell, *The Great Rifle Controversy: Search for the Ultimate Infantry Weapon from World War II through Vietnam and Beyond* (Stackpole Books, 1984), 218.
163 Murphy, *Hill Fights*, 115.
164 Jeffrey Elbies, "They Were Soldiers Once," PopPhoto, December 17, 2008, https://www.popphoto.com/how-to/2008/12/they-were-soldiers-once/.
165 Murphy, *Hill Fights*, 201.
166 *M16 Maintenance and Repair Manual: Army TM 9-1005-319-23&P Air Force to 11 W3-5-5-42* (Department of Defense, 1991), section 12–13c.
167 Will Eisner, "The M16A1 Rifle: Operation and Preventive Maintenance (DA Pam 750-30)," June 28, 1968, https://archive.org/details/1968m16A1.
168 "Eisner Awards," Wikipedia, last updated May 13, 2025, https://en.wikipedia.org/wiki/Eisner_Awards.
169 Will Eisner, *Last Day in Vietnam: A Memory* (Dark Horse Comics, 2000), 4.
170 Eisner, *Last Day in Vietnam*, 5.
171 C.J. Chivers, *The Gun* (Simon and Schuster, 2011), 269.
172 "M16 Rifle," Wikipedia, last updated May 2, 2024, https://en.wikipedia.org/wiki/M16_rifle.
173 David H. Hackworth and Julie Sherman, *About Face: The Odyssey of an American Warrior* (Touchstone, 1990), 434–5.
174 Larry Kahaner, *AK-47: The Weapon that Changed the Face of War* (Wiley, 2007), 24.
175 Kahaner, *AK-47*, 23.
176 Chivers, *Gun*, 188.
177 Ezell, *Great Rifle Controversy*, 220.
178 Kofi Annan, "Small Arms, Big Problems," United Nations, July 10, 2001, https://www.un.org/sg/en/content/sg/articles/2001-07-10/small-arms-big-problems.
179 "Catherine Leroy: Photographer 1944–2006," Dotation Catherine Leroy, https://dotationcatherineleroy.org/en/.
180 Aaron Smith, Skye Toor, and Patrick van Kessel, "Many Turn to YouTube for Children's Content, News, How-to Lessons," Pew Research Center, November 7, 2018, https://www.pewresearch.org/internet/2018/11/07/many-turn-to-youtube-for-childrens-content-news-how-to-lessons/.
181 Christina Farr, "Doctors are Turning to YouTube to Learn How to Do Surgical Procedures, But There's No Quality Control," CNBC, November 24, 2019, https://www.cnbc.com/2019/11/24/doctors-are-watching-surgical-procedures-on-youtube.html.
182 Mark Fauenfelder, "Leaky Faucet Fix," Recomendo: Issue No. 327, Cool Tools, October 16, 2022, https://kk.org/cooltools/lex-fridman-podcast-consensus-app-leaky-faucet-fix/.
183 I'm grateful to the following responders to my query on Twitter (now X) about great repair videos and great videos on how to make great videos (https://twitter.com/stewartbrand/status/1607803329698201601): @thinkyparts, @idlebell, @makerjak, @kwiens, @dustinbajer, @davidkennerly, @ruizdurazo, @matisse_enzer, @ltownzag, @aaron_salus, @intjonathan, and @jhong.

184 Thinky Parts (@thinkyparts), Twitter (now X), November 28, 2022, https://twitter.com/thinkyparts/status/1597404857681735680. The user appears to have left Twitter since leaving this comment.

185 Adam (@idlebell), "I have rebuilt my entire car using Timmy the Tool Man and some manuals," Twitter (now X), December 27, 2022, https://twitter.com/idlebell/status/1607822523583930368.

186 Todd Osgood, "Best Knife Brand? Benchmade, Buck, Zero Tolerance, Spyderco, Cold Steel, Kershaw, SOG, CRKT, Ontario," posted February 6, 2022, by Project Farm, YouTube, 18 min., 54 sec., https://www.youtube.com/watch?v=wVQ3raLq4LQ&t=1006s.

187 Eric Tozzi, "Rare Antique Fractal Vise [Restoration]," posted June 24, 2021, by Hand Tool Rescue, YouTube, 36 min., 19 sec., https://youtu.be/QBeOgGt_oWU.

188 Muir and Gregg, *Volkswagen*, 427.

189 Jerome, *Truck*, 9.

190 Jonathan Waldman, *Rust: The Longest War* (Simon and Schuster, 2015), 3.

191 Zaki Ahmad, *Principles of Corrosion Engineering and Corrosion Control* (Elsevier, 2006), 2.

192 Gerhardus Koch, et al., "International Measures of Prevention, Application, and Economics of Corrosion Technologies Study," NACE International, March 1, 2016, http://impact.nace.org/documents/Nace-International-Report.pdf.

193 "World Steel in Figures: 2022," World Steel Association, April 30, 2022, https://worldsteel.org/data/world-steel-in-figures-2022/.

194 Vaclav Smil, *Still the Iron Age: Iron and Steel in the Modern World* (Elsevier Science, 2016).

195 Waldman, *Rust*, 164.

196 Waldman, *Rust*, 165.

197 Waldman, *Rust*, 195.

198 Jean Hatzfeld, *Machete Season: The Killers in Rwanda Speak* (Farrar, Straus and Giroux, 2006), 79.

199 Hatzfeld, *Machete Season*, 79.

200 "Stainless Steel," Wikipedia, last updated May 1, 2024, https://en.wikipedia.org/wiki/Stainless_steel.

201 Waldman, *Rust*, 281.

202 For how it works, look up "galvanic corrosion" online.

203 Waldman, *Rust*, 21.

204 The Wikipedia entry on the conservation and restoration of the Statue of Liberty has more of the story, as does the chapter "A High-Maintenance Lady" in Jonathan Waldman's *Rust*. "Conservation-restoration of the Statue of Liberty," Wikipedia, last updated November 12, 2024, https://en.wikipedia.org/wiki/Conservation-restoration_of_the_Statue_of_Liberty; Waldman, *Rust*, 13.

205 James S. Powell, "Taking a Look Under the Hood: The October War and What Maintenance Approaches Reveal about Military Operations," The Institute of Land Warfare, Land Warfare Paper 128 (August 2019), 12, https://www.ausa.org/sites/default/files/publications/LWP-128-Taking-a-Look-under-the-Hood-The-October-War-and-What-Maintenance-Approaches-Reveal-about-Military-Operations.pdf.

206 Powell, "Under the Hood," 21.

207 Avraham Adan, *On the Banks of the Suez: An Israeli General's Personal Account of the Yom Kippur War* (Presidio Press, 1980), 203.

208 Powell, "Under the Hood," 20.

209 Powell, "Under the Hood," 33.

210 Kenneth M. Pollack, *Armies of Sand: The Past, Present, and Future of Arab Military Effectiveness* (Oxford University Press, 2019), 378–80.

211 Pollack, *Armies of Sand*, 379; Sania Hamady, *Temperament and Character of the Arabs* (Hassell Street Press, 2021), 35.

212 Pollack, *Armies of Sand*, 384–85.

213 Norvell De Atkine, "Why Arabs Lose Wars," *Middle East Quarterly* 6, no. 4 (1999), https://www.meforum.org/middle-east-quarterly/why-arabs-lose-wars.

214 Pollack, *Armies of Sand*, 380.

215 Kenneth M. Pollack, *Arabs at War: Military Effectiveness, 1948–1999* (University of Nebraska Press, 2004), 129.

216 John Gulick, "Two Streams into One," in *Readings in Arab Middle Eastern Societies and Cultures*, ed. Abdulla M. Lutfiyya and Charles W. Churchill (Mouton, 1970), 342.

217 De Atkine, "Why Arabs Lose Wars."

218 De Atkine, "Why Arabs Lose Wars."

219 De Atkine, "Why Arabs Lose Wars."

220 *ATP 4-33: Maintenance Operations* (Department of the Army, 2019), A-2.

221 *ATP 4-33*, A-2.

222 Powell, "Under the Hood," 5.

223 Pollack, *Arabs at War*, 568.

224 Powell, "Under the Hood," 30.

225 Powell, "Under the Hood," 15.

226 Pollack, *Arabs at War*, 130.

227 Simon Dunstan, *The Yom Kippur War 1973 (2): The Sinai* (Bloomsbury Publishing, 2012), 92.

228 Peng Guangqian and Yao Youzhi, eds., *Science of Military Strategy* (Military Publishing House, 2005), 280, quoted in Powell, "Under the Hood," 1.

229 Powell, "Under the Hood," 29.

230 *FM 4-0, Sustainment Operations* (US Government Printing Office, 2019), 1.

231 *FM 4-0*, 1–6.

232 Deployable Training Division, "Insight and Best Practices Focus Paper: Mission Command," 2nd ed., Joint Staff J7, Joint Training, January 2020, https://www.jcs.mil/Portals/36/Documents/Doctrine/fp/missioncommand_fp_2nd_ed.pdf.

233 Stephen Bungay, "The Road to Mission Command: The Genesis of a Command Philosophy," *The British Army Review* 137 (Summer 2005): 2, https://studylib.net/doc/7824018/the-genesis-of-a-command-philosophy.

234 Bungay, "Mission Command," 3.

235 Bungay, "Mission Command," 6.

236 Trevor Dupuy, *A Genius for War: German Army and General Staff 1807–1945* (Macdonald & Janes, 1977), 253–54.

237 Michael Flynn and Chuck Schrankel, "Applying

Mission Command through the Operations Process," *Military Review* (March–April 2013), https://www.armyupress.army.mil/Portals/7/military-review/Archives/English/Military Review_20130430_art006.pdf.

238 John T. Nelsen II, "'Auftragstaktik': A Case for Decentralized Battle," *Parameters* 17, no. 1 (September 1987), 22–27, https://doi.org/10.55540/0031-1723.1460.

239 *DA PAM 750-3, Soldiers' Guide for Field Maintenance Operations* (Department of the Army, 2013), 3.

240 *DA PAM 750-3*, 15.

241 Norman M. Wade, *SMFLS5: The Sustainment & Multifunctional Logistics SMARTbook*, 5th ed., (Lightning Press, 2021), 4-16.

242 *ATP 4-33*, 3, 28–29.

243 Wade, *SMFLS5*, 5-10.

244 Peter Sandborn and William Lucyshyn, *System Sustainment: Acquisition and Engineering Processes for the Sustainment of Critical and Legacy Systems*, World Scientific Series on Emerging Technologies 4 (World Scientific, 2022), 1.

245 Sandborn and Lucyshyn, *System Sustainment*, v, 14, 17.

246 Sandborn and Lucyshyn, *System Sustainment*, 3, 89.

247 Sandborn and Lucyshyn, *System Sustainment*, 3.

248 Charles C. Mann, email to author, October 19, 2023.

249 Naveed Jamali, David Brennan, and Tom O'Connor, "Exclusive: US Expects Kyiv to Fall in Days as Ukraine Source Warns of Encirclement," *Newsweek*, February 25, 2022, https://www.newsweek.com/us-expects-kyiv-fall-days-ukraine-source-warns-encirclement-1682326.

250 Phillips Payson O'Brien, "People Forgot How War Actually Works," *The Atlantic*, February 24, 2023, https://www.theatlantic.com/ideas/archive/2023/02/russia-ukraine-war-one-year-national-identity/673192/.

251 Daniel Michaels and Matthew Luxmoore, "The 19th-Century Technology Driving Russia's Latest Gains in Ukraine: Railroads," *Wall Street Journal*, June 14, 2022, https://www.wsj.com/articles/the-19th-century-technology-driving-russias-latest-gains-in-ukraine-railroads-11655218602.

252 Brad Lendon, "What Images of Russian Trucks Say About Its Military's Struggles in Ukraine," CNN, April 14, 2022, https://www.cnn.com/2022/04/14/europe/ukraine-war-russia-trucks-logistics-intl-hnk-ml/index.html.

253 Trent Telenko (@TrentTelenko), "This is a thread that will explain the implied poor Russian Army truck maintenance practices based on this photo of a Pantsir-S1 wheeled gun-missile system's right rear pair of tires below & the operational implications during the Ukrainian mud season," Twitter (now X), March 2, 2022, https://x.com/TrentTelenko/status/1499164245250002944.

254 Trent Telenko (@TrentTelenko), "Alright Lady's & Gentlemen, boys and girls, it is time for another Truck logistics thread for this latest Russian invasion of Ukraine. In it we are going to discuss the concept of "Operational Attrition" as applied to the Russian Army truck fleet in combat," Twitter (now X), March 20, 2022, https://twitter.com/TrentTelenko/status/1505370275273183239.

255 Lendon, "Russian Trucks."

256 Antony Beevor, "Russia's New Winter War: Could Putin Go the Way of Napoleon and Hitler?" *Foreign Affairs*, December 29, 2022, https://www.foreignaffairs.com/russian-federation/russias-new-winter-war.

257 Jack Detsch, "How Ukraine Learned to Fight," *Foreign Policy*, March 1, 2023, https://foreignpolicy.com/2023/03/01/how-ukraine-learned-to-fight/.

258 Jim Garamone, "NCOs Key to Ukrainian Military Successes Against Russia," US Department of Defense, February 28, 2023, https://www.defense.gov/News/News-Stories/Article/Article/3313982/ncos-key-to-ukrainian-military-successes-against-russia/.

259 Jim Garamone, "Training Key to Ukrainian Advantages in Defending Nation," US Department of Defense, September 6, 2022, https://www.defense.gov/News/News-Stories/Article/Article/3149975/training-key-to-ukrainian-advantages-in-defending-nation/.

260 Jen Judson, "US Army Goes Virtual to Help Ukraine Maintain Weapons," *Defense News*, February 1, 2023, https://www.defensenews.com/land/2023/01/31/us-army-goes-virtual-to-help-ukraine-maintain-weapons/.

261 Patrick Tucker, "US Soldiers Provide Telemaintenance as Ukranians MacGyver Their Weapons," Defense One, September 18, 2022, https://www.defenseone.com/technology/2022/09/us-soldiers-provide-telemaintenance ukrainians-macgyver-their-weapons/377306/.

262 Marc Champion, "8 Years of Combat Hardened Ukraine's Army into a Fighting Force," *Stars and Stripes*, October 10, 2022, https://www.stripes.com/theaters/europe/2022-10-10/ukraine-military-transformation-russia-7638600.html.

263 Thomas Gibbons-Neff and Marc Santora, "Ukrainian Offensive Seen as Reshaping the War's Contours," *New York Times*, September 11, 2022, https://www.nytimes.com/2022/09/10/world/europe/ukraine-offensive-izium-donbas.html.

264 Mykhailo Fedorov, "Announcing Ukraine's Version of Delta," Facebook post, October 26, 2022, https://www.facebook.com/mykhailofedorov.com.ua/posts/pfbid0t7z33MF42vmCrTiBZJxk9dQHFgcwG6sgS6ge2SWLWZQ3kr6y5YM8MChXdR7TBxmLl.

265 "Delta (Situational Awareness System)," Wikipedia, last updated April 8, 2024, https://en.wikipedia.org/wiki/Delta_(situational_awareness_system).

266 Yaroslav Trofimov, Micah Maidenberg, and Drew FitzGerald, "Ukraine Leans on Elon Musk's Starlink in Fight against Russia," *Wall Street Journal*, July 16, 2022, https://www.wsj.com/articles/ukraine-leans-on-elon-musks-starlink-in-fight-against-russia-11657963804.

267 Walter Isaacson, *Elon Musk* (Simon and Schuster, 2023), 434.

268 Sam Schechner and Daniel Michaels, "Ukraine Has Digitized Its Fighting Forces on a Shoestring," *Wall Street Journal*, January 3, 2023, https://www.wsj.com/articles/ukraine-has-digitized-its-fighting-forces-on-a-shoe string-11672741405.

269 David Axe, "Ukraine Is Capturing Russia's Old T-62 Tanks. Will It Use Them?" *Forbes*, October 4, 2022, https://www.forbes.com/sites/davidaxe/2022/10/04/ukraine-is-capturing-russias-old-t-62-tanks-will-it-use-them/.

270 Daniel Boffey, "The Ukraine Repair Shop: Where Russian Tanks Go to Change Sides," *The Guardian*, February 3, 2023, https://www.theguardian.com/world/2023/feb/03/the-ukraine-repair-shop-where-russian-tanks-go-to-change-sides.

271 Jakub Janovsky et al., "Attack on Europe: Documenting Russian Equipment Losses During the Russian Invasion of Ukraine," Oryx, February 24, 2022, https://www.oryxspioenkop.com/2022/02/attack-on-europe-documenting-equipment.html.

272 Isabelle Khurshudyan, Paul Sonne, Serhiy Morgunov, and Kamila Hrabchuk, "Inside the Ukrainian Counteroffensive that Shocked Putin and Reshaped the War," *Washington Post*, December 29, 2022, https://www.washington post.com/world/2022/12/29/ukraine-offensive-kharkiv-kherson-donetsk/.

273 David Axe, "The Ukrainians Are Converting Worthless Russian Tanks into Priceless Engineering Vehicles," *Forbes*, February 13, 2023, https://www.forbes.com/sites/davidaxe/2023/02/13/the-ukrainians-are-converting-worthless-russian-tanks-into-priceless-engineering-vehicles/.

274 Boffey, "Ukraine Repair Shop."

275 Ashlee Vance, *Elon Musk: Tesla, SpaceX, and the Quest for a Fantastic Future* (HarperCollins, 2015), 268.

276 "Will Car Dealerships Survive the EV Revolution?" Aria, January 3, 2018, https://www.ariasystems.com/resources/do-evs-mean-the-end-of-the-road-for-car-dealers/.

277 Richard Morgan, "Engine vs Electric Motor," video, posted January 23, 2022, by Electric Classic Cars, YouTube, 17:20, https://youtu.be/5XLf-elHdec.

278 Richard Morgan, "Petrol vs Batteries," video, posted January 31, 2022, by Electric Classic Cars, YouTube, 27:44, https://youtu.be/opF1si_APs.

279 Richard Morgan, "Tech Talk—Electric Car Charging," video, posted February 12, 2022, by Electric Classic Cars, YouTube, 21:35, https://youtu.be/i25JcDCbQnk.

280 Dave VanderWerp, "Our 2019 Tesla Model 3 Was a Learning Experience," *Car and Driver*, May 2022, https://www.caranddriver.com/reviews/a30209598/2019-tesla-model-3-reliability-maintenance/.

281 "New Consumer Reports Analysis Shows Rising Gas Prices Ramp Up Savings for EV Owners," *Consumer Reports*, March 10, 2022, https://advocacy.consumerreports.org/press_release/new-consumer-reports-analysis-shows-rising-gas-prices-ramp-up-savings-for-ev-owners/.

282 Isaacson, *Elon Musk*, 284–85.

283 Isaacson, *Elon Musk*, 441.

284 Eric Berger, "The Falcon Heavy Is an Absurdly Low-Cost Heavy Lift Rocket," *Ars Technica*, February 14, 2018, https://arstechnica.com/science/2018/02/three-years-of-sls-development-could-buy-86-falcon-heavy-launches/.

285 Matthew C. Weinzierl, Kylie Lucas, and Mehak Sarang, "SpaceX, Economies of Scale, and a Revolution in Space Access," Harvard Business School Case 720-027, April 2020 (Revised October 2021), https://www.hbs.edu/faculty/Pages/item.aspx?num=57679.

286 Isaacson, *Elon Musk*, 437.

287 Elon Musk, "All Our Patent Are Belong to You," Tesla, June 12, 2014. The original Tesla blog post has been removed, but it is available to read in full at https://chargedevs.com/newswire/tesla-shares-all-of-its-patented-technology/.

288 Austin Ramzy, "On the Streets of China, Electric Bikes Are Swarming," *Time*, June 14, 2009, https://content.time.com/time/world/article/0,8599,1904334,00.html.

289 Rob Siegel, "Are Lucas Electricals as Bad as Everyone Says?" Hagerty, May 13, 2019, https://www.hagerty.com/media/maintenance-and-tech/lucas-electricals-as-bad-as-everyone-says/.

290 Matthew Carter, "The New Rolls-Royce Phantom 2017: A Work of Art," Luxury London, October 4, 2017, https://luxurylondon.co.uk/lifestyle/drive/motoring/the-new-rolls-royce-phantom-2017-a-work-of-art/.

291 "Rolls-Royce Maintenance Pricing," Kelley Blue Book, https://www.kbb.com/rolls-royce/maintenance-schedules/.

292 Jonathan M. Gitlin, "The 2024 Rolls-Royce Spectre Proves EVs Make the Best Luxury Cars," *Ars Technica*, July 3, 2023, https://arstechnica.com/cars/2023/07/silent-smooth-sublime-driving-the-electric-2024-rolls-royce-spectre/.

293 Jeremy Taylor, "Is This the World's Most Luxurious Electric Car?" *Country & Town House*, May 2024, https://www.countryandtownhouse.com/culture/rolls-royce-spectre-green-lane/.

294 Albert Borgmann, *Crossing the Postmodern Divide* (University of Chicago Press, 1992), 122.

Caption Notes

Figure 17

* David Grimstead, "Once Upon a Time in London," PreWarCar.com, January 24, 2022, https://www.prewarcar.com/once-upon-a-time-in-london.

Figure 29

* Daniel Walker Howe, *What Hath God Wrought: The Transformation of America, 1815–1848*, Oxford History of the United States 5 (Oxford University Press, 2007), 64.

Figure 43

* David A. Hounshell, *From the American System to Mass Production, 1800–1932: The Development of Manufacturing Technology in the United States*, Studies in Industry and Society 4 (Johns Hopkins University Press, 1984), 209.

Figure 47

* Henry Ford and Samuel Crowther, *Moving Forward* (Doubleday, 1930), 203, 212.

Figure 54

* John Muir and Tosh Gregg, *How to Keep Your Volkswagen Alive: A Manual of Step-by-Step Procedures for the Compleat Idiot* (Avalon Publishing, 2001), 208.

Figure 56

* Haynes, *Pontiac G6: 2005 Thru 2009* (Haynes North America, Inc., 2009), https://archive.org/details/pontiacg6automot0000imho/.

Figure 58

* *Model T Ford Service* (Ford Motor Company, 1927), 210.

Figure 59

* Charlie Huenemann, "Encyclopédie," Huenemanniac, March 13, 2015, https://huenemanniac.com/2015/03/13/encyclopedie/.

† Philipp Blom, *Enlightening the World: Encyclopédie, the Book that Changed the Course of History* (Macmillan, 2005), xxv.

Figure 65

* Benjamin Woolley, *Heal Thyself: Nicholas Culpeper and the Seventeenth-Century Struggle to Bring Medicine to the People* (HarperCollins, 2004), 314.

† Nicholas Culpeper, *A Directory for Midwives: Or, a Guide for Women, in Their Conception, Bearing, and Suckling Their Children* (John Streater, 1651), 38.

Figure 66

* Christina Hardyment, *Dream Babies: Childcare Advice from John Locke to Gina Ford* (Frances Lincoln, 2007), 240.

Figure 67

* Joseph Moxon, *Mechanick Exercises: Or, the Doctrine of Handy-works* (D. Midwinter and T. Leigh, 1703), 3.

Figure 68

* Joseph Moxon, *Mechanick Exercises: Or, the Doctrine of Handy-works Applied to the Art of Printing* (J. Moxon, 1683), 201.

Figure 69

* Moxon, *Art of Printing*, 213.

Figure 90

* Ryan Kluftinger, "7 Minute Motorcycle Teardown—Mechanic Crash Course," posted March 28, 2021, by FortNine, YouTube, 7:07, https://youtu.be/rL6O-jHjSp8.

Figure 98

* "Corrosion Identification," posted March 15, 2024, by CNATT MicroLearning, YouTube, 9:41, https://www.youtube.com/watch?v=32bqVhi4Ijl.

Figure 110

* Simon Dunstan, *Centurion vs T-55: Yom Kippur War 1973* (Bloomsbury Publishing, 2022), 75.

Figure 117

* Combined Arms Center, Mission Command Center of Excellence, "Field Manual 3-0, Operations," US Army STAND-TO!, October 10, 2017, https://www.army.mil/standto/archive/2017/10/10/.

Figure 118

* Emma Brazell, "Ukraine News: Convoy of Russian Tanks Now Stretches for 40 Miles," *Metro*, March 1, 2022, https://metro.co.uk/2022/03/01/ukraine-news-convoy-of-russian-tanks-now-stretches-for-40-miles-16193665/.

† Lolita C. Baldor and Robert Burns, "Explainer: Is Stuck Convoy in Ukraine a Setback for Russia?" AP News, March 3, 2022, https://apnews.com/article/russia-ukraine-kyiv-europe-moscow-0479970c33745de8f630fc9b5c82a793.

Figure 139

* Walter Isaacson, *Elon Musk* (Simon and Schuster, 2023), 338.

Figure 140

* Hosea W. Libbey, electric bicycle, US Patent 596,272, filed November 8, 1895, and issued December 28, 1897, https://patents.google.com/patent/US596272.

Bibliography

Adan, Avraham. *On the Banks of the Suez: An Israeli General's Personal Account of the Yom Kippur War*. Presidio Press, 1980.

Ahmad, Zaki. *Principles of Corrosion Engineering and Corrosion Control*. Elsevier, 2006.

Alder, Ken. *Engineering the Revolution: Arms and Enlightenment in France, 1763–1815*. University of Chicago Press, 2010.

Annan, Kofi. "Small Arms, Big Problems." United Nations, July 10, 2001. https://www.un.org/sg/en/content/sg/articles/2001-07-10/small-arms-big-problems.

Aria. "Will Car Dealerships Survive the EV Revolution?" January 3, 2018. https://www.ariasystems.com/resources/do-evs-mean-the-end-of-the-road-for-car-dealers/.

ATP 4-33: Maintenance Operations. Department of the Army, 2019.

Axe, David. "The Ukrainians Are Converting Worthless Russian Tanks into Priceless Engineering Vehicles." *Forbes*, February 13, 2023. https://www.forbes.com/sites/davidaxe/2023/02/13/the-ukrainians-are-converting-worthless-russian-tanks-into-priceless-engineering-vehicles/.

Axe, David. "Ukraine Is Capturing Russia's Old T-62 Tanks. Will It Use Them?" *Forbes*, October 4, 2022. https://www.forbes.com/sites/davidaxe/2022/10/04/ukraine-is-capturing-russias-old-t-62-tanks-will-it-use-them/.

Baboian, Robert, E. Blaine Cliver, and E. Lawrence Bellante, eds. *The Statue of Liberty Restoration: Proceedings of the Statue of Liberty, Today for Tomorrow Conference, October 20–22, 1986, New York City, New York*. National Association of Corrosion Engineers, 1990.

Baldor, Lolita C., and Robert Burns. "Explainer: Is Stuck Convoy in Ukraine a Setback for Russia?" AP News, March 3, 2022. https://apnews.com/article/russia-ukraine-kyiv-europe-moscow-0479970c33745de8f630fc9b5c82a793.

Basalla, George. *The Evolution of Technology*. Cambridge University Press, 1989.

Beers, Mark H., ed. *The Merck Manual of Medical Information: Home Edition. Pocket Books*, 2004.

Beevor, Antony. "Russia's New Winter War: Could Putin Go the Way of Napoleon and Hitler?" *Foreign Affairs*, December 29, 2022. https://www.foreignaffairs.com/russian-federation/russias-new-winter-war.

Bennet, Glin. "Psychological Breakdown at Sea: Hazards of Singlehanded Ocean Sailing." *British Journal of Medical Psychology* 47 (1974): 189. https://doi.org/10.1111/j.2044-8341.1974.tb02284.x.

Berger, Eric. "The Falcon Heavy Is an Absurdly Low-Cost Heavy Lift Rocket." *Ars Technica*, February 14, 2018. https://arstechnica.com/science/2018/02/three-years-of-sls-development-could-buy-86-falcon-heavy-launches/.

"Bernard Moitessier." Produced by Fabrice Florin. Posted August 31, 2012, by Videowest TV. YouTube, 8 min., 01 sec. https://www.youtube.com/watch?v=PtmnOL-LSqE.

Blom, Philipp. *Enlightening the World: Encyclopédie, the Book that Changed the Course of History*. Macmillan, 2005.

Bly, Nellie. *Around the World in Seventy-Two Days and Other Writings*. Penguin, 2014.

Boffey, Daniel. "The Ukraine Repair Shop: Where Russian Tanks Go to Change Sides." *The Guardian*, February 3, 2023. https://www.theguardian.com/world/2023/feb/03/the-ukraine-repair-shop-where-russian-tanks-go-to-change-sides.

Borgmann, Albert. *Crossing the Postmodern Divide*. University of Chicago Press, 1992.

Brazell, Emma. "Ukraine News: Convoy of Russian Tanks Now Stretches for 40 Miles." *Metro*, March 1, 2022. https://metro.co.uk/2022/03/01/ukraine-news-convoy-of-russian-tanks-now-stretches-for-40-miles-16193665/.

Bungay, Stephen. "The Road to Mission Command: The Genesis of a Command Philosophy." *The British Army Review* 137 (Summer 2005). https://studylib.net/doc/7824018/the-genesis-of-a-command-philosophy.

Carr, Benjamin. "Motorcycle vs. Car Accident Statistics (2024)." AutoInsurance.org. Last updated April 18, 2024. https://www.autoinsurance.org/motorcycle-vs-car-accidents/.

Carter, Matthew. "The New Rolls-Royce Phantom 2017: A Work of Art." Luxury London, October 4, 2017. https://luxurylondon.co.uk/lifestyle/drive/motoring/the-new-rolls-royce-phantom-2017-a-work-of-art/.

Champion, Marc. "8 Years of Combat Hardened Ukraine's Army into a Fighting Force." *Stars and Stripes*, October 10, 2022. https://www.stripes.com/theaters/europe/2022-10-10/ukraine-military-transformation-russia-7638600.html.

Chivers, C.J. *The Gun*. Simon and Schuster, 2011.

Classic.com. "Rolls-Royce Silver Ghost (1909 to 1926)." https://www.classic.com/m/rolls-royce/silver-ghost/.

Colvin, Fred H. *60 Years with Men and Machines: An Autobiography*. McGraw-Hill, 1947.

Combined Arms Center, Mission Command Center of Excellence. "Field Manual 3-0, Operations." US Army STAND-TO!, October 10, 2017. https://www.army.mil/standto/archive/2017/10/10/.

Consumer Reports. "New Consumer Reports Analysis Shows Rising Gas Prices Ramp Up Savings for EV Owners." March 10, 2022. https://advocacy.consumerreports.org/press_release/new-consumer-reports-analysis-shows-rising-gas-prices-ramp-up-savings-for-ev-owners/.

"Corrosion Identification." Posted March 15, 2024, by CNATT MicroLearning. YouTube, 9:41. https://www.youtube.com/watch?v=32bqVhi4Ijl.

Crawford, Matthew B. *Shop Class as Soulcraft: An Inquiry into the Value of Work*. Penguin, 2009.

Crawford, Matthew B. "Why Robert Pirsig's 'Zen and the Art of Motorcycle Maintenance' Still Resonates Today." *Smithsonian Magazine*, October 2020. https://www.smithsonianmag.com/smithsonian-institution/robert-pirsig-zen-art-motorcycle-maintenance-resonates-today-180975768/.

Culpeper, Nicholas. *A Directory for Midwives: Or, a Guide for Women, in Their Conception, Bearing, and Suckling Their Children*. John Streater, 1651.

DA-PAM 750-3, Soldiers' Guide for Field Maintenance Operations. US Department of the Army, 2013.

De Atkine, Norvell. "Why Arabs Lose Wars." *Middle East Quarterly* 6, no. 4 (1999). https://www.meforum.org/middle-east-quarterly/why-arabs-lose-wars.

Deployable Training Division. "Insight and Best Practices Focus Paper: Mission Command." 2nd ed. Joint Staff J7, Joint Training, January 2020. https://www.jcs.mil/Portals/36/Documents/Doctrine/fp/missioncommand_fp_2nd_ed.pdf.

Detsch, Jack. "How Ukraine Learned to Fight." *Foreign Policy*, March 1, 2023. https://foreignpolicy.com/2023/03/01/how-ukraine-learned-to-fight/.

Dotation Catherine Leroy. "Catherine Leroy: Photographer 1944–2006." https://dotationcatherineleroy.org/en/.

Dunstan, Simon. *Centurion vs T-55: Yom Kippur War 1973*. Bloomsbury Publishing, 2022.

Dunstan, Simon. *The Yom Kippur War 1973 (2): The Sinai*. Bloomsbury Publishing, 2012.

Dupuy, Trevor. *A Genius for War: German Army and General Staff 1807–1945*. Macdonald & Janes, 1977.

Edgerton, David. *The Shock of the Old: Technology and Global History Since 1900*. Oxford University Press, 2011.

Eisner, Will. *Last Day in Vietnam: A Memory*. Dark Horse Comics, 2000.

Eisner, Will. "The M16A1 Rifle: Operation and Preventive Maintenance (DA Pam 750-30)." June 28, 1968. https://archive.org/details/1968m16A1.

Elbies, Jeffrey. "They Were Soldiers Once." PopPhoto, December 17, 2008. https://www.popphoto.com/how-to/2008/12/they-were-soldiers-once/.

Encyclopedia.com. "Moitessier, Bernard." *Encyclopedia of World Biography*. https://www.encyclopedia.com/history/encyclopedias-almanacs-transcripts-and-maps/moitessier-bernard.

Ezell, Edward Clinton. *The Great Rifle Controversy: Search for the Ultimate Infantry Weapon from World War II through Vietnam and Beyond*. Stackpole Books, 1984.

Fallows, James. "M-16: A Bureaucratic Horror Story." *The Atlantic*, June 1, 1981. https://www.theatlantic.com/magazine/archive/1981/06/m-16-a-bureaucratic-horror-story/545153/.

Farr, Christina. "Doctors are Turning to YouTube to Learn How to Do Surgical Procedures, But There's No Quality Control." CNBC, November 24, 2019. https://www.cnbc.com/2019/11/24/doctors-are-watching-surgical-procedures-on-youtube.html.

Fauenfelder, Mark. "Leaky Faucet Fix." Recomendo: Issue No. 327, Cool Tools, October 16, 2022. https://kk.org/cooltools/lex-fridman-podcast-consensus-app-leaky-faucet-fix/.

Flynn, Michael, and Chuck Schrankel. "Applying Mission Command through the Operations Process." *Military Review* (March–April 2013). https://www.armyupress.army.mil/Portals/7/military-review/Archives/English/MilitaryReview_20130430_art006.pdf.

FM 3-0, Operations. US Government Publishing Office, 2017.

FM 4-0, Sustainment Operations. US Government Publishing Office, 2019.

Ford, Henry, and Samuel Crowther. *Moving Forward*. Doubleday, 1930.

Forgeng, Jeffrey L. *The Medieval Art of Swordsmanship: Royal Armouries MS I.33*. Royal Armouries Museum, 2018.

Frankel, Todd C., Shawn Boburg, Josh Dawsey, Ashley Parker, and Alex Horton. "The Gun that Divides a Nation." *Washington Post*, March 27, 2023. https://www.washingtonpost.com/nation/interactive/2023/ar-15-america-gun-culture-politics/.

Furbank, Philip Nicholas. *Diderot: A Critical Biography*. Knopf, 1992.

Garamone, Jim. "NCOs Key to Ukrainian Military Successes Against Russia." US Department of Defense, February 28, 2023. https://www.defense.gov/News/News-Stories/Article/Article/3313982/ncos-key-to-ukrainian-military-successes-against-russia/.

Garamone, Jim. "Training Key to Ukrainian Advantages in Defending Nation." US Department of Defense, September 6, 2022. https://www.defense.gov/News/News-Stories/Article/Article/3149975/training-key-to-ukrainian-advantages-in-defending-nation/.

Gibbons-Neff, Thomas, and Marc Santora. "Ukrainian Offensive Seen as Reshaping the War's Contours." *New York Times*, September 11, 2022. https://www.nytimes.com/2022/09/10/world/europe/ukraine-offensive-izium-donbas.html.

Gitlin, Jonathan M. "The 2024 Rolls-Royce Spectre Proves EVs Make the Best Luxury Cars." *Ars Technica*, July 3, 2023. https://arstechnica.com/cars/2023/07/silent-smooth-sublime-driving-the-electric-2024-rolls-royce-spectre/.

Grimstead, David. "Once Upon a Time in London." PreWarCar.com, January 24, 2022. https://www.prewarcar.com/once-upon-a-time-in-london.

Guangqian, Peng, and Yao Youzhi, eds. *Science of Military Strategy*. Military Publishing House, 2005.

Gulick, John. "Two Streams into One." In *Readings in Arab Middle Eastern Societies and Cultures*, edited by Abdulla M. Lutfiyya and Charles W. Churchill. Mouton, 1970.

Hackworth, David H., and Julie Sherman. *About Face: The Odyssey of an American Warrior*. Touchstone, 1990.

Hamady, Sania. *Temperament and Character of the Arabs*. Hassell Street Press, 2021.

Hamilton, Peter. "The Lada: A Cultural Icon." In *Autopia: Cars and Culture*, edited by Peter Wollen and Joe Kerr. Reaktion Books, 2002.

Hardyment, Christina. *Dream Babies: Childcare Advice from John Locke to Gina Ford*. Frances Lincoln, 2007.

Hargrave, Jocelyn E. "Joseph Moxon: A Re-Fashioned Appraisal." *Script & Print: Bulletin of the Bibliographical Society of Australia and New Zealand* 39, no. 3 (2015): 163–81. https://search.informit.org/doi/10.3316/INFORMIT.473337499287786.

Hatzfeld, Jean. *Machete Season: The Killers in Rwanda Speak*. Farrar, Straus and Giroux, 2006.

Haynes. *Pontiac G6: 2005 Thru 2009*. Haynes North America, Inc., 2009. https://archive.org/details/pontiacg6automot0000imho/.

Herlihy, David V. *Bicycle: The History*. Yale University Press, 2004.

Hertling, Mark. "I Commanded US Army Europe. Here's What I Saw in the Russian and Ukrainian Armies." The Bulwark, April 10, 2022. https://www.thebulwark.com/i-commanded-u-s-army-europe-heres-what-i-saw-in-the-russian-and-ukrainian-armies/.

Hounshell, David A. *From the American System to Mass Production, 1800–1932: The Development of Manufacturing Technology in the United States*. Studies in Industry and Society 4. Johns Hopkins University Press, 1984.

Howe, Daniel Walker. *What Hath God Wrought: The Transformation of America, 1815–1848*. Oxford History of the United States 5. Oxford University Press, 2007.

Huenemann, Charlie. "Encyclopédie." Huenemanniac, March 13, 2015. https://huenemanniac.com/2015/03/13/encyclopedie/.

Isaacson, Walter. *Elon Musk*. Simon and Schuster, 2023.

Jamali, Naveed, David Brennan, and Tom O'Connor. "Exclusive: US Expects Kyiv to Fall in Days as Ukraine Source Warns of Encirclement." *Newsweek*, February 25, 2022. https://www.newsweek.com/us-expects-kyiv-fall-days-ukraine-source-warns-encirclement-1682326.

Janovsky, Jakub, Naalsio, Aloha, Dan, Kemal, and Alexander Black. "Attack on Europe: Documenting Russian Equipment Losses During the Russian Invasion of Ukraine." Oryx, February 24, 2022. https://www.oryxspioenkop.com/2022/02/attack-on-europe-documenting-equipment.html.

Jerome, John. *Truck: On Rebuilding a Worn-Out Pickup and Other Post-Technological Adventures*. University Press of New England, 2014.

Judson, Jen. "US Army Goes Virtual to Help Ukraine Maintain Weapons." *Defense News*, February 1, 2023. https://www.defensenews.com/land/2023/01/31/us-army-goes-virtual-to-help-ukraine-maintain-weapons/.

Kahaner, Larry. *AK-47: The Weapon that Changed the Face of War*. Wiley, 2007.

Kelley Blue Book. "Rolls-Royce Maintenance Pricing." https://www.kbb.com/rolls-royce/maintenance-schedules/.

Khurshudyan, Isabelle, Paul Sonne, Serhiy Morgunov, and Kamila Hrabchuk. "Inside the Ukrainian Counteroffensive that Shocked Putin and Reshaped the War." *Washington Post*, December 29, 2022. https://www.washingtonpost.com/world/2022/12/29/ukraine-offensive-kharkiv-kherson-donetsk/.

Kluftinger, Ryan. "7 Minute Motorcycle Teardown—Mechanic Crash Course." Posted March 28, 2021, by FortNine. YouTube, 7:07, https://youtu.be/rL6O-jHjSp8.

Knox-Johnston, Robin. *A World of My Own: The First Ever Non-Stop Solo Round the World Voyage*. Adlard Coles Nautical, 1969.

Koch, Gerhardus, Jeff Varney, Neil Thompson, Oliver Moghissi, Melissa Gould, and Joe Payer. "International Measures of Prevention, Application, and Economics of Corrosion Technologies Study." NACE International, March 1, 2016. http://impact.nace.org/documents/Nace-International-Report.pdf.

Kurin, Richard. *The Smithsonian's History of America in 101 Objects*. Penguin, 2013.

Lendon, Brad. "What Images of Russian Trucks Say About Its Military's Struggles in Ukraine." CNN, April 14, 2022. https://www.cnn.com/2022/04/14/europe/ukraine-war-russia-trucks-logistics-intl-hnk-ml/index.html.

Libbey, Hosea W. Electric bicycle, US Patent 596,272. Filed November 8, 1895. Issued December 28, 1897. https://patents.google.com/patent/US596272.

Long, Derek Albert. *At the Sign of Atlas: The Life and Work of Joseph Moxon, a Restoration Polymath*. Shaun Tyas, 2013.

M16 Maintenance and Repair Manual: Army TM 9-1005-319-23&P Air Force to 11 W3-5-5-42. Department of Defense, 1991.

MacDonald, Alistair. "Scottish Enlightenment." British Council, July 2016. https://www.britishcouncil.org/research-insight/scottish-enlightenment.

Marshall Steam Museum at Auburn Heights. "1916 Rauch and Lang Electric Brougham." https://auburnheights.org/automobile/1916-rauch-and-lang-electric-brougham/.

Martin, Taylor. "The Infamously Terrible Lada Riva Is Also One of the Best-Selling Cars of All Time." MotorBiscuit, November 15, 2021. https://www.motorbiscuit.com/terrible-lada-riva-sixth-best-selling-car/.

Michaels, Daniel, and Matthew Luxmoore. "The 19th-Century Technology Driving Russia's Latest Gains in Ukraine: Railroads." *Wall Street Journal*, June 14, 2022. https://www.wsj.com/articles/the-19th-century-technology-driving-russias-latest-gains-in-ukraine-railroads-11655218602.

Model T Ford Service. Ford Motor Company, 1927.

Moitessier, Bernard. *A Sea Vagabond's World*. Sheridan House, 1995.

Moitessier, Bernard. *The Long Way*. Sheridan House, 1971.

Morgan, Richard. "Engine vs Electric Motor." Posted January 23, 2022, by Electric Classic Cars. YouTube, 17:20. https://youtu.be/5XLf-elHdec.

Morgan, Richard. "Petrol vs Batteries." Posted January 31, 2022, by Electric Classic Cars. YouTube, 27:44. https://youtu.be/ opF1si_APs.

Morgan, Richard. "Tech Talk—Electric Car Charging." Posted February 12, 2022, by Electric Classic Cars. YouTube, 21:35. https:// youtu.be/ i25JcDCbQnk.

Moxon, Joseph. *Mechanick Exercises: Or, the Doctrine of Handy-Works*. D. Midwinter and T. Leigh, 1703.

Moxon, Joseph. *Mechanick Exercises: Or, the Doctrine of Handy-works Applied to the Art of Printing*. J. Moxon, 1683.

Muir, John, and Tosh Gregg. *How to Keep Your Volkswagen Alive: A Manual of Step-by-Step Procedures for the Compleat Idiot*. Avalon Publishing, 2001.

Murphy, Edward F. *The Hill Fights: The First Battle of Khe Sanh*. Presidio Press, 2007.

Musk, Elon. "All Our Patent Are Belong to You." Tesla, June 12, 2014.

National Park Service. "Thomas Blanchard." Last updated March 25, 2023. https://www.nps.gov/spar/learn/historyculture/thomas-blanchard-and-his-lathe.htm.

Nelsen, John T., II. "'Auftragstaktik': A Case for Decentralized Battle." *Parameters* 17, no. 1 (September 1987): 21–34. https://doi.org/10.55540/0031-1723.1460.

Nichols, Peter. *A Voyage for Madmen*. HarperCollins, 2009.

Nietzsche, Friedrich. *The Will to Power*. Dover Publications, 2019.

Norman, Jeremy. "John Wilkinson Invents the First Machine Tool: A Boring Machine for Cylinders and Cannons." Jeremy Norman's HistoryofInformation.com. Last updated July 15, 2024. https://historyofinformation.com/detail.php?id=4755.

O'Brien, Phillips Payson. "People Forgot How War Actually Works." *The Atlantic*, February 24, 2023. https://www.theatlantic.com/ideas/archive/2023/02/russia-ukraine-war-one-year-national-identity/673192/.

Osgood, Todd. "Best Knife Brand? Benchmade, Buck, Zero Tolerance, Spyderco, Cold Steel, Kershaw, SOG, CRKT, Ontario." Posted February 6, 2022, by Project Farm. YouTube, 18 min., 54 sec. https://www.youtube.com/watch?v=wVQ3raLq4LQ&t=1006s.

Pirsig, Robert M. *Zen and the Art of Motorcycle Maintenance: An Inquiry into Values*. Harper Collins, 2009.

Pollack, Kenneth M. *Arabs at War: Military Effectiveness, 1948–1991*. University of Nebraska Press, 2004.

Pollack, Kenneth M. *Armies of Sand: The Past, Present, and Future of Arab Military Effectiveness*. Oxford University Press, 2019.

Powell, James S. "Taking a Look Under the Hood: The October War and What Maintenance Approaches Reveal about Military Operations." The Institute of Land Warfare, Land Warfare Paper 128. August 2019. https://www.ausa.org/sites/default/files/publications/LWP-128-Taking-a-Look-under-the-Hood-The-October-War-and-What-Maintenance-Approaches-Reveal-about-Military-Operations.pdf.

Ramzy, Austin. "On the Streets of China, Electric Bikes Are Swarming." *Time*, June 14, 2009. https://content.time.com/time/world/article/0,8599,1904334,00.html.

Reid, Carlton. "Reclaiming the Roads." Works in Progress, July 21, 2022. https://worksinprogress.co/issue/reclaiming-the-roads.

Reid, John S. "A Tale of Invention: The Birth of the Modern Bicycle." University of Aberdeen, 2012. https://homepages.abdn.ac.uk/nph120/meteo/Bicycles.pdf.

Robespierre, Maximilien. "On the Principles of Political Morality." Marxists.org. http://marxists.org/history/france/revolution/robespierre/1794/political-morality.htm.

Roser, Christoph. *"Faster, Better, Cheaper" in the History of Manufacturing: From the Stone Age to Lean Manufacturing and Beyond*. CRC Press, 2016.

Rousseau, Jean-Jacques. *The Confessions of Jean-Jacques Rousseau, Book VI*. Privately Printed for Members of the Aldus Society, 1903. https://gutenberg.org/files/3913/3913-h/3913-h.htm.

Royal National Lifeboat Institution. "A Golden Anniversary." March 13, 2019. https://rnli.org/magazine/magazine-featured-list/2019/march/a-golden-anniversary.

Sandborn, Peter, and William Lucyshyn. *System Sustainment: Acquisition and Engineering Processes for the Sustainment of Critical and Legacy Systems*. World Scientific Series on Emerging Technologies 4. World Scientific, 2022.

Schechner, Sam, and Daniel Michaels. "Ukraine Has Digitized Its Fighting Forces on a Shoestring." *Wall Street Journal*, January 3, 2023. https://www.wsj.com/articles/ukraine-has-digitized-its-fighting-forces-on-a-shoestring-11672741405.

Schiffer, Michael Brian. *Taking Charge: The Electric Automobile in America*. Smithsonian Institution Scholarly Press, 1994.

Schmidt, Peter A. *Hall's Military Breechloaders*. Andrew Mowbray Pub, 1995.

Sennett, Richard. *The Craftsman*. Yale University Press, 2008.

Siegel, Rob. "Are Lucas Electricals as Bad as Everyone Says?" Hagerty, May 13, 2019. https://www.hagerty.com/media/maintenance-and-tech/lucas-electricals-as-bad-as-everyone-says/.

Sir Robin Knox-Johnston: Sailing Legend. Directed by Clifford Webb. Posted May 14, 2020, by Clipper Round the World Yacht Race. YouTube, 56 min., 34 sec. https://youtu.be/WdIIYr1GdIs.

Smil, Vaclav. *Still the Iron Age: Iron and Steel in the Modern World*. Elsevier Science, 2016.

Smith, Aaron, Skye Toor, and Patrick Van Kessel. "Many Turn to YouTube for Children's Content, News, How-To Lessons." Pew Research Center, November 7, 2018. https://www.pewresearch.org/internet/2018/11/07/many-turn-to-youtube-for-childrens-content-news-how-to-lessons/.

Smith, Merritt Roe. *Harpers Ferry Armory and the New Technology: The Challenge of Change*. Cornell University Press, 1977.

Smith, Merritt Roe, ed. *Military Enterprise and Technological Change: Perspectives on the American Experience*. MIT Press, 1985.

Smithsonian. "'Zen Motorcycle' Takes Final Journey into the Smithsonian's Collections." December 17, 2019. https://www.si.edu/newsdesk/releases/zen-motorcycle-takes-final-journey-smithsonians-collections.

Snyder, Gary. "Riprap." Poetry Foundation. https://www.poetryfoundation.org/poems/47178/riprap.

Swiss Environmental Action Foundation. *Dry Stone Walls: Basics, Construction, Significance*. Scheidegger and Spiess, 2018.

Taylor, Jeremy. "Is This the World's Most Luxurious Electric Car?" *Country & Town House*, May 2024. https://www.countryandtownhouse.com/culture/rolls-royce-spectre-green-lane/.

Technology.org. "How to Repair M777 or HIMARS in Ukraine? You Will Need an Online Chat for That." October 11, 2022. https://www.technology.org/2022/10/11/how-to-repair-m777-or-himars-in-ukraine-you-will-need-an-online-chat-for-that/.

Timothy Hughes Rare & Early Newspapers. "Nellie Bly Interview with Susan B. Anthony." https://www.rarenewspapers.com/view/621269?acl=851761768&imagelist=1.

Tomalin, Nicholas, and Ron Hall. *The Strange Last Voyage of Donald Crowhurst*. Quercus, 1970.

Tozzi, Eric. "Rare Antique Fractal Vise [Restoration]." Posted June 24, 2021, by Hand Tool Rescue. YouTube, 36 min., 19 sec. https://youtu.be/QBeOgGt_oWU.

Trofimov, Yaroslav, Micah Maidenberg, and Drew FitzGerald. "Ukraine Leans on Elon Musk's Starlink in Fight against Russia." *Wall Street Journal*, July 16, 2022. https://www.wsj.com/articles/ukraine-leans-on-elon-musks-starlink-in-fight-against-russia-11657963804.

Tucker, Patrick. "US Soldiers Provide Telemaintenance as Ukranians MacGyver Their Weapons." Defense One, September 18, 2022. https://www.defenseone.com/technology/2022/09/us-soldiers-provide-telemaintenanceukrainians-macgyver-their-weapons/377306/.

Vance, Ashlee. *Elon Musk: Tesla, SpaceX, and the Quest for a Fantastic Future*. HarperCollins, 2015.

VanderWerp, Dave. "Our 2019 Tesla Model 3 Was a Learning Experience." *Car and Driver*, May 2022. https://www.caranddriver.com/reviews/a30209598/2019-tesla-model-3-reliability-maintenance/.

Wade, Norman M. *SMFLS5: The Sustainment & Multifunctional Logistics SMARTbook*. 5th ed. Lightning Press, 2021.

Waldman, Jonathan. *Rust: The Longest War*. Simon and Schuster, 2015.

Weinzierl, Matthew C., Kylie Lucas, and Mehak Sarang. "SpaceX, Economies of Scale, and a Revolution in Space Access." Harvard Business School Case 720-027, April 2020 (Revised October 2021). https://www.hbs.edu/faculty/Pages/item.aspx?num=57679.

White, E.B. *Farewell to Model T: From Sea to Shining Sea*. New York Review Books, 2003.

Wikipedia. "Conservation-restoration of the Statue of Liberty." Last updated November 12, 2024. https://en.wikipedia.org/wiki/ Conservation-restoration_of_the_Statue_of_ Liberty.

Wikipedia. "Delta (Situational Awareness System)." Last updated April 8, 2024. https://en.wikipedia.org/wiki/Delta_(situational_awareness_system).

Wikipedia. "Eisner Awards." Last updated May 13, 2025. https://en.wikipedia.org/wiki/Eisner_Awards.

Wikipedia. "Ford Model T." Last updated June 20, 2025. https://en.wikipedia.org/wiki/Ford_Model_T.

Wikipedia. "John Muir (engineer)." Last updated January 18, 2024. https://en.wikipedia.org/wiki/John_Muir_(engineer).

Wikipedia. "List of Best-Selling Automobiles." Last updated May 3, 2024. https://en.wikipedia.org/wiki/List_of_best-selling_automobiles.

Wikipedia. "M16 Rifle." Last updated May 2, 2024. https://en.wikipedia.org/wiki/M16_rifle.

Wikipedia. "Nicholas Culpeper." Last updated April 13, 2024. https://en.wikipedia.org/wiki/Nicholas_Culpeper.

Wikipedia. "RTFM." Last updated June 28, 2024. https://en.wikipedia.org/wiki/RTFM.

Wikipedia. "Samuel Colt." Last updated April 2, 2024. https://en.wikipedia.org/wiki/Samuel_Colt.

Wikipedia. "Samuel Colt's Manufacturing Company." Last updated April 13, 2024. https://en.wikipedia.org/wiki/Colt's_Manufacturing_Company.

Wikipedia. "Scottish Enlightenment." Last updated July 29, 2024. https://en.wikipedia.org/wiki/Scottish_Enlightenment.

Wikipedia. "Stainless Steel." Last updated May 1, 2024. https://en.wikipedia.org/wiki/Stainless_steel.

Winchester, Simon. *The Perfectionists: How Precision Engineers Created the Modern World*. HarperCollins, 2018.

Woolley, Benjamin. *Heal Thyself: Nicholas Culpeper and the Seventeenth-Century Struggle to Bring Medicine to the People*. HarperCollins, 2004.

World Steel Association. "World Steel in Figures: 2022." April 30, 2022. https://worldsteel.org/data/world-steel-in-figures-2022/.

Index

Notes

About *Maintenance: Of Everything, Part One*

Maintenance is what keeps everything going. It's what keeps life going. Yet it's also easy to shirk or defer—until the thing breaks, the system falters, and everything stops. The first in a multi-volume work, *Maintenance: Of Everything, Part One* offers a comprehensive overview of the civilizational importance of maintenance. Spanning the maintenance of sailboats, motorcycles, automobiles, and weapons—with absorbing detours into the evolution of precision in manufacturing, the enduring importance of manuals, sustainment in the military, and the battle against corrosion—Stewart Brand invites us to understand the profound impact maintenance has on our daily lives. *Maintenance: Of Everything, Part One* is a wide-ranging and provocative call to expand what we mean by "maintenance," and a powerful argument for why taking responsibility for maintaining something can be a radical act.

About the Author

Stewart Brand is cofounder of The Long Now Foundation, Global Business Network, the Hackers Conference, and the WELL. He created and edited the National Book Award-winning *Whole Earth Catalog* from 1968 to 1998. His books include *The Clock of the Long Now* (1999), *How Buildings Learn* (1994), *The Media Lab* (1987), and *Whole Earth Discipline* (2009). He graduated from Stanford with a degree in biology and served as an infantry officer in the US Army.